INDEPENDENT LEARNING PROJECT FOR ADVANCED CHEMISTRY

ILPAC

second edition

4

INORGANIC

s-BLOCK ELEMENTS
THE HALOGENS
THE PERIODIC TABLE

REVISED BY ANN LAINCHBURY JOHN STEPHENS ALEC THOMPSON

JOHN MURRAY

ACKNOWLEDGEMENTS

We are grateful to CLEAPSS/ASE Laboratory Standards Committee for ensuring that the text meets with current safety recommendations.

Thanks are due to the following examination boards for permission to reproduce questions from past A-level papers: Associated Examining Board: Exercise 66, p. 73 (1980); Exercise 67, p. 74 (1979); Exercise 94, p. 95 (1978). Joint Matriculation Board: s-Block End-of-unit test 5, p. 37 (1991); 7, p. 37 (1992). Halogens End-of-unit test 2, p. 92 (1992); 4, p. 92 (1992); 6, p. 92 (1991); 9, p. 93 (1990); 10, p. 93 (1990). Periodic Table End-of-unit test 11, p. 143 (1992). Teacher-marked Exercise, p. 116 (1978). Oxford and Cambridge Schools Examination Board: Exercise 7, p. 9 (Salters, 1992). Teacher-marked Exercise, p. 16 (1976). Discussion exercise, p. 40 (1992). s-Block End-of-unit test 6, p. 37 (1990); 8, p. 37 (1991); 9, p. 37 (1991). Halogens End-of-unit test 5, p. 92, (1991). Periodic Table End-of-unit test 12, p. 143 (1991); 13, p. 143 (1991). Southern Universities Joint Board: Exercise 65, p. 73 (1980); Exercise 68, p. 76 (1980); Exercise 69, p. 76 (1979); Exercise 71, p. 78 (1977); Exercise 95, p. 128 (1980). University of Cambridge Local Examinations Syndicate: Periodic Table Part A test 14, p. 119 (1974). Periodic Table End-of-unit test 12, p. 143; 13, p. 143 (1991). University of London Examination and Assessments Council: Exercise 5, p. 8 (N 1974); Teacher-marked Exercise, p. 32 (L 1980); Teacher-marked Exercise, second choice, p. 35 (L 1993); s-Block End-of-unit test 1, p. 36 (L 1989); 2, p. 36 (L 1991); 3, p. 36 (L 1993); 4, p. 36 (L 1988); 10, p. 37 (L 1993); 11, p. 38 (L 1988); 12, p. 38 (L 1981); 13, p. 38 (1984 and 1990); Exercise 41, p. 50 (L 1978); Exercise 64, p. 70 (1976). Exercise 76, p. 83 (1977); Teacher-marked Exercise, p. 70 (1981); Experiment 10, p. 88 (1979); Experiment 11, p. 90 (1974); Halogens Part A test 2, p. 66 (1990); 3, p. 66 (1978). Halogens End-of-unit test 1, p. 92 (1993); 3, p. 92 (1993); 7, p. 93 (1992); 8, p. 93 (1989); 11, p. 93 (1990); 12 (1994). Exercise 96, p. 128 (1973). Teacher-marked Exercise, p. 134 (1978); p. 138 (1979); p. 140 (1976); Periodic Table Part A test 1–4, p. 117 (1980); 5, p. 117 (N 1976); 6, p. 118 (1990); 7, p. 118 (1976); 8, p. 118 (1979); 9, p. 118 (1978); 10, p. 118 (1988); 15, p. 119 (1977). Periodic Table End-of-unit test 1–5, p. 142 (1981); 6–10, p. 142 (1989); 14, p. 143 (N 1979); 15, p. 144 (1976); 17, p. 144 (1989). University of Oxford Delegacy of Local Examinations: Teacher-marked exercise, first choice, p. 35 (1981). Teacher-marked Exercise, p. 70 (1978). Periodic Table Part A test 12, p. 119 (1980). Welsh Joint Education Committee: Periodic Table End-of-unit test 16, p. 144 (1990); 18, p. 144 (1977). (The examination boards accept no responsibility whatsoever for the accuracy or method of working in the answers given.)

Photographs reproduced by kind permission of AERE Technology (p. 9); Peter Gould (p. 11, p. 46, p. 47, p. 103); Farrell Grehan/Science Photo Library (p. 25); Science Photo Library (p. 29, p. 108, p. 116). All other photographs by the Last Resort Picture Library. The assistance provided by the staff and students of Roding Valley High School, Loughton, Essex and Tuxford School, Tuxford, Newark, Nottinghamshire for the photographs of the experiments is gratefully acknowledged.

The extract starting on p. 95 is taken from *The Essential Chemical Industry* with kind permission from the Chemical Industry Education Centre at the University of York.

The publishers have made every effort to trace the copyright holders, but if they have inadvertently overlooked any, they will be pleased to make the necessary arrangements at the earliest opportunity.

Original material produced by the Independent Learning Project for Advanced Chemistry sponsored by the Inner London Education Authority

First edition published 1983
by John Murray (Publishers) Ltd
50 Albemarle Street
London W1X 4BD

Second edition 1995

British Library Cataloguing in Publication Data
A catalogue record for this book is available from the British Library

ISBN 0-7195-5334-2

Design and layouts by John Townson/Creation
Illustrations by Barking Dog Art

Produced by Gray Publishing
Typeset in 10/12 pt Times and Helvetica

Printed in Great Britain by St Edmundsbury Press Ltd, Bury St Edmunds

CONTENTS

s-BLOCK ELEMENTS

THE HALOGENS

THE PERIODIC TABLE

Symbols used in ILPAC

Computer program

Discussion

Experiment

Model-making

Reading

Revealing Exercise

Video programme

A- level question

A-level part question

A-level question; Special Paper

A-level supplementary question

International hazard symbols

Corrosive

Explosive

Harmful or irritant

Highly flammable

Oxidising

Radioactive

Toxic

s-BLOCK ELEMENTS

INTRODUCTION

In this unit we deal with the elements and compounds of Groups I and II (the s-block). To remind you of the elements in these groups, we include their symbols, group names and atomic numbers in the outline Periodic Table in Fig. 1 below.

Figure 1

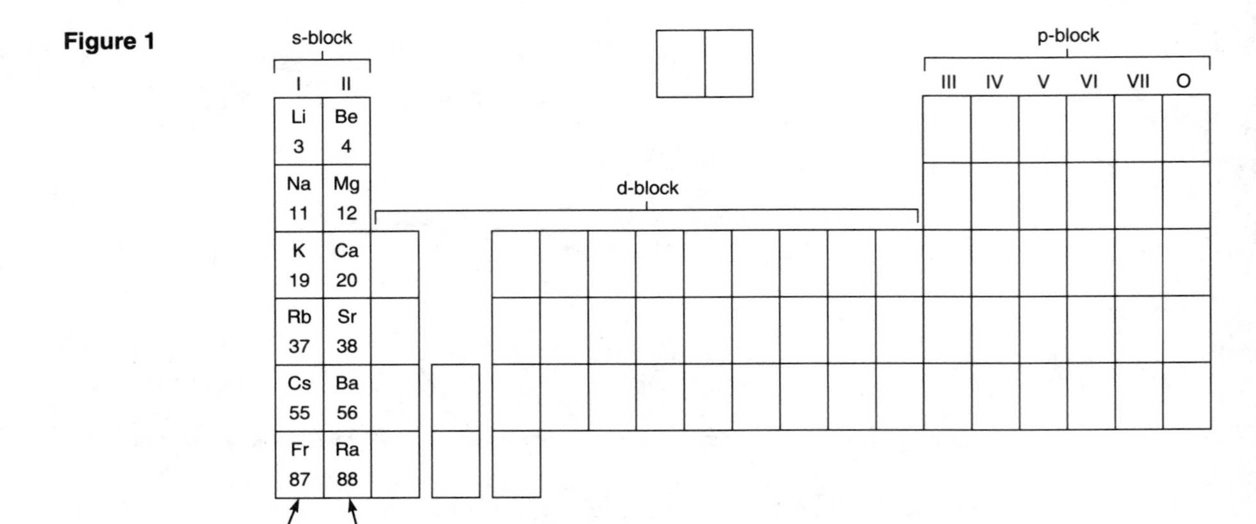

We deal with Groups I and II concurrently so that we can make comparisons between them, as well as consider the trends in properties within each group.

Since this is a short unit, and there is no obvious progression of difficulty in the subject matter, we have not divided it into two parts. Consequently there is no Part A test.

In the first section of the unit we deal with the physical and chemical properties of the elements. (The distinction between physical and chemical properties is not rigid; we simply use the terms as convenient labels for organising information.) Then we consider the properties of some of the compounds of the s-block elements.

In an appendix we consider briefly some of the industrial chemistry of these elements and their compounds.

There are three experiments in this unit.

Pre-knowledge

Before you start work on this unit, you should be able to:

1. Identify the s-, p- and d-blocks in the Periodic Table.
2. State the names and symbols of the first four elements in Groups I and II.
3. Describe the usual appearance of the elements lithium, sodium, potassium, magnesium and calcium.
4. Describe the reactions of sodium, potassium and calcium with water, and write equations.
5. Write an equation for the reaction of calcium oxide with water.
6. Write equations for the reactions between magnesium and dilute acids.
7. State the effect of heat on sodium carbonate and calcium carbonate.
8. Name the brown gas given off when certain nitrates are heated.
9. Describe simple chemical tests for
   a oxygen,
   b hydrogen,
   c carbon dioxide,
   d sulphate ions,
   e carbonates and hydrogencarbonates.
10. Perform flame tests and state the flame colours for lithium, sodium, potassium, calcium, strontium and barium.
11. State the meaning of the terms
   a ionisation energy,
   b electron affinity,
   c electronegativity,
   d atomic and ionic radii,
   e acidic, basic and amphoteric oxides,
   f oxidation and reduction,
   g oxidation number,
   h polarising power of a cation,
   i polarisability of an anion.
12. State and apply the following simple solubility guidelines:
   a all metal nitrates are soluble in water,
   b most metal chlorides are soluble in water,
   c most metal sulphates are soluble in water,
   d all sodium, potassium and ammonium salts are soluble in water.

Pre-test

To find out whether you are ready to start, try the following test which is based on the pre-knowledge items. You should not spend more than 45 minutes on this test. Hand your answers to your teacher for marking.

1. D is a white crystalline solid which, when heated, produces a mixture of two gases. One is brown and poisonous; the other is colourless and relights a glowing splint. The solid gives an orange-red flame test. Suggest what D may be and give an equation for its decomposition. (3)
2. E is a white crystalline solid which is soluble in water and gives a yellow flame test. Its aqueous solution gives a white precipitate with acidified barium chloride solution. Identify E and give an equation for its reaction with barium chloride solution. (3)
3. Describe the effect of dilute hydrochloric acid on
   a calcium carbonate, $CaCO_3$,
   b magnesium ribbon, Mg,
   c solid sodium hydrogencarbonate, $NaHCO_3$. (6)
4. **a** Complete and balance the equations shown below. State the oxidation number for each atom appearing in each equation.
   i) $Na(s) + H_2O(l) \rightarrow$
   ii) $Na(s) + Cl_2(g) \rightarrow$ (4)
   b For each of the above reactions state which atom is oxidised and which is reduced. (2)
5. Y is a soft metal, easily cut with a knife. When placed in water it floats, melts and ignites with a lilac-coloured flame. Identify Y. (1)
6. This question concerns the following ions:

   Li^+, Be^{2+}, K^-, CO_3^{2-}, O^{2-} and F^-

   a Place the cations in order of increasing polarising power. (1)
   b Put the anions in order of increasing polarisability. (1)
   c Which combination of cation and anion will produce a compound with the greatest covalent character? Explain your answer. (2)
7. State whether the solution formed in each of the following cases is acidic, alkaline or neither. Give a reason for each answer.
   a Calcium oxide, CaO, added to water.
   b Sodium chloride, NaCl, added to water.
   c Lithium oxide, Li_2O, added to water. (6)
8. Write thermochemical equations to specify:
   a the first ionisation energy of sodium,
   b the first electron affinity of oxygen. (4)
9. What two simple tests would help you to decide whether or not an oxide is amphoteric? (2)

(Total: 35 marks)

THE s-BLOCK ELEMENTS

To obtain a simple overall picture of the s-block elements we suggest that you read the introduction to the s-block (or to Groups I and II if they are treated separately) in your textbook(s). Also, skim the rest of the chapter(s) so that you know how the detailed information on these elements is organised.

In the first part of the unit we are concerned with the chemistry of the elements themselves. For convenience, we consider physical and chemical properties separately. We shall regard as physical properties those which are not necessarily linked with specific chemical reactions, and which can be given numerical values, but these distinctions are rather arbitrary.

PHYSICAL PROPERTIES

We begin with some properties associated with the behaviour of single atoms. For convenience, we refer to these as **atomic properties**.

OBJECTIVES

When you have finished this chapter you should be able to:

- write down the **electronic configurations** of the first four elements in Groups I and II, using the s, p and d notation;
- explain, in terms of atomic structure, the trends in Groups I and II, in (a) **atomic and ionic radii**, (b) **ionisation energy**, (c) **electronegativity**;
- state the **oxidation numbers** shown by the elements of Groups I and II in their compounds.

Most of the physical and chemical properties of an element are directly related to its atomic structure. You now spend a short time revising the electron arrangements of the s-block elements.

1.1 Electronic configurations

In the first exercise we want you to recall what you have already learned about writing electronic configurations and explore some of their implications in the case of the s-block elements.

EXERCISE 1
Answers on page 145

a Write down the electronic configurations of the first four elements in Groups I and II using the s, p and d notation.
b Why are these elements placed in Groups I and II?
c How do the configurations of lithium and beryllium differ from those of the other members of their groups?
d What are the charges on ions of Groups I and II? Explain.

In the last exercise, the emphasis was on the similarities between elements in the same group. Equally important, however, are the regular changes that take place down a group as each extra shell of electrons is added. These trends help you to predict the properties of elements which appear lower down the groups and which you may not study in any detail.

We now go on to identify trends in atomic and ionic radii of Groups I and II.

1.2 Atomic and ionic radii

You should be familiar with these terms from ILPAC Volume 3, Bonding and Structure. The next exercise concerns the variation of these radii in the s-block.

EXERCISE 2

Answers on page 145

Study Fig. 2 and then answer the questions below.

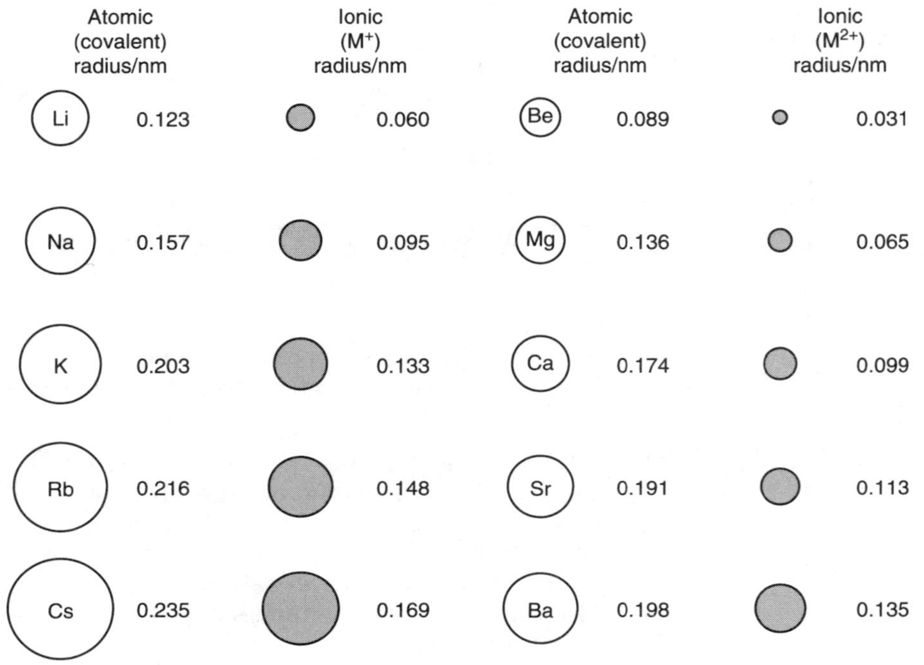

Figure 2
Atomic and ionic radii of the s-block elements.

	Atomic (covalent) radius/nm	Ionic (M^+) radius/nm		Atomic (covalent) radius/nm	Ionic (M^{2+}) radius/nm
Li	0.123	0.060	Be	0.089	0.031
Na	0.157	0.095	Mg	0.136	0.065
K	0.203	0.133	Ca	0.174	0.099
Rb	0.216	0.148	Sr	0.191	0.113
Cs	0.235	0.169	Ba	0.198	0.135

a From your knowledge of atomic structures explain why:

i) atomic and ionic size increase down each group;

ii) Group I atoms and ions are larger than their Group II neighbours in the same period.

b Which of the Group II atoms is similar in size to the lithium atom?

c Which of the Group II ions is similar in size to the lithium ion?

The similarity in size of the lithium and magnesium ions leads to a number of chemical similarities in the compounds of the two elements. We discuss this later in the unit, in Chapter 5.

Now that you have seen the trends in atomic size we go on to examine ionisation energies.

1.3 Ionisation energies

In the Atomic Structure unit of ILPAC Volume 1, you learned how ionisation energy is related to the structure of the atom. In the following exercise you will see how this property varies in Groups I and II.

EXERCISE 3
Answers on page 145

Copy Table 1 and enter the values using your data book. Then answer the questions below.

Table 1

Element	Ionisation energy/kJ mol^{-1} First	Second	Third
Li			
Na			
K			
Rb			
Cs			3300
Be			
Mg			
Ca			
Sr			
Ba			3390

a For each element in Group I, explain why the first ionisation energy is so much smaller than the other two.
b Explain the relatively large difference between the second and third ionisation energies for all Group II elements.
c Describe and explain the trend in ionisation energies as each group is descended.
d How do you expect the reactivity of the elements to change on going down each group? Explain your answer.
e How would you expect the reactivity of the elements to change going across from Group I to Group II in the same period?

The predictions you have made in Exercise 3**d** and **e** will be tested when you deal with the chemical properties of the elements later in this unit.

A property directly related to ionisation energy is electronegativity, which we now discuss.

1.4 Electronegativity

You were first introduced to this term (and electropositivity) in ILPAC Volume 3, Bonding and Structure, where you used it to predict the ionic and covalent character of bonds, and linked it to polarising power.

You also learned in that volume that electronegativity decreases down each group and increases across each period. In the next exercise you use your knowledge of ionisation energies to explain these trends in the s-block elements.

EXERCISE 4
Answers on page 146

a Explain why electronegativity decreases as both Groups I and II are descended.
b Why does electronegativity increase from Group I to Group II in the same period?
c Which of the s-block elements is the most electropositive?
d Which of the s-block elements is least likely to form an ionic compound with chlorine?

In Volume 3, you considered another atomic property of the s-block elements – the light emitted from their excited ions. You will use these flame colours to identify some s-block cations in The Halogens unit of this volume.

You should now be able to do the next exercise, which is taken from an A-level paper.

EXERCISE 5
Answers on page 146

a What is the electronic configuration, in terms of s, p and d electrons, of
  i) the beryllium atom,
  ii) the barium atom?

b i) What is the oxidation state common to both elements in their compounds?
  ii) State, in terms of ionisation energies, why there is little likelihood of a higher oxidation state for either element.
  iii) To what group of the Periodic Table do these two elements belong?

c i) Which of the two elements has the higher first ionisation energy? Give a reason for this.
  ii) Would their ions be smaller or larger than their atoms? Give a reason for this.

Now we look at those physical properties of the elements which depend not only on the nature of individual atoms, but also on the way they are linked together in the bulk material.

OBJECTIVES

When you have finished this section you should be able to:

- state and explain the trends in **melting points** and **boiling points** within Groups I and II;
- describe and explain the difference in **hardness** for the s-block metals.

1.5 Melting points and boiling points

We start this section by considering the trends in melting points and boiling points of the s-block elements.

Most of the differences in bulk properties can be interpreted in terms of the strengths of metallic bonds. The strengths of these bonds are dependent on the following factors:

a atomic size,
b number of electrons in the outer shell of each atom,
c metallic crystal structure.

Remembering these points, and what you have already learned about metallic bonding in ILPAC Volume 3, Bonding and Structure, attempt the next exercise.

EXERCISE 6
Answers on page 146

Look up the melting points of the elements in Groups I and II using your data book. For each group in turn, plot the melting point values on the vertical axis against atomic number on the horizontal axis, on the same piece of graph paper. Then answer the questions below.

a What is the general trend in each group? (Look for a simple overall trend, e.g. increase or decrease, ignoring the occasional 'hiccup'.)

b Suggest an explanation for the trends in terms of 'atomic' size. (Hint: think of the delocalised electrons as a type of 'cement' holding the ions together. Thin 'cement' leads to weak metallic bonding.)

c Why does each Group II element have a higher melting point than the Group I element in the same period?

d Liquid sodium has been used as a coolant in some nuclear reactors. Give reasons why you think it is preferable to water. (Use your data book.)

Sodium is used as a coolant in the nuclear reactor at Dounray.

The graph in Fig. 3 shows that similar trends exist in the boiling points of the s-block elements.

Figure 3
The boiling points of the s-block elements.

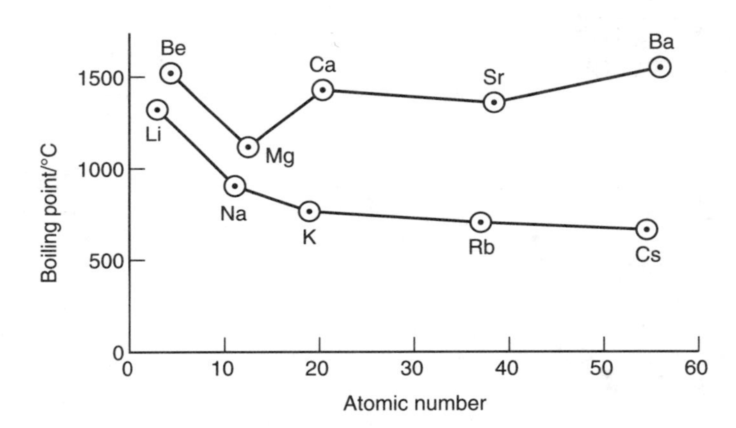

The changes in Group I are irregular and this is partly due to differences in crystal structure of the metals in this group. The following exercise deals with the type of crystal structure found in the s-block elements.

EXERCISE 7

Answer on page 147

Look up the structures of the metals in Groups I and II in your data book. How does this help explain the irregularities in Fig. 3 for Group II?

You should remember that there is no simple relationship between crystal structure and melting point and boiling point. We can only conclude that crystal structure affects physical properties.

We now turn to one of the more easily observed properties of the s-block elements – their hardness as metals.

1.6 Hardness

You probably already know that all the alkali metals are soft enough to be cut with a knife, whereas the first three alkaline earth metals are not. In the following exercise you suggest explanations for this.

Cutting a slice from a lump of sodium held under oil.

EXERCISE 8
Answers on page 147

a Give a reason, based on the simple model of metallic bonding, to explain why Group II elements are much harder to cut than Group I elements.
b Explain why the metals from each group become easier to cut with increasing atomic number.

The last few sections have given you a picture of the physical nature and characteristics of the s-block elements. We now go on to consider their chemical properties, and test the predictions you have made, on the basis of ionisation energies, concerning the reactivity of the elements.

CHAPTER 2

CHEMICAL PROPERTIES

The s-block elements are the most reactive metals in the whole Periodic Table and combine directly with the majority of non-metals. We have selected four reactions to illustrate trends in reactivity. (You will not handle beryllium or its compounds because they are very toxic.)

OBJECTIVES

When you have finished this chapter you should be able to:

- illustrate **trends in reactivity** by reference to the reactions of s-block elements with **water**, **dilute acids**, **oxygen and nitrogen**;
- identify the **types of oxide** formed by the s-block elements as **basic** or amphoteric;
- state how the various **oxides of s-block elements** react with water, giving equations for the reactions.

Most textbooks have a section on the chemical reactions of the s-block elements, either taken together, or in a separate chapter for each group. Read about these reactions, noting particularly the ones mentioned in the objectives above.

We start this chapter with the reactions of the s-block elements with water.

2.1 Reaction with water

This reaction is often used to illustrate the general trend of increasing reactivity from the top of Groups I and II to the bottom. If you haven't seen the reactions of lithium, sodium, potassium, magnesium and calcium with water, ask your teacher to demonstrate them. Now do the next exercises, which are concerned with the reactivity of the s-block elements towards water.

A piece of potassium rushing about on the surface of some water as it reacts.

EXERCISE 9
Answers on page 147

a Write a general equation for the reaction between an alkali metal and water, using M as the symbol for a metal.
b When the alkali metals react with water, a flame is seen for potassium but not for sodium. Why is this?

EXERCISE 10
Answers on page 147

a Describe the reaction between calcium and water, and write an equation.
b Magnesium can also be shown to react with water, using the apparatus in Fig. 4.

Figure 4

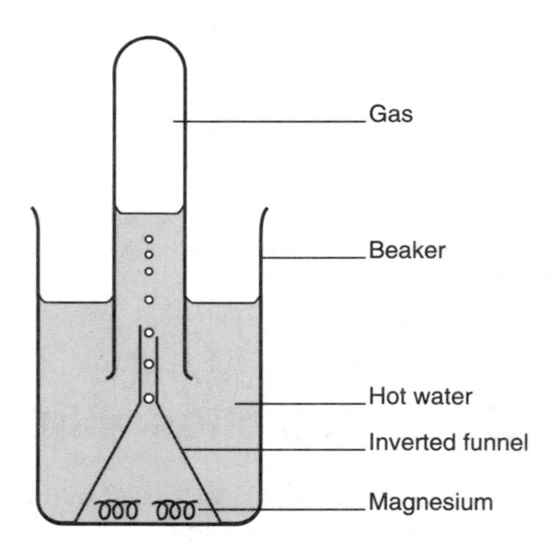

i) Why is **hot** water used in the experiment?
ii) What is the gas produced and how is it tested?

c How would you expect beryllium and barium to react with water?

EXERCISE 11
Answers on page 148

Figure 5 shows an experiment which demonstrates that hot magnesium reacts vigorously with steam.

Figure 5

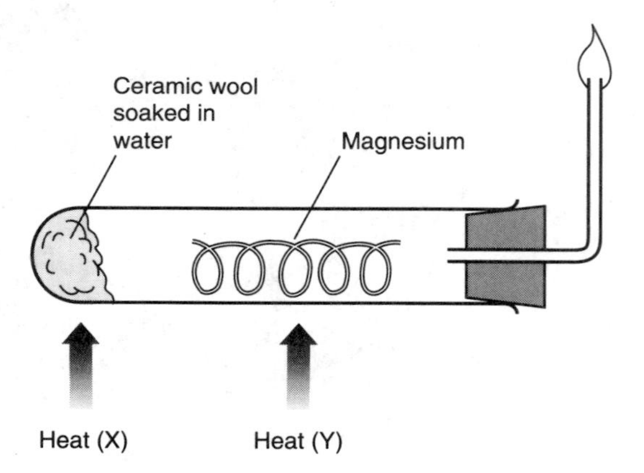

a Select from the following the best position(s) for the Bunsen burner:
i) position (Y) only;
ii) position (X) only;
iii) (Y) initially then (X);
iv) (X) initially then (Y);
v) (Y) at first, then alternating between (X) and (Y).

b Explain your answer to **a**.
c Write a balanced equation for the reaction taking place.

Next, we consider the reaction of the s-block elements with dilute acids.

2.2 Reaction with dilute acids

Here we restrict our discussion to dilute, non-oxidising acids, namely hydrochloric acid and sulphuric acid. Some organic acids such as dilute ethanoic (acetic) acid would react in much the same way. Dilute nitric acid reacts with s-block elements in a more complex way as you will find out in ILPAC Volume 12.

You already know how magnesium reacts with dilute acids from your pre-A-level course. In the next exercise, you are asked to predict the reactions of other elements with dilute acids.

EXERCISE 12
Answers on page 148

a How would you expect beryllium to react with dilute sulphuric and hydrochloric acids?

b Which of the following acids will produce hydrogen at a faster rate when added to magnesium ribbon?
i) 0.1 M hydrochloric acid,
ii) 0.1 M ethanoic acid.
Explain your answer.

c Why is it dangerous to place the alkali metals in dilute acids?

Another sign of the high reactivity of s-block elements is the ease with which they combine with oxygen, forming various oxides.

2.3 Reaction with oxygen

You have probably seen sodium burning in air with a yellow flame, but the white product remaining is not pure sodium oxide, Na_2O, as you might expect. In fact, it is mainly sodium peroxide, Na_2O_2.

With the exception of lithium and beryllium, all s-block elements produce more than one oxide. In addition to the monoxides you met in your pre-A-level course, there are also some peroxides and superoxides. The three types of oxide are all ionic, and the ions are related as follows:

$$\underset{\text{monoxide}}{O^{2-}} \xrightarrow{\frac{1}{2}O_2} \underset{\text{peroxide}}{O_2^{2-}} \xrightarrow{O_2} \underset{\text{superoxide}}{2O_2^-}$$

Read about these oxides in your textbook(s). (Superoxides are sometimes called hyperoxides.) You should know which oxide(s) is/are formed when each element is burned in an adequate supply of oxygen or air. Also look for the reactions of these oxides with water and find out which monoxide is amphoteric. You should then be able to do the exercises which follow.

EXERCISE 13
Answers on page 148

a Use the flow scheme given above to:
i) write an equation for the conversion of sodium monoxide to sodium peroxide,
ii) suggest the conditions under which sodium monoxide might be prepared.

b i) Which of the oxides shown in the flow scheme is not normally formed by Group II elements?
ii) Write down the names and formulae of the oxides formed directly by the alkaline earth metals.
iii) When barium peroxide is heated, it decomposes to produce a colourless gas. Write an equation for this decomposition.

An important point about most s-block monoxides is that they are basic. The next exercise is concerned with one s-block monoxide which is amphoteric.

EXERCISE 14

Answers on page 148

a Which s-block monoxide is amphoteric?

b Give equations to show how this oxide reacts with:

i) sodium hydroxide solution,

ii) dilute nitric acid.

Peroxides are also basic, although when they react with water, they not only produce the hydroxides of the metals but also other products. The next short experiment illustrates this point.

EXPERIMENT 1 Reaction between sodium peroxide and water

Aim

The purpose of this experiment is to identify the products formed when sodium peroxide, Na_2O_2, reacts with water.

Introduction

When the s-block monoxides dissolve in water, they produce hydroxide ions which make the resulting solutions alkaline. For example,

$$CaO\ (s) + H_2O\ (l) \rightarrow Ca(OH)_2\ (aq)$$

In this experiment, you will note the pH of the resulting solution when sodium peroxide, Na_2O_2, reacts with water, and identify other products which are also formed.

One of the products you will be asked to test for is hydrogen peroxide, H_2O_2. A very sensitive test for this is one which involves shaking it with orange potassium dichromate(VI) solution, $K_2Cr_2O_7$, dilute sulphuric acid and 2-methylbutan-1-ol, $C_5H_{11}OH$. If a blue colour develops in the organic layer, then hydrogen peroxide is present.

(The blue colour is thought to be due to CrO_5, which contains O–O bonds and is stable in 2-methylbutan-1-ol but not in water.)

Requirements

- safety spectacles
- 4 test-tubes in rack
- Bunsen burner and bench mat
- spatula
- sodium peroxide, Na_2O_2
- distilled water
- wood splints
- 3 dropping pipettes
- universal indicator
- potassium dichromate(VI) solution, 0.02 M $K_2Cr_2O_7$
- dilute sulphuric acid, 2 M H_2SO_4
- 2-methylbutan-1-ol (amyl alcohol), $C_5H_{11}OH$

HAZARD WARNING

2-Methylbutan-1-ol is highly flammable. Therefore you **must**:

- **keep the stopper on the bottle when not in use;**
- **keep the liquid away from flames.**

Sodium peroxide is corrosive and a powerful oxidant. Therefore you **must**:

- **wear safety spectacles;**
- **avoid contact with skin.**

Procedure

1. Cautiously add about 0.1 g of sodium peroxide to about 3 cm^3 of distilled water in a test-tube, and immediately test the gas evolved. (What are the possibilities?)
2. To the resulting solution add a few drops of universal indicator.
3. Put a few grains (less than 0.1 g) of sodium peroxide in a test-tube and add the following reagents, in order: 3 cm^3 of distilled water, 3 drops of potassium dichromate solution, 1 cm^3 of 2-methylbutan-1-ol and 3 cm^3 of dilute sulphuric acid. Shake gently and let the two layers separate.
4. Record your observations and conclusions in a copy of Results Table 1.

Results Table 1

Experiment	Observation	Conclusion
Sodium peroxide added to water and universal indicator	Colour of gas . . . . Effect on glowing splint . . . . pH of solution . . .	The gas is . . . . .
Sodium peroxide plus water, added to acidified dichromate solution plus 2-methylbutan-1-ol	Colour of organic (top) layer . . . . Colour of aqueous layer	The colour of the organic layer shows. . . . .

(Specimen results on page 148.)

Questions

Answers on page 148

1. At 0°C, sodium peroxide reacts with water without the evolution of oxygen. Hydrogen peroxide is detected at this temperature.
   a Write an equation for this reaction.
   b The evolution of oxygen at higher temperatures is believed to be due to a secondary reaction. Write an equation for this secondary reaction.
   c What products are likely to be obtained if sodium peroxide is added to very hot water? Give a balanced equation.
2. **a** Predict the reaction between barium peroxide and ice-cold water. Give a balanced equation in your answer.
   b Hydrogen peroxide can be prepared in the laboratory by adding barium peroxide to ice-cold dilute sulphuric acid.
   i) Write an equation for this reaction.
   ii) Why do you think dilute sulphuric acid is used in place of water?

3. All s-block oxides (apart from BeO) are basic oxides and thus react with water to form hydroxides, and with acidic substances to form salts. How would you expect the following oxides to react with carbon dioxide?
   i) Na_2O, ii) Na_2O_2, iii) KO_2.

You should now be able to do the following Teacher-marked Exercise, which is taken from a past A-level paper. We suggest that, before you start, you discuss with fellow students and/or your teacher what is meant by the phrase 'most economical to carry' in the context of the question.

EXERCISE
Teacher-marked

1. ^{18}O is a stable oxygen isotope. By means of equations, show how it would be possible to obtain from $H_2{}^{18}O$ samples of **a** $^{18}O_2$ (g), **b** a solution of $H_2{}^{18}O_2$ in $H_2{}^{18}O$.
2. The atmosphere in a manned spacecraft needs to be purified from exhaled carbon dioxide and replenished with oxygen. Write equations for the reactions between carbon dioxide and **a** lithium oxide, Li_2O, **b** sodium peroxide, Na_2O_2, and **c** potassium superoxide, KO_2.
   Which of the following systems would be the most economical to carry in a spacecraft for regeneration of the atmosphere? Give your reasons.
   i) lithium oxide and liquid oxygen,
   ii) sodium peroxide and liquid oxygen,
   iii) potassium superoxide alone.
   (Use relative atomic masses to the nearest whole number.)

We have already mentioned that lithium and beryllium are not typical of their groups. A further illustration of this is provided by the formation of their oxides. Table 2 summarises the facts about the s-block oxides. Study this table and the following paragraphs in preparation for a Revealing Exercise.

Table 2
Oxides of the s-block elements

Type of oxide	Elements which form oxides directly in an adequate supply of air	Elements which form oxides indirectly by other methods
Monoxide, O^{2-}	Li Be Mg Ca Sr Ba	all Group I and II
Peroxide, $O_2{}^{2-}$	Na Ba	all except Be
Superoxide, $O_2{}^{-}$	K Rb Cs	Na (with difficulty)

Atomic and ionic size play a very important role in determining both the chemical behaviour and structure of the s-block compounds. For example, as you learned in ILPAC Volume 3, Bonding and Structure, small cations have a high polarising effect on large anions. This leads to a degree of covalent character in ionic compounds and so affects the chemical properties of such compounds (e.g. those of Li and Be).

Furthermore, the relative sizes of the cations and anions can determine the type of structure adopted – in many cases the radii are such that no stable structure can form at all.

In the following Revealing Exercise, you explore some possible reasons for the variety of oxides formed by the s-block elements.

EXERCISE
Revealing

Q1 How does the polarising power of the cation change as Groups I and II are descended? Explain your answer.

A1 Polarising power decreases as each group is descended. The smaller the cation, the greater its polarising power (for the same charge). Since ionic size increases down each group, then polarising power decreases.

Q2 How does the polarising power of Li^+ compare with that of Be^{2+}? Explain your answer.

A2 Be^{2+} has a greater polarising power than Li^+. This is because Be^{2+} is smaller and more highly charged than Li^+. Be^{2+}, therefore, distorts the charge clouds around an anion more.

Q3 Which of the following anions is more easily polarised – the peroxide ion, O_2^{2-}, or the monoxide ion, O^{2-}? Explain your answers.

A3 Peroxide ion. It is much larger than the monoxide ion and its electron cloud is therefore more easily distorted.

Q4 Explain, in terms of ionic size and polarising power, why it is extremely difficult to prepare lithium peroxide and why there are no reports at all that beryllium peroxide has been prepared.

A4 The small cations greatly distort the electron cloud around the peroxide ions. The more the electron cloud is distorted, the more likely it is for the compound to decompose. Because Be^{2+} distorts the anion more than Li^+, beryllium peroxide is even more unstable than lithium peroxide.

It is also rather difficult for very small cations such as Li^+ and Be^{2+} to be surrounded by large peroxide ions in a stable crystal lattice.

Q5 Why does barium form a peroxide more readily than any other element in its group?

A5 It is the largest cation in its group and therefore has the least polarising power. It is also more able to form a stable crystal structure with large peroxide ions, since its larger size gives more room for large peroxide ions to pack around it.

Q6 Suggest reasons why, of all the s-block elements, only K, Rb and Cs readily form superoxides.

A6 The larger size of K^+, Rb^+ and Cs^+ ions allows superoxide ions to pack comfortably around them. Ba^{2+} is very slightly larger than K^+ but still does not easily form a superoxide because it is more polarising than K^+. (See Fig. 2, page 6 for ionic radii.)

Other anomalies in the chemistry of lithium and beryllium can be seen by considering the reactions between nitrogen and the s-block elements. Furthermore, these reactions illustrate the diagonal relationship between lithium and magnesium.

2.4 Reaction with nitrogen

Some of the s-block metals, when burned in air, form nitrogen-containing compounds called nitrides. Such two-element compounds are often called binary compounds.

Look up nitrides in your textbook(s). Find out which s-block elements form them and note their formulae. This will help you to do the next exercise.

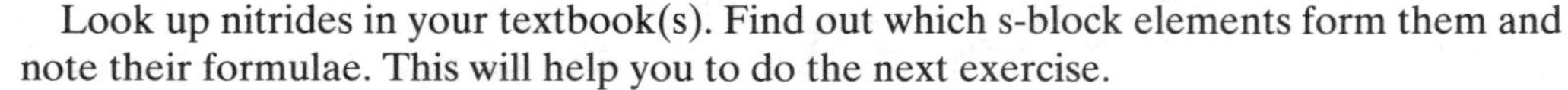

EXERCISE 15
Answers on page 149

a Write down the formulae of the nitrides formed by direct reaction between the s-block elements and nitrogen.
b Give balanced equations for the reactions between nitrogen and i) lithium, ii) magnesium.
c Are lithium and beryllium typical of their groups regarding nitride formation? Explain.
d How does nitride formation illustrate the diagonal relationship between lithium and magnesium?

Most of the reactions you have studied so far in this unit involve reduction and oxidation (redox), with the s-block metals behaving as reducing agents. The chemical reactions of the s-block metals can be summarised by the following half-equation:

$$\mathbf{M \rightarrow M^{n+} + ne^-}$$

↑	↑	
metal	**electron**	**where $n = 1$ for Group I metals**
		$n = 2$ for Group II metals

In the next section, we consider the trends in reducing power of the s-block elements and also link electron loss to metallic character.

2.5 General properties related to electron loss

OBJECTIVES

When you have finished this section you should be able to:

- state and explain the **trends in reducing power** of the Group I and II elements;
- state and explain the trends in **metallic character** in each group;
- illustrate the powerful **reducing properties** of the s-block elements by referring to their **reactions with hydrogen**.

The next exercise links ionisation energies to the reducing powers of the elements in Groups I and II.

EXERCISE 16
Answers on page 149

Use ionisation energies to predict the trends in reducing power as Groups I and II are descended.

The s-block elements have many uses as reducing agents in both organic and inorganic chemistry: e.g. sodium in ethanol, and sodium/mercury amalgam are commonly used in organic chemistry while sodium and magnesium are used in the manufacture of titanium.

In ILPAC Volume 3, Bonding and Structure, you learned that metals are usually defined in terms of their chemical properties, i.e. a metal is an element which tends to form positive ions by losing electrons in chemical reactions. It follows from this that **the greater the tendency to lose electrons, the more metallic the element becomes**. With this statement in mind, attempt the next exercise.

EXERCISE 17
Answers on page 149

a How does metallic character change as Groups I and II are descended?
b In the s-block, which is:
i) the most metallic element,
ii) the least metallic element?
c Support your answer in **b** ii) by referring to the acid–base nature of its oxide.

You will know from your pre-A-level course that hydrogen is a good reducing agent. Only a more powerful reducing agent will be able to force an electron into a hydrogen atom and thus reduce it. Most of the s-block elements are able to do this when they react with hydrogen gas at temperatures up to 700°C. The resulting binary compounds are called hydrides.

2.6 Reaction with hydrogen

Read about the s-block hydrides in your textbook(s). Find out which s-block hydrides are formed by direct combination with hydrogen, and what type of structure they possess. Then you should be able to do the following exercise.

EXERCISE 18
Answers on page 149

a Which s-block elements react directly with hydrogen?
b Write equations for the reactions between hydrogen and i) sodium, ii) calcium.
c Which of the s-block hydrides are classified as i) ionic and ii) covalent?
d How would you demonstrate that the ionic hydrides contain the H^- ion?

You will deal with the reactions of the hydrides with water in The Periodic Table unit of this volume.

In order to consolidate your knowledge about the elements, attempt the following Teacher-marked Exercise which is taken from an A-level essay paper. Before you start answering the question, look through your notes to remind yourself of the important points.

EXERCISE
Teacher-marked

Explain the meaning of the terms 'first electron affinity', 'first ionisation energy' and 'electronegativity'. Discuss the trends in first ionisation energy and electronegativity in Groups I and II of the Periodic Table. In each case, relate your answer to the chemical properties of the elements.

Mention and explain three other trends which occur in one or both of these periodic groups.

Discuss briefly the relationships which exist between the two groups of elements.

Having studied the chemistry of the elements and a few compounds, we now concentrate on some other important s-block compounds.

THE s-BLOCK COMPOUNDS

In your study of the elements the atypical behaviour of lithium and beryllium became apparent and, furthermore, similarities between lithium and magnesium were beginning to emerge. These points will also be illustrated as you work through the compounds of the s-block metals, starting with their thermal decompositions.

THE EFFECT OF HEAT ON SOME s-BLOCK COMPOUNDS

In this chapter you will test the effect of heat on the solid nitrates and carbonates of Groups I and II, and briefly refer to their hydrogencarbonates, hydroxides and sulphates.

OBJECTIVES

When you have finished this chapter you should be able to:
- state the effect of **heat on the nitrates and carbonates** of the s-block elements;
- state and explain the trends in **thermal stabilities** of the nitrates and carbonates for each group.

You start this chapter with an experiment. We advise you to work in pairs and divide the tasks so that you do not use too much laboratory time.

EXPERIMENT 2 Heating the nitrates and carbonates of the s-block elements

Aim

The aim of this experiment is two-fold: to identify the products of thermal decomposition and to estimate the order of thermal stability of these compounds.

Introduction

In this experiment you heat small samples of the nitrate and carbonate of each element, using the same size flame. You then note the time taken to detect the products of decomposition. Your pre-A-level experience should enable you to recognise nitrogen dioxide, NO_2 (brown gas), produced from nitrates, and carbon dioxide, CO_2, from carbonates. In order to save time, we suggest that you work in pairs, one student on each part of the experiment.

Requirements

- safety spectacles
- 30 test-tubes
- 2 test-tube racks
- labels for test-tubes
- solid nitrates and carbonates (anhydrous if possible) of Groups I and II
- 2 spatulas
- retort stand, clamp and boss
- bent delivery tube to fit test-tubes
- lime-water
- 2 Bunsen burners and mats
- 2 stop-clocks (or watches)
- 2 test-tube holders
- wood splints
- hydrochloric acid, dilute, 2 M HCl

HAZARD WARNING

Barium compounds are toxic if swallowed or absorbed through the skin.
- **Avoid contact with skin.**

Nitrogen dioxide is a toxic gas.
- **Heat nitrates in a fume cupboard.**

Nitrates are strong oxidising agents.
- **Do not allow pieces of glowing splint to drop onto hot nitrates.**

Procedure A

Effect of heat on carbonates.

1. Set up two rows of four or five test-tubes each.
2. Label the test-tubes in the first row with the names of the Group I carbonates, and the second row with the names of the Group II carbonates.
3. To each test-tube add a spatula-measure of the appropriate carbonate.
4. For the first carbonate, set up the apparatus as shown in Fig. 6.

Figure 6

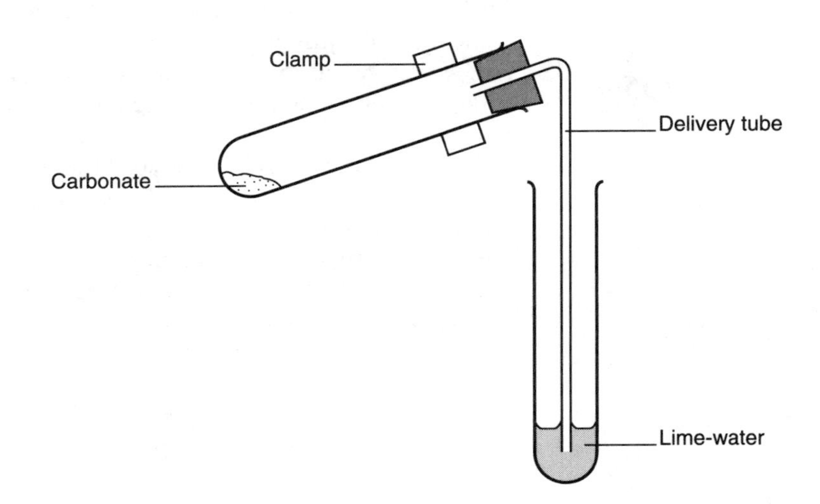

5. Start the clock at the moment you begin heating the carbonate by holding the end of the tube just above the inner blue cone of a roaring Bunsen flame. It is important that you can reproduce this method of heating so that your comparisons with other carbonates will be valid.
6. Note the time for the lime-water to just turn milky (if it does at all) and, before removing the flame, prevent 'suckback' by lifting the delivery tube out of the lime-water. This is simply done by lifting the clamp and stand.
7. Repeat the heating procedure for each carbonate in turn, making sure that the tube height and the flame size are the same for each one.
8. Record your results in a copy of Results Table 2.

Results Table 2
Effect of heat on the s-block carbonates

Carbonate	Time to detect CO_2	Observations
Li_2CO_3		
Na_2CO_3		
K_2CO_3		
Rb_2CO_3*		
Cs_2CO_3*		
$MgCO_3$		
$CaCO_3$		
$SrCO_3$		
$BaCO_3$		

*If available.
(Specimen results on page 149.)

Procedure B

Effect of heat on nitrates. (To be done in a fume cupboard.)

9. Heat small quantities of sodium nitrate and magnesium nitrate separately, in clean test-tubes. In each case, test for oxygen and note the appearance of any brown fumes. (This will give you an idea of the products you can expect when Groups I and II nitrates are heated.)
10. Set up two rows of four test-tubes each containing the appropriate nitrates, as you did for the carbonates.
11. Start the clock at the moment you begin heating the first nitrate by holding the end of the test-tube just above the blue cone of a roaring Bunsen flame.
12. Test for oxygen at short regular intervals (place the glowing splint in the same part of the test-tube) and also look for the first signs of a brown gas. (A white background is helpful.)
13. In a copy of Results Table 3, record the time for the first appearance of brown fumes or when oxygen is detected. (Whichever method of detection you choose for one member of a group you must also apply to the other members of the same group.) Continue heating for another minute.
14. Repeat steps 11, 12 and 13 for the other nitrates in turn.
15. To the **cold** solid residue remaining after each nitrate is heated add a few drops of dilute hydrochloric acid and warm.

Results Table 3
Effect of heat on the s-block nitrates

Nitrate	Time to detect O_2 or NO_2	Observations	Effect of adding dilute HCl to cold residue
$LiNO_3$			
$NaNO_3$			
KNO_3			
$RbNO_3$*			
$CsNO_3$*			
$Mg(NO_3)_2$			
$Ca(NO_3)_2$			
$Sr(NO_3)_2$			
$Ba(NO_3)_2$			

*If available.
(Specimen results on page 150.)

Questions
Answers on page 150

1. Explain why many of these nitrates rapidly turn into colourless liquids on first heating, but on further heating become white solids again, before they decompose. (Hint: look at the formulae of the nitrates on the reagent bottles.)
2. Which of the nitrates and carbonates of Group I most resemble those of Group II in their reaction to heat?
3. Describe the trend in thermal stability of the nitrates and carbonates as each group is descended.
4. How do Group I nitrates and carbonates compare with their Group II counterparts in terms of thermal stability?
5. Write balanced equations, where applicable, for the thermal decompositions of:
   a lithium nitrate and lithium carbonate,
   b potassium nitrate and potassium carbonate,
   c magnesium nitrate and magnesium carbonate.
6. Why are brown fumes produced when dilute HCl is added to the cold residue obtained when many of the Group I nitrates are heated?

The reactions you have just dealt with are those of the anions. The more the cation distorts the anion, the more likely the anion will undergo decomposition. Using this idea and what you already know about the polarising effect of cations on large polarisable anions, do the following exercises.

EXERCISE 19
Answers on page 150

a Explain why the thermal stabilities of the nitrates and carbonates of Groups I and II increase as each group is descended.
b Why is sodium carbonate much more stable to heat than magnesium carbonate?

EXERCISE 20
Answers on page 151

The decomposition temperatures* of the Group II carbonates are shown below, in °C.

$BeCO_3$	$MgCO_3$	$CaCO_3$	$SrCO_3$	$BaCO_3$
~100	540	900	1290	1360

*Decomposition temperature is the temperature at which the pressure of CO_2 reaches one atmosphere. Some CO_2 can be detected below this temperature.

a Suggest why beryllium carbonate is particularly unstable. (In fact, it must be kept in an atmosphere of CO_2.)
b Why is lithium carbonate (which decomposes at approximately 900°C) much more stable than beryllium carbonate?
c Why do you think carbon dioxide is not detected if barium carbonate is heated in a Bunsen flame?

The model we used previously to explain the comparative thermal stabilities of the s-block nitrates and carbonates can easily be applied to other s-block compounds with large polarisable anions. These include hydrogencarbonates, sulphates and even hydroxides, all of which we discuss below.

3.1 The hydrogencarbonates, sulphates and hydroxides

OBJECTIVES

When you have finished this section you should be able to:

- predict the trends in thermal stabilities for the s-block of the following solids:
  i) hydrogencarbonates,
  ii) sulphates,
  iii) hydroxides;
- state the products of thermal decomposition (if any) of the following s-block compounds:
  i) hydrogencarbonates,
  ii) sulphates,
  iii) hydroxides.

We start by considering the hydrogencarbonates.

3.2 The hydrogencarbonates

Read about the effect of heat on hydrogencarbonates and find out which s-block hydrogencarbonates exist as solids. You should then be able to do the following exercise.

EXERCISE 21
Answers on page 151

a Suggest a reason why lithium hydrogencarbonate is the only Group I hydrogencarbonate which does not exist as a solid.
b Write an equation to show the effect of heat on sodium hydrogencarbonate.
c Explain the following facts:
  i) self-raising flour, which is often used to make cakes, contains sodium hydrogencarbonate (sometimes called by its old name – sodium bicarbonate, or baking powder);
  ii) stalagmites and stalactites form in limestone ($CaCO_3$) caves.
d In what way is lithium hydrogencarbonate similar to magnesium hydrogencarbonate?
e How would you distinguish between sodium carbonate and sodium hydrogencarbonate?
f Predict the trend in thermal stability of the Group I hydrogencarbonates.
g Suggest reasons why no Group II hydrogencarbonates exist as solids (they do exist in aqueous solution).

Stalagmites and stalactites inside Blanchard Spring Caverns, Arkansas, U.S.A.

We now consider the s-block sulphates.

3.3 The sulphates

Read about the effect of heat on the s-block sulphates so that you can do the exercise which follows.

EXERCISE 22
Answers on page 151

All Group I sulphates are thermally stable whereas some decomposition does occur with Group II sulphates at high temperatures.

a Magnesium sulphate decomposes at about 600°C. Write the equation for this decomposition.

b What trend would you expect in the thermal stability of the sulphates as Group II is descended? Give a reason for your answer.

We now ask you to make some predictions about the s-block hydroxides.

3.4 The hydroxides

You are probably already familiar with the solid hydroxides of sodium and potassium from your pre-A-level work. They are white deliquescent solids and are sold as pellets, sticks or flakes.

Read about the effect of heat on the s-block hydroxides so that you can answer the questions in the exercise which follows.

EXERCISE 23
Answers on page 151

a Predict which of the two groups, I or II, has the more thermally stable hydroxides.
b Predict the trend in the thermal stability of the s-block hydroxides as each group is descended.
c Do the data in Table 3 back up the trend you predicted in **b**? Explain.
d Do you think that lithium hydroxide will be different from the other Group I hydroxides in terms of thermal stability? Give an equation if you think it is relevant.

Table 3

Compound	ΔH°(298 K) for the reaction $M(OH)_2\,(s) \rightarrow MO\,(s) + H_2O\,(l)$
$Be(OH)_2$	+54 kJ mol^{-1}
$Mg(OH)_2$	+81 kJ mol^{-1}
$Ca(OH)_2$	+109 kJ mol^{-1}
$Sr(OH)_2$	+127 kJ mol^{-1}
$Ba(OH)_2$	+146 kJ mol^{-1}

The s-block hydroxides have many commercial uses, e.g. sodium hydroxide is the cheapest industrial alkali and is used in the manufacture of rayon, paper, soap, oven-cleaners, etc. We include a short study of the manufacture of sodium hydroxide in the appendix to this unit (pages 39–43).

A suspension of magnesium hydroxide in water (sometimes called milk of magnesia) is used to treat acid indigestion, because it is a weak alkali.

The fact that magnesium hydroxide forms a suspension in water indicates that, unlike most Group I hydroxides, it is not very soluble in water. We take a closer look at the solubility of s-block compounds in the next chapter.

CHAPTER 4 THE SOLUBILITY OF THE s-BLOCK COMPOUNDS IN WATER

Most of the alkali metal salts are soluble in water but this is not true of the alkaline earths, which have a large number of insoluble salts.

In this chapter we will examine the trends in solubility for various Group II compounds and illustrate more anomalous properties of lithium.

OBJECTIVES

When you have finished this chapter you should be able to:

- state the **trends in solubility** of the following Group II compounds: **a** hydroxides, **b** chlorides, **c** sulphates, **d** sulphites, **e** carbonates;
- explain why
  - **a** **barium chloride** solution is used to detect the presence of sulphate ions;
  - **b** **barium hydroxide** solution can be used to detect small quantities of carbon dioxide.

We begin this section with an experiment in which you examine qualitatively the trends in solubility of various Group II compounds.

EXPERIMENT 3 The solubility of some salts of Group II elements

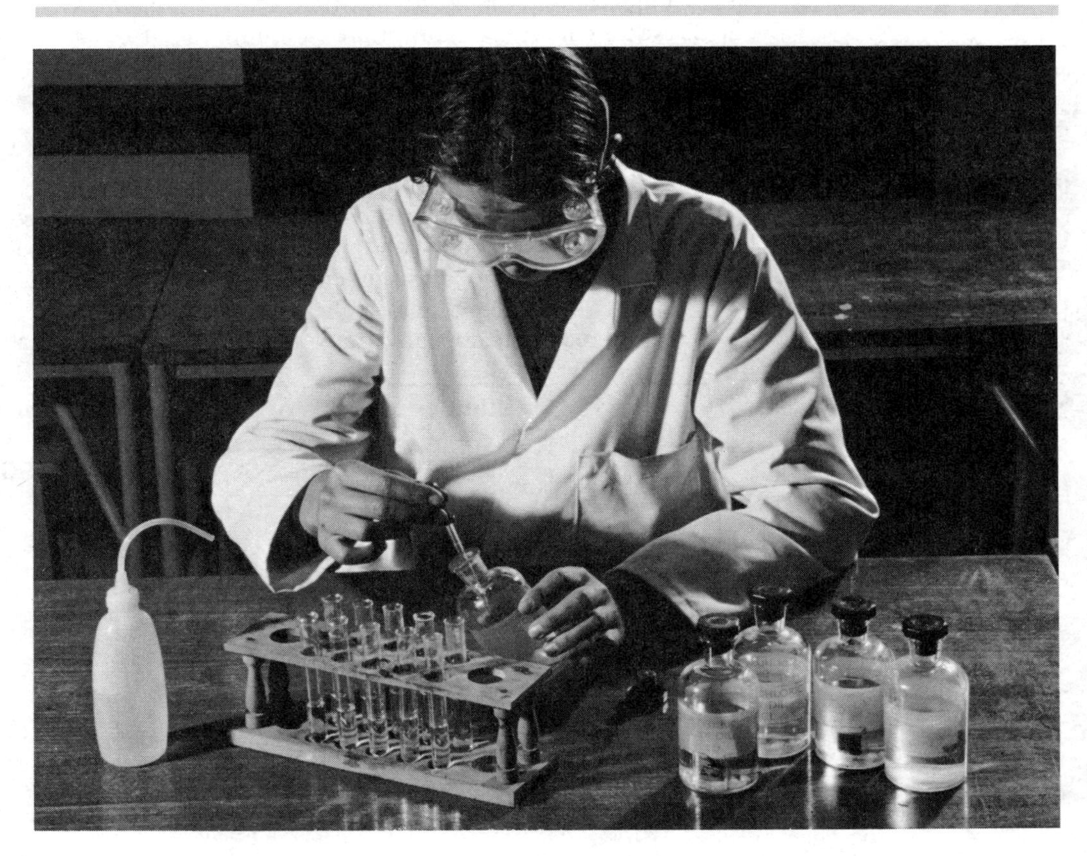

Aim

The aim of this experiment is to demonstrate the trends in solubility of the Group II carbonates, sulphates, sulphites and hydroxides.

Introduction

In this experiment, you add each of the anion solutions to 1 cm^3 of each cation solution provided, drop by drop, until the first sign of a precipitate appears. For each salt, the solubility is proportional to the number of drops of anion solution added.

Requirements

- 16 test-tubes
- 4 test-tube racks
- labels for test-tubes
- 5 teat pipettes (marked off at 1 cm^3)
- 0.1 M solutions of the following cations: Mg^{2+}, Ca^{2+}, Sr^{2+}, Ba^{2+}
- 1.0 M solution of OH^- ions
- 0.5 M solution of SO_4^{2-} and SO_3^{2-} ions
- 0.05 M solution of CO_3^{2-} ions
- distilled water

HAZARD WARNING

- 1.0 M solutions of OH^- ions are corrosive. Therefore you must wear safety spectacles;
- Solutions of sulphite ions, SO_3^{2-}, release a toxic gas, sulphur dioxide if acid is added. Take care with disposal of these solutions, especially if you suffer from asthma.

Procedure

1. Set up four rows of four test-tubes each.
2. For each row, label the first test-tube Mg^{2+}, the second test-tube Ca^{2+}, the third test-tube Sr^{2+} and the fourth test-tube Ba^{2+}.
3. Add 1 cm^3 of the appropriate cation solution to each test-tube, using a teat pipette with a 1 cm^3 mark.
4. Label the first row of test-tubes OH^-, the second row SO_4^{2-}, the third row SO_3^{2-} and the fourth row CO_3^{2-}.
5. Add the solution of OH^-, drop by drop, with shaking, to each cation solution in the first row, until the first sign of a precipitate appears.
6. Record the number of drops of OH^- solution used in a copy of Results Table 4.
7. Repeat steps 5 and 6 with the remaining anions and cations.
8. If a precipitate appears suddenly, during the addition of a drop, then you should classify the precipitate as slight (s) or heavy (h).
9. If no precipitate appears after 40 drops, then write '40+' and regard the salt as soluble.

Results Table 4

Cation solution	Number of drops of anion solution added to give a precipitate			
	OH^-	SO_4^{2-}	SO_3^{2-}	CO_3^{2-}
Mg^{2+}				
Ca^{2+}				
Sr^{2+}				
Ba^{2+}				

(Specimen results on page 152.)

Questions

Answers on page 152

For Group II, what are the trends in solubility of the salts listed below?

a hydroxides,
b sulphates,
c sulphites,
d carbonates.

The exercises which follow extend your knowledge of the solubility of the s-block compounds. You will need to refer to Table 4. Note that solubilities can be quoted in a variety of different units, but they always specify either an amount or a mass of solute dissolved in a given quantity of either solvent or solution.

Table 4 Solubilities of Group II compounds in water at 298 K

Singly charged anions		Doubly charged anions	
Compound	**Solubility /mol per 100 g of water**	**Compound**	**Solubility /mol per 100 g of water**
$MgCl_2$	5.6×10^{-1}	$MgCO_3$	1.3×10^{-4}
$CaCl_2$	5.4×10^{-1}	$CaCO_3$	0.13×10^{-4}
$SrCl_2$	3.5×10^{-1}	$SrCO_3$	0.07×10^{-4}
$BaCl_2$	1.5×10^{-1}	$BaCO_3$	0.09×10^{-4}
$Mg(NO_3)_2$	4.9×10^{-1}	$MgSO_4$	3600×10^{-4}
$Ca(NO_3)_2$	6.2×10^{-1}	$CaSO_4$	11×10^{-4}
$Sr(NO_3)_2$	1.6×10^{-1}	$SrSO_4$	0.62×10^{-4}
$Ba(NO_3)_2$	0.4×10^{-1}	$BaSO_4$	0.009×10^{-4}
$Mg(OH)_2$	0.020×10^{-3}	$MgCrO_4$	8500×10^{-4}
$Ca(OH)_2$	1.5×10^{-3}	$CaCrO_4$	870×10^{-4}
$Sr(OH)_2$	3.4×10^{-3}	$SrCrO_4$	5.9×10^{-4}
$Ba(OH)_2$	15×10^{-3}	$BaCrO_4$	0.011×10^{-4}

EXERCISE 24

Answers on page 152

a Identify the group trends in solubility for each type of salt listed in Table 4.
b Do the solubilities given above for the carbonates, sulphates and hydroxides agree with your findings in Experiment 3?
c Do singly or doubly charged anions give the more insoluble compounds?

EXERCISE 25

Answers on page 152

a The X-ray photograph in Fig. 7 shows the human stomach (black region) filled with a suspension of barium sulphate (called barium meal). The stomach can be seen because X-rays are strongly absorbed by barium compounds. (This technique is often used to detect stomach ulcers.)

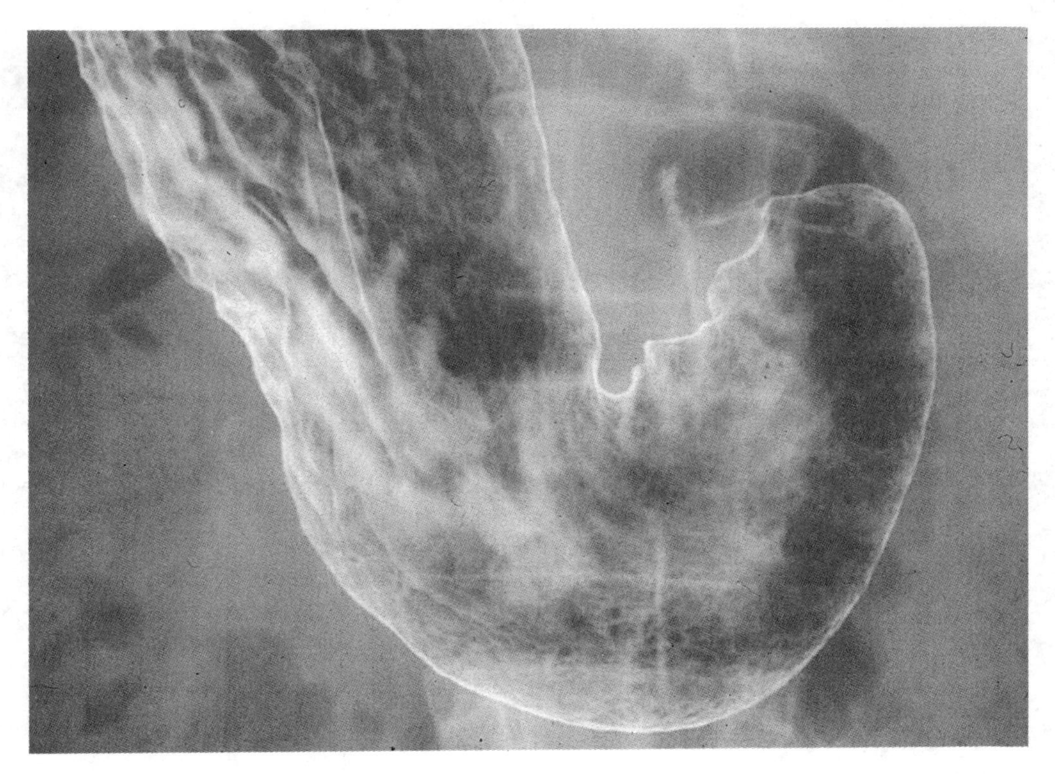

Figure 7 Double-contrast barium meal X-ray image of a healthy human stomach, showing the contoured appearance of its lining.

If barium compounds are (generally speaking) very poisonous, why can barium sulphate be swallowed as barium meal without harming the patient?

b Barium chloride solution is often used to confirm the presence of sulphate ions by adding it to the suspected sulphate solution, previously acidified with dilute hydrochloric acid.
   i) Why is barium chloride solution used, and what would you observe in the test-tube if it were mixed as described above?
   ii) Write an ionic equation for the reaction between barium ions and sulphate ions.
   iii) What is the purpose of the dilute hydrochloric acid?

c Barium hydroxide solution is occasionally used instead of lime-water, $Ca(OH)_2$ (aq), for detecting small quantities of carbon dioxide. It is also used instead of sodium hydroxide in titrations where it is important to exclude dissolved carbonate ions.
   i) Suggest one reason why barium hydroxide might be preferred in these uses.
   ii) State any disadvantage(s) of using barium hydroxide solution.
   iii) Write an equation for the reaction between barium hydroxide solution and carbon dioxide.

The next exercise concerns the solubilities of some compounds of alkali metals.

EXERCISE 26
Answers on page 153

a Look up and record the solubilities of the carbonates and hydroxides of Group I elements.
b What are the trends in solubility of the Group I carbonates and hydroxides?
c Do these trends agree with those of the Group II carbonates and hydroxides?
d Are the hydroxides and carbonates of Group I more or less soluble than those of Group II? (See Table 4.)
e Does the general statement about divalent anions forming less soluble salts compared with univalent anions apply to the Group I hydroxides and carbonates?

You have seen that, for each type of s-block compound, there is a group trend in solubility, but the trends are not always the same. In the next section we give some explanations for this.

4.1 Factors determining the solubility of salts

OBJECTIVES

When you have finished this section you should be able to:
- relate the **solubility** of a salt to the **standard enthalpy of solution**;
- show that enthalpy of solution is the difference between **lattice enthalpy** and **hydration enthalpy**;
- show that both lattice enthalpy and hydration enthalpy (and therefore solubility) depend on the charge and radius of the ions concerned.

Detailed explanations for the varying trends in solubility are notoriously difficult and you are expected only to make suggestions about the different factors which influence solubility. As you saw in ILPAC Volumes 2 (Chemical Energetics) and 3 (Bonding and Structure), the two main factors are:

1. the energy input required to separate the ions in the crystal lattice (equal, but opposite in sign, to the lattice enthalpy), and
2. the energy released when the separated ions make bonds with the surrounding water molecules (hydration enthalpy), as shown in Fig. 8.

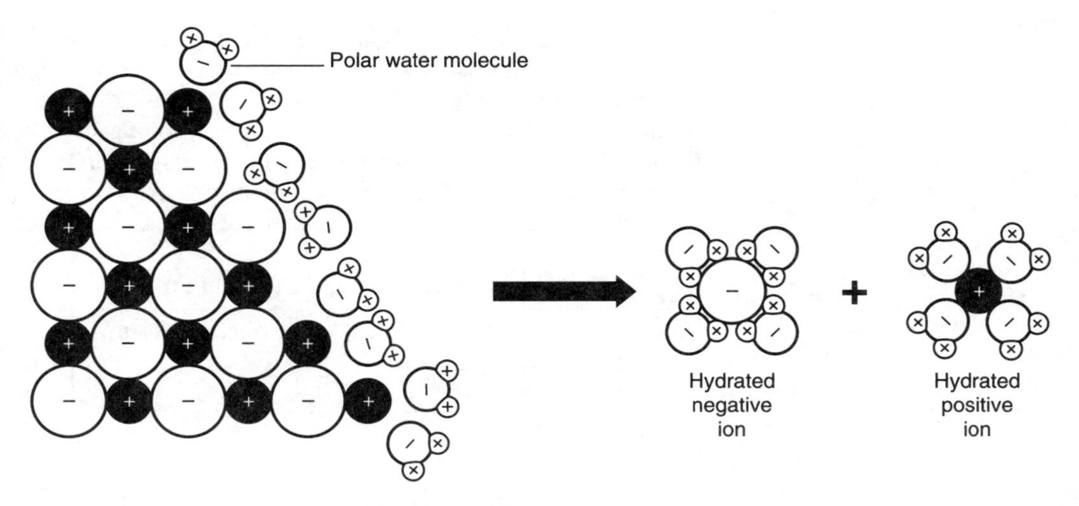

Figure 8
We have shown only one layer of attached water molecules surrounding each ion. There may be several layers, especially around small, highly charged ions.

The difference between these two energy terms is, of course, known as the enthalpy change of solution

$$\Delta H^{\ominus}_{\text{solution}} = \Delta H^{\ominus}_{\text{hydration}} - \Delta H^{\ominus}_{\text{lattice}}$$

Make sure that you understand this by doing the following exercise.

EXERCISE 27

Answers on page 153

a Draw a Hess cycle to show how the enthalpy of solution of anhydrous magnesium chloride, $MgCl_2$, can be found by considering the change as taking place in two stages via separate gaseous ions. Calculate the enthalpy of solution, using the following data:
$\Delta H_{\text{lat}}(MgCl_2) = -2526\ \text{kJ mol}^{-1}$; $\Delta H_{\text{hyd}}(Mg^{2+}) = -1920\ \text{kJ mol}^{-1}$;
$\Delta H_{\text{hyd}}(Cl^-) = -364\ \text{kJ mol}^{-1}$.
b Represent the changes on an energy-level diagram.
c Would you expect $MgCl_2$ to be soluble in water? Explain your answer.

In general terms, if the energy released is greater than the energy input, i.e. if $\Delta H^{\ominus}_{\text{solution}}$ is negative, we expect the crystals to dissolve in water. Clearly, this is not the whole story. You are probably aware that some salts dissolve readily even though they have a positive value for $\Delta H^{\ominus}_{\text{solution}}$. (Try, for example, dissolving some ammonium nitrate in water in a test-tube – you will feel the tube getting cooler!). We cannot adequately explain this without reference to changes in free energy, ΔG, and entropy, ΔS, which are not included in most A-level syllabuses. However, it is generally true that solubility increases as $\Delta H^{\ominus}_{\text{solution}}$ becomes more negative (or less positive). You will find this easier to understand by looking at the energy-level diagrams in Fig. 9.

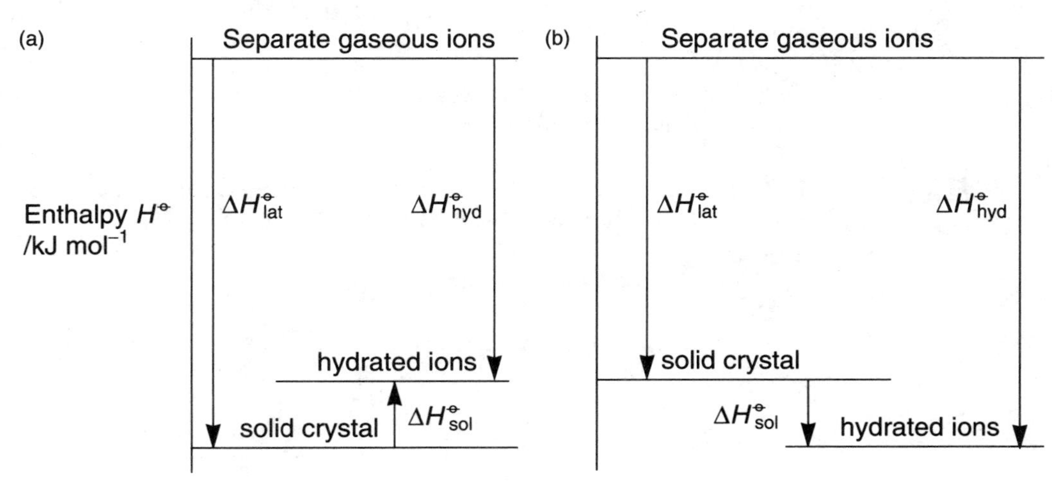

Figure 9
(a) Positive $\Delta H^{\ominus}_{\text{sol}}$ for an insoluble salt.
(b) Negative $\Delta H^{\ominus}_{\text{sol}}$ for a soluble salt.

Both $\Delta H^{\ominus}_{hydration}$ and $\Delta H^{\ominus}_{lattice}$ are large negative quantities and the difference between them, $\Delta H^{\ominus}_{solution}$, is usually relatively small. It is, therefore, not easy to predict, in any individual case, whether $\Delta H^{\ominus}_{solution}$ will be positive or negative. It is even more difficult to predict, or explain, the trends in solubility down a group because we have to consider the effect that the increasing size of the cations has on both $\Delta H^{\ominus}_{hydration}$ and $\Delta H^{\ominus}_{lattice}$ for any particular anion. The general conclusions are summarised below.

	Effect on ΔH_{hyd}	**Effect on ΔH_{lat}**	**Effect on $\Delta H_{solution}$ and solubility**
Increasing cation radius	Becomes less negative	Becomes less negative	Usually ΔH_{hyd} changes more than ΔH_{lat} so that ΔH_{sol} becomes less negative and solubility decreases. However, the opposite is true for very small anions, e.g. F^- and OH^-

The situation is rather simpler when we compare similar salts in Groups I and II. The effect of slightly decreasing radius as we go along a period is masked by the much greater effect of doubling the charge.

	Effect on ΔH_{hyd}	**Effect on ΔH_{lat}**	**Effect on $\Delta H_{solution}$ and solubility**
Increasing cation charge	Becomes more negative	Becomes more negative	ΔH_{lat} changes more than ΔH_{hyd} so that ΔH_{sol} becomes less negative and solubility decreases

You are not likely to have to give a full explanation of all these points but, by referring to your notes on lattice enthalpy and hydration enthalpy from ILPAC Volumes 3 and 4, you should be able to go part of the way in the next two exercises.

EXERCISE 28

Answers on page 154

a Why does the enthalpy of hydration of an ion become less negative as ionic radius increases?

b Why does the lattice enthalpy of an ionic salt become less negative as ionic radius increases?

c The lattice enthalpy of an ionic solid has been shown to be inversely proportional to the square of the internuclear distance (the sum of the radii of the anion and cation).

$$\text{Lattice enthalpy} \propto \frac{1}{(r_{anion} + r_{cation})^2}$$

Use this relationship to explain why the effect on lattice enthalpy of increasing cationic radius is so much greater when anionic radius is very small.

EXERCISE 29

Answers on page 154

The solubility of a salt in water depends upon the lattice energy of the salt and the **hydration energies** of its ions.

a Consider a salt ($M^{2+}A^{2-}$) and write equations (with state symbols) which illustrate the processes associated with these terms:

i) lattice energy,

ii) hydration energy.

b Below is an incomplete diagram of an energy cycle representing the dissolving of the salt $M^{2+}A^{2-}(s)$ in water. Complete a copy of the diagram (showing state symbols) and mark on it the **enthalpy (heat) change of solution**, **lattice energy** and **hydration energy**.

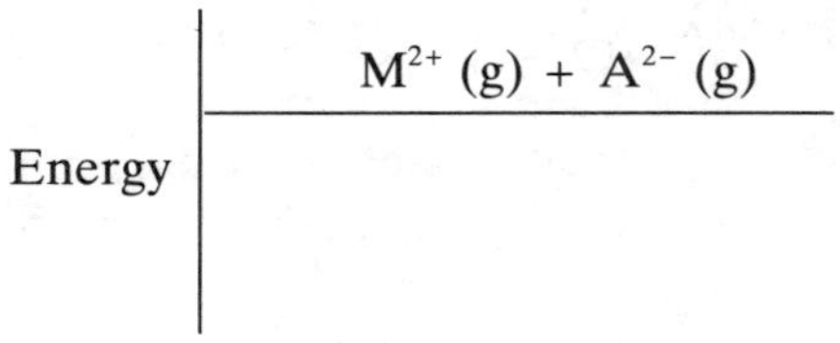

Energy

$M^{2+}(g) + A^{2-}(g)$

c The lattice energies of the sulphates of the elements of Group II do not differ very greatly throughout the group. Explain why magnesium sulphate is readily soluble in water whereas barium sulphate is very sparingly soluble.

Similarities between lithium and magnesium are not evident in the solubilities of their compounds but we have already noted some similarities in other properties. In the next section, we bring together these similarities and discuss the nature of the 'diagonal relationship' between lithium and magnesium.

CHAPTER 5

THE DIAGONAL RELATIONSHIP BETWEEN LITHIUM AND MAGNESIUM

Because of the relative positions of lithium and magnesium in the Periodic Table, their similarities are often referred to as indicating a 'diagonal relationship'. Such a relationship can also be identified between other elements in the first two periods, e.g. beryllium and aluminium, boron and silicon.

OBJECTIVES

When you have finished this chapter you should be able to:

- list some physical and chemical properties which illustrate the **similarities between lithium and magnesium;**
- give an explanation for this **diagonal relationship**.

In the next exercise, you bring together information from various parts of this unit.

EXERCISE 30

Answers on page 155

Copy and complete Table 5, which shows both the diagonal relationship between lithium and magnesium, and also the atypical behaviour of lithium in Group I. We have filled in some parts to give you an idea of the amount of detail you need.

Table 5

Property	Li	Rest of Group I	Mg
Oxide formation	Li_2O (monoxide) formed by direct combination		
Nitride formation			
Effect of heat on nitrates		Stable nitrites (NO_2^-) and oxygen produced	
Effect of heat on carbonates			MgO formed with CO_2
Effect of heat on hydroxides		Thermally stable	
Physical state of hydrogencarbonates	$LiHCO_3$ does not exist as a solid		
Solubility of carbonates	Sparingly soluble		
Solubility of hydroxides		Soluble	

The next exercise shows how similarities in atomic properties between lithium and magnesium can provide an explanation for their diagonal relationship.

EXERCISE 31

Answers on page 155

A

a How does the polarising power of Li^+ compare with that of Be^{2+}?
b How does the polarising power of Mg^{2+} compare with that of Be^{2+}?
c How do you think the polarising power of Li^+ compares with that of Mg^{2+}?
d How does your answer to **c** provide an explanation for similarities such as those observed when the nitrates and carbonates of lithium and magnesium are heated?

In order to consolidate your knowledge of the chemistry of the s-block elements, we suggest that you attempt **one** of the questions which follow as a Teacher-marked Exercise. Look through your notes and make a rough plan before you start writing.

EXERCISE
Teacher-marked

Either
The s-block of the Periodic Table contains Group IA, the alkali metals, and Group IIA, the alkaline earths. Give an account of these two groups of elements and their compounds, paying particular attention to similarities and differences within the groups.
Or
Give an account of the chemistry of the elements of Group II in the Periodic Table and their compounds and draw attention to any differences between them and those of the elements of Group I. Chemical trends should be explained, where appropriate, in terms of the energy changes involved.

End-of-unit test

To find out how well you have learned the material in this unit, try the test which follows. Read the notes below before starting.
1. You should spend about 90 minutes on this test.
2. Hand your answers to your teacher for marking.

In questions 1 to 4 one or more of the suggested responses may be correct.
Answer as follows:
A if **1**, **2**, and **3** are correct,
B if **1** and **2** only are correct,
C if **2** and **3** only are correct,
D if **1** only is correct,
E if **3** only is correct.

Directions summarised				
A	B	C	D	E
1, 2, 3	**1, 2**	**2, 3**	**1**	**3**
correct	only	only	only	only

1. Which of the following properties of the alkali metals increase with increasing atomic number?
   1 Atomic volume.
   2 First ionisation energy.
   3 Melting point. (1)

2. Lithium and magnesium resemble each other in that their
   1 carbonates are decomposed by heat
   2 nitrates give nitrogen dioxide and oxygen on heating
   3 ions colour a Bunsen flame. (1)

3. In Group II of the Periodic Table, which of the following properties increase from magnesium to barium?
   1 Solubility of the sulphates.
   2 Solubility of the hydroxides.
   3 Thermal stability of the carbonates. (1)

4. Francium has the highest relative atomic mass of the Group I elements. It may be predicted that
   1 only oxygen would be given off as a gas when francium nitrate is heated
   2 the bonding in francium chloride would show predominantly covalent character
   3 francium sulphate would be precipitated from solution if dilute sulphuric acid were added to a solution of francium nitrate. (1)

5. Locate the element rubidium (Rb) in Group I of the Periodic Table. Predict which one of the following statements is **not** correct.
   A Rubidium has a lower first ionisation energy than potassium.
   B Rubidium has a larger ionic radius than potassium.
   C Rubidium reacts more vigorously in water than does potassium.
   D Rubidium chloride is soluble in water.
   E Rubidium carbonate is insoluble in water. (1)

6. Beryllium behaves slightly differently in several respects from the other Group II metals. Which of the following statements is true **only** for beryllium?
   A The metal forms a peroxide MO_2 when heated in a plentiful supply of oxygen.
   B The nitrate gives the monoxide, oxygen and nitrogen dioxide on heating.
   C The carbonate gives the monoxide and carbon dioxide on heating.
   D The metal reacts readily with cold water.
   E The hydroxide is amphoteric. (1)

7. Which one of the following is the correct and complete observation when barium metal is added to a large excess of water?
   A No reaction.
   B Forms a colourless solution.
   C Forms a colourless solution with effervescence.
   D Forms a dense white precipitate.
   E Forms a coloured solution with effervescence. (1)

8. Which of the following statements concerning magnesium is correct? It forms
   A an ionic hydride, an insoluble sulphate, and ionic salts containing a +2 cation;
   B an ionic hydride, an insoluble sulphate, and two series of ionic salts containing +1 and +2 cations;
   C a covalent hydride, an insoluble sulphate, and two series of ionic salts containing +1 and +2 cations;
   D a covalent hydride, a soluble sulphate, and ionic salts containing a +2 cation;
   E an ionic hydride, a soluble sulphate, and ionic salts containing a +2 cation. (1)

9. Radium is the element below barium in the Periodic Table. In the separation of radium from other radioactive species, which one of the following processes is likely to be effective?
   A Precipitation of the chloride from aqueous solution.
   B Precipitation of the sulphate from aqueous solution.
   C Distillation of the volatile chloride.
   D Extraction of the chloride into ethoxyethane (diethyl ether).
   E Extraction of the sulphate into ethoxyethane. (1)

10. **S** is a white solid which, on strong heating, evolves a colourless, weakly acidic gas. When a flame test is carried out on the residue, a red flame is obtained. Which one of the following compounds is **S** most likely to be?
   A Calcium nitrate.
   B Calcium carbonate.
   C Magnesium carbonate.
   D Barium carbonate.
   E Strontium nitrate. (1)

11. This question concerns the alkaline earth elements in Group II of the Periodic Table.
   a The following is a table of metallic and ionic radii.

Element	Metallic radius /nm	Ionic radius M^{2+}/nm
Beryllium	0.112	0.030
Magnesium	0.160	0.065
Calcium	0.197	0.094
Strontium	0.215	0.110
Barium	0.221	0.134

   How do you account for the fact that
   i) for all elements the ionic radius is smaller than the metallic radius,
   ii) the metallic radius increases from beryllium to barium,
   iii) the radius of the K^+ ion is greater than the radius of the Ca^{2+} ion although both ions have the same electronic configuration? (4)

   b Explain why $BeCl_2$ (g) is a covalent and linear molecule but $MgCl_2$ (s) is ionic. (4)
   c State with reasons which of the ions in the table has the least exothermic molar enthalpy of hydration. (3)
   d Magnesium sulphate is very soluble in water whereas barium sulphate is not. Suggest what factors are relevant in accounting for this. (4)

12. Although lithium and magnesium are in different groups of the Periodic Table, they show many chemical similarities.
   a How do you account for this? (3)
   b Give **one** property of the metals or their compounds to illustrate the similarity. (2)

13. Suggest explanations for each of the following statements which refer to Group IA, the alkali metals.
   a Only lithium reacts with nitrogen to form a nitride. (3)
   b On heating, lithium nitrate forms an oxide, whereas the nitrates of the other metals in the group form nitrites. (3)
   c Lithium forms only one oxide, whereas the other alkali metals each form at least two oxides. (3)
   d Some of the compounds of lithium have a partially covalent character. (3)
   e The solubility of the fluorides increase in the order $Mg < Ca < Sr < Ba$ but the reverse is true for the corresponding chlorides. (3)

(Total: 45 marks)

APPENDIX: Some industrial chemistry of the s-block elements

In this appendix, we select some important industrial processes for you to study in outline. We also direct you to consider very briefly some of the uses of s-block elements and their compounds. Industrial processes, including key factors influencing the design and siting of chemical plants, are discussed in more detail in ILPAC Volume 8, Functional Groups.

OBJECTIVES

When you have finished this appendix you should be able to:

- discuss briefly the principles underlying the extraction of the s-block elements;
- describe in outline the **extraction of sodium** by the **Downs process**;
- describe in outline the **extraction of magnesium** from sea-water;
- describe in outline the **manufacture of sodium hydroxide** by electrolysis;
- state some **uses of the s-block elements** and their compounds.

The s-block elements are, of course, too reactive to be found 'native', i.e. in an uncombined state. Their high reactivity also means that their compounds are generally very stable, and extraction of the metals from them requires a substantial input of energy. This energy input is usually made by means of electrolysis.

A.1 The Downs process for the extraction of sodium

Read about the extraction of sodium in a suitable textbook. Look for an account of the Downs process and ignore any reference to the Castner process, which has long been obsolete. Use what you find to help you with the following exercises.

EXERCISE 32
Answers on page 155

a The standard enthalpy change of formation of sodium chloride is -411 kJ mol^{-1}. What does this tell you about the extraction of sodium?

b Why is it necessary to use sodium chloride in its molten state rather than in aqueous solution for the extraction of sodium by electrolysis?

c How is the sodium chloride obtained?

EXERCISE 33
Answers on page 155

Make a copy of Fig. 10 and label the parts A to G as you answer the questions.

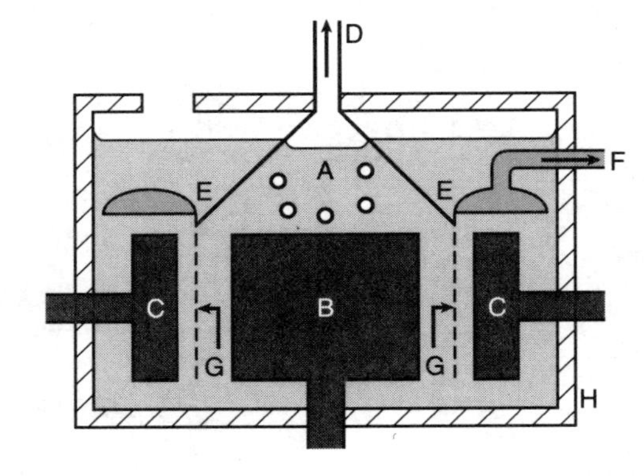

Figure 10
The Downs cell for the extraction of sodium.

a What does the melt (A) consist of?
b What is the purpose of the calcium chloride?
c Why is calcium not discharged at the cathode?
d B and C are the electrodes. Which is which?
e What are the products at the anode and cathode (D and F)?
f Why is the anode made of graphite rather than a metal?
g What is G and what is its purpose?
h Why does the steel tank have a refractory lining (H)?

The extraction of calcium and magnesium by electrolysis is similar in many ways to the extraction of sodium, but suitable electrolytes are not so readily available.

A.2 The extraction of magnesium from sea-water

Read about the extraction of magnesium from sea-water in your textbook(s). We suggest that you study only an electrolytic method and that you concentrate on the **Dow process** for obtaining the electrolyte because this is the method used in the U.K. (The Dow process uses hydrochloric acid and hydrogen chloride gas.)

The next two exercises are about the preparation of the electrolyte and the one following is about the electrolysis.

EXERCISE 34
Answers on page 156

a Write an equation for the thermal decomposition of the mineral dolomite, $MgCO_3 \cdot CaCO_3$.
b How does the addition of calcined (i.e. strongly heated) dolomite to sea-water cause the precipitation of magnesium hydroxide?
c The magnesium hydroxide is then converted to hydrated magnesium chloride by adding hydrochloric acid and crystallising. How are the crystals converted to anhydrous magnesium chloride ready for electrolysis?

In order to appreciate some of the economic factors associated with the extraction of magnesium, we suggest you discuss, with the rest of your group and/or your teacher, answers to the following exercise.

EXERCISE
Discussion

The Special Products Division of Steetley Quarry Products Ltd at Hartlepool produces up to 250×10^3 tonnes of magnesium oxide each year. The raw materials are sea-water and dolomite (magnesian limestone: $MgCO_3 \cdot CaCO_3$).

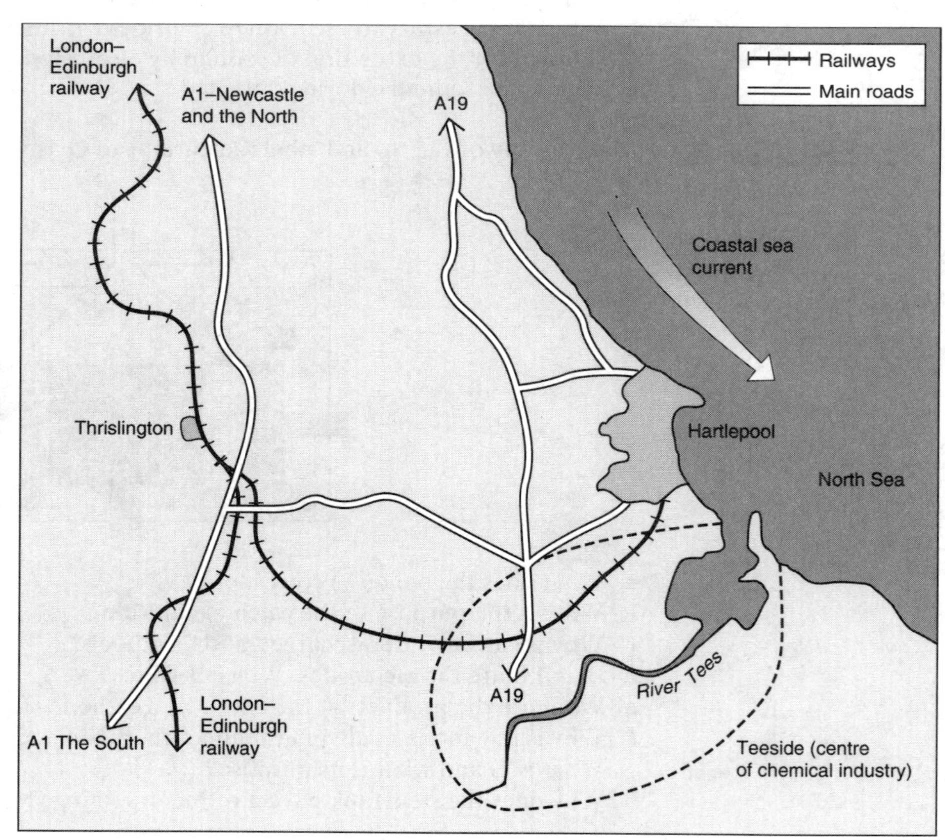

The dolomite is quarried at Thrislington and is decomposed on the site by strong heating at about 1450°C to produce the mixed oxide, $MgO{\cdot}CaO$

$$MgCO_3{\cdot}CaCO_3\ (s) \rightarrow MgO{\cdot}CaO\ (s) + 2CO_2\ (g) \qquad \text{(equation 1)}$$

The oxide is carried by rail to Hartlepool, where a controlled amount of water is added to hydrate it to a mixture of magnesium hydroxide and calcium hydroxide

$$MgO{\cdot}CaO\ (s) + 2H_2O\ (l) \rightarrow Mg(OH)_2\ (s) + Ca(OH)_2\ (s) \qquad \text{(equation 2)}$$

This is then added to sea-water which contains about 1270 mg of magnesium, in the form of $Mg^{2+}(aq)$, per dm^3. Magnesium hydroxide is precipitated by the reaction

$$Ca(OH)_2\ (s) + Mg^{2+}\ (aq) \rightarrow Mg(OH)_2\ (s) + Ca^{2+}\ (aq) \qquad \text{(equation 3)}$$

and this adds to the magnesium hydroxide already present from equation 2.

The precipitate is filtered and heated to decompose it to magnesium oxide.

The Hartlepool operation started in 1937. At first, locally mined coal provided the fuel for heating; later, oil was used. Today's process makes use of imported coal from Poland.

a State *three* factors which made Hartlepool a favourable location in which to establish this process.

b i) Calculate the percentage of the mass of dolomite which is lost when it is decomposed to the mixed oxide. (Relative atomic masses: C = 12, O = 16, Mg = 24, Ca = 40.)

ii) Suggest why it is more economical to carry out this stage of the process at Thrislington rather than at Hartlepool.

c i) Describe the general pattern of the solubilities of the hydroxides of the Group II elements.

ii) Outline how this solubility pattern is used in the Steetley process.

d What advantage did the Hartlepool site possess for the changes of fuel from local coal to oil, and then to Polish coal?

The next exercise deals with the electrolysis.

EXERCISE 35

Answers on page 156

Make a copy of Fig. 11 and label the parts A to F as you answer the questions.

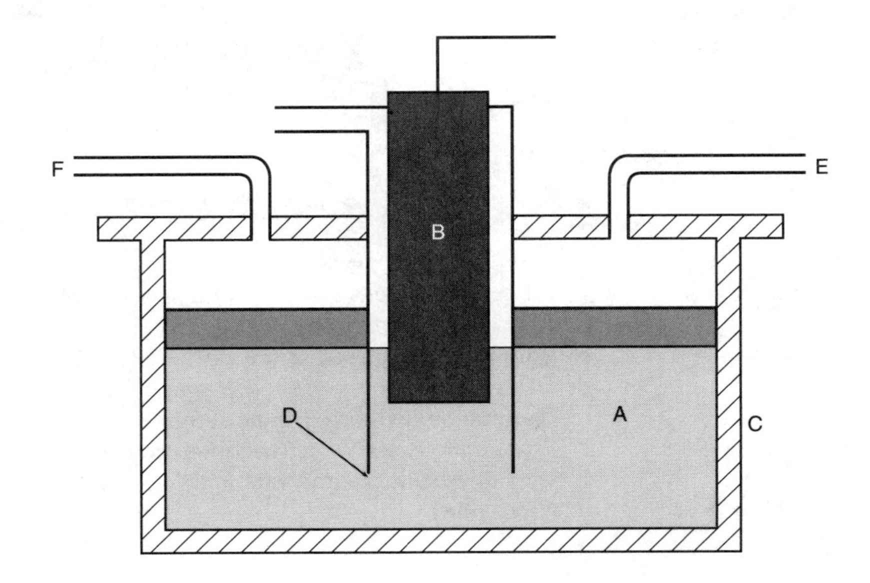

Figure 11
The extraction of magnesium by electrolysis.

a Why is a little sodium chloride added to the molten magnesium chloride electrolyte (A)?
b Label the anode and cathode (B and C).
c Why is the anode made of graphite rather than a metal?
d What is D and what is its purpose?
e What is passed in and out of the cell at E and F and why is this necessary?
f Suggest two or three reasons why you might expect magnesium to be more expensive than sodium. Base your answer on differences between the two extraction procedures.
g Suggest what precautions must be taken to protect workers in the plant and local residents.
h By considering your answer to **g**, the availability of raw materials, the energy requirements and the distribution of the products, suggest the characteristics of an ideal site for magnesium extraction.

Another important application of electrolysis is the manufacture of sodium hydroxide, which we now consider.

A.3 The manufacture of sodium hydroxide

Read about the manufacture of sodium hydroxide in an electrolytic cell which has a **flowing mercury** cathode. There are several types of cell, which go by different names but they are otherwise very similar. You may find references to cells named after **Castner, Kellner** or **Solvay**; any one of these will do. We suggest that you do not study the alternative diaphragm cell, which is not as important in the U.K. as it is elsewhere, and that you ignore any reference to the Gossage process, which is obsolete. Only the most modern books will deal with membrane cells, which are steadily replacing flowing mercury cells. This is at least partly due to environmental concerns about the discharge of effluent containing mercury. However, at the time of writing, mercury cells are still very important.

EXERCISE 36
Answers on page 157

Copy Fig. 12 and label the parts A to G as you answer the questions.

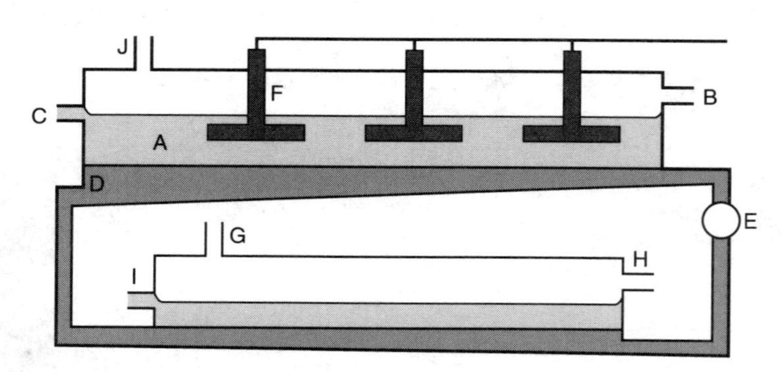

Figure 12
A flowing mercury cell for the manufacture of sodium hydroxide.

a What is the electrolyte (A), and how is it obtained?
b Why is it necessary to keep the electrolyte flowing through the upper cell (B and C)?
c Why is mercury used as the cathode (D and E)?
d Titanium has now replaced graphite for the anodes (F). What two properties must titanium have in order to be suitable?
e Write equations for the reactions occurring in each compartment. (Label G, H, I and J.)
f Why does sodium amalgam react with water in the lower compartment but not in the upper one?

The flowing mercury cell is just as important for the manufacture of chlorine as it is for the production of sodium hydroxide. Because of this, we have included another exercise in The Halogens unit of this volume. This exercise concerns the membrane cell as well.

A.4 Uses of s-block elements and compounds

The final exercise in this appendix refers to the uses of some s-block elements and their compounds. Read the relevant sections of your textbook to help you with those uses which are not already familiar to you.

EXERCISE 37

Answers on page 157

For each of the following products, name one s-block element or simple compound which is an important constituent.

a Gunpowder.
b Bath salts.
c Epsom salts.
d Indigestion remedy.
e Oven cleaner.
f Grit for icy roads.
g Coolant in nuclear reactors.
h Baking powder.
i Compound fertiliser providing the three major plant nutrients.
j Fertiliser for correcting acidity.
k Cement.
l A very light strong alloy.

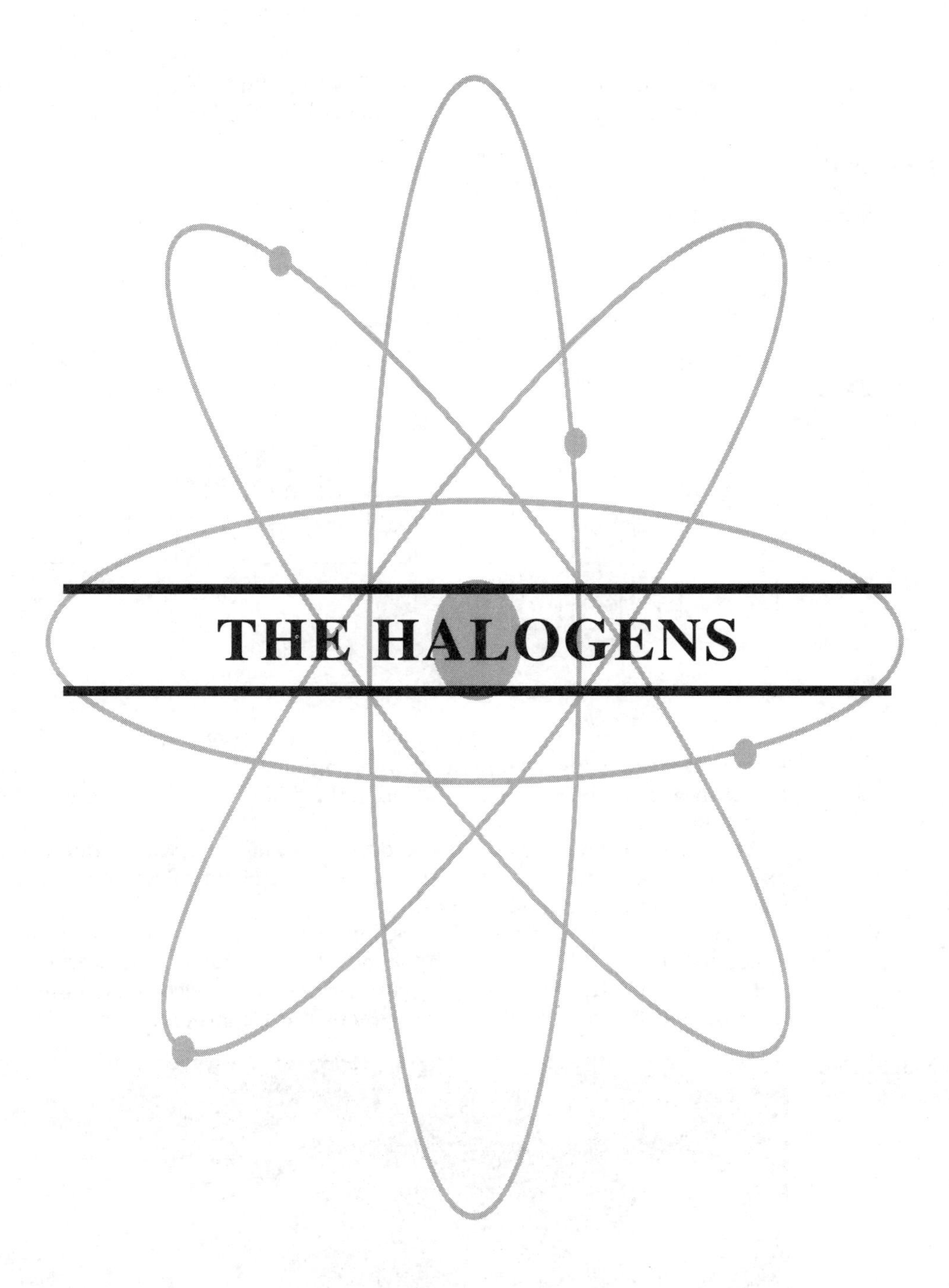
THE HALOGENS

INTRODUCTION

In this unit we deal with the elements and compounds of Group VII (the halogens), whose symbols we include in the outline Periodic Table below (Fig. 13).

Figure 13

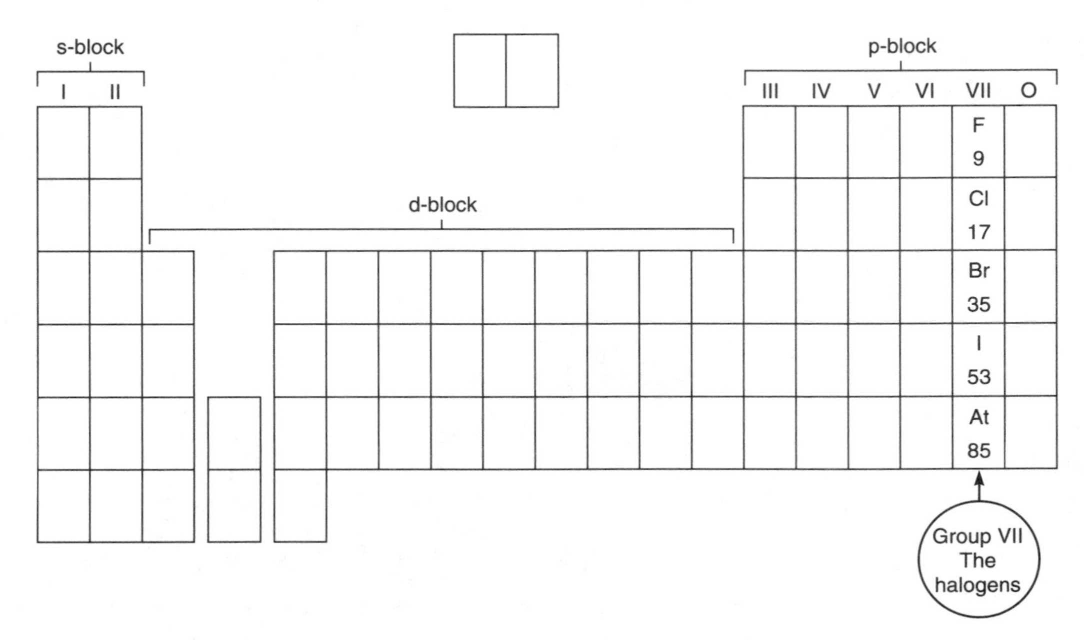

In Part A we deal with the physical and chemical properties of the elements. In Part B we consider the halogen compounds. Throughout, we focus attention on similarities and trends in selected properties, as we did in the first unit of this volume, the s-Block Elements.

At the end of the unit you are asked to carry out 'observation and deduction' exercises, which enable you to identify, by simple chemical analysis, various inorganic substances which contain halogens.

There are eight experiments in this unit, but some of them are very short. There is an appendix to this unit, dealing with the industrial production of chlorine.

There are two ILPAC video programmes designed to accompany this unit. They are not essential, but you should try to see them at the appropriate times if they are available.

Aluminium and iodine reacting together.

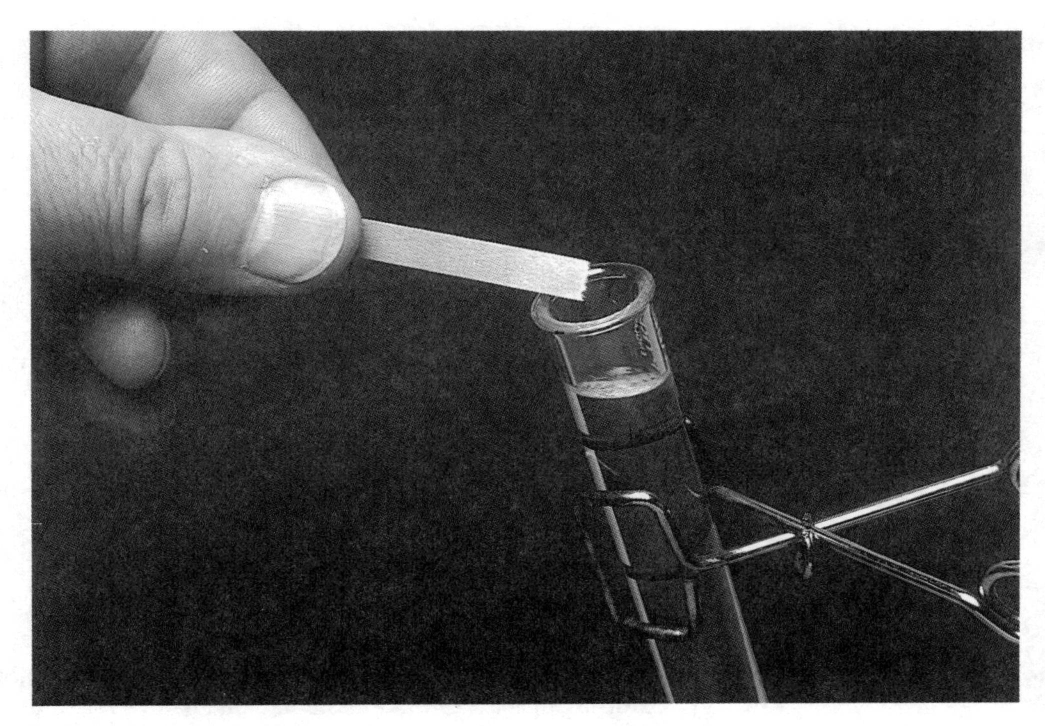
Identifying unknown substances.

Pre-knowledge

Before you start work on this unit, you should be able to:

1. State the names and symbols of the first four elements in Group VII.
2. Describe the usual appearance of the elements chlorine, bromine and iodine.
3. State simple chemical tests for the following:
   a chloride ions,
   b chlorine gas,
   c hydrogen chloride gas.
4. Explain why dry hydrogen chloride is neutral to litmus whereas its aqueous solution is acidic.
5. State the meaning of the following terms:
   a electron affinity,
   b van der Waals forces,
   c isoelectronic.
6. With reference to acids, explain the difference between the terms:
   a weak and dilute,
   b strong and concentrated.
7. Describe how chlorine is prepared in the laboratory.
8. In general terms, state the relative solubilities of ionic and covalent substances in polar and non-polar solvents.

Pre-test

To find out whether you are ready to start Part A, try the following test which is based on the pre-knowledge items. You should not spend more than 30 minutes on this test. Hand your answers to your teacher for marking.

1. Identify the following substances:
   a X is a black, shiny solid which produces a violet vapour when heated. (1)
   b Y is a light, green-yellow gas which bleaches moist litmus paper. (1)
2. Z is a colourless gas, neutral to litmus when dry, and produces white fumes with ammonia. When the gas is dissolved in water, the aqueous solution is acidic to litmus and produces a white precipitate with a silver nitrate solution.
   a Identify Z. (1)
   b What are the white fumes? Give a balanced equation. (2)
   c Give an equation for the formation of the white precipitate. (1)
   d Why is Z neutral to dry litmus as a gas but acidic in aqueous solution? (1)
3. '2 M ethanoic acid is weaker than 2 M hydrochloric acid'. What does this statement mean? (2)
4. Define the term 'electron affinity' and illustrate your answer with an electronic equation. (2)
5. Figure 14 below shows the laboratory preparation of chlorine, which makes use of the oxidising properties of potassium manganate(VII) . Study it and answer the questions which follow.

Figure 14

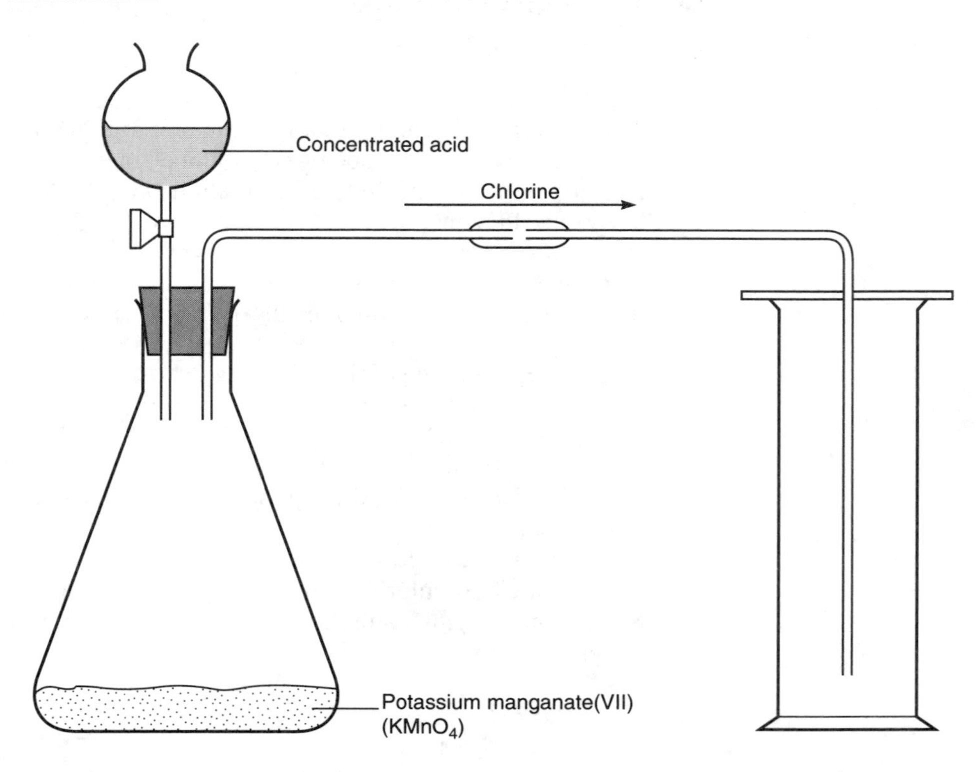

   a Name the concentrated acid which should be used. (1)
   b Is it necessary to heat the conical flask for chlorine to be generated? (1)
   c Why is chlorine collected by the upward displacement of air? (1)
   d Suggest one other solid which could be used in place of potassium manganate(VII). (1)

(Total: 15 marks)

THE HALOGENS

The Group VII elements, the halogens, are reactive non-metals. Within the group there are well-defined trends in physical and chemical properties.

The first element in the group, fluorine, is anomalous, just as lithium and beryllium are in Groups I and II respectively. Astatine, at the bottom, is radioactive, as are francium and radium in the s-block. Not much is known about this element except that it seems to be typical of its group as far as its chemical properties are concerned.

To obtain a simple overall picture of the halogens, we suggest that you read the introduction to them in your textbook(s).

We deal with the halogens under similar headings to those used for the s-block elements. We therefore start this unit by considering the physical properties of these elements.

PHYSICAL PROPERTIES OF THE HALOGENS

Again we begin with some properties associated with the nature of single atoms; for convenience, we refer to these as atomic properties.

OBJECTIVES

When you have finished this chapter you should be able to:

- state the **electron configurations** of the Group VII elements and recognise the similarities between them;
- describe and explain the trends in **atomic and ionic radii**, **electron affinity** and **electronegativity** as the halogen group is descended;
- state and explain the trend in the **bond dissociation energies** of the halogen molecules as their relative molecular masses increase.

6.1 Electron configuration

We start with this property for both the atoms and ions of Group VII because it influences the physical and chemical properties of the elements and their compounds.

EXERCISE 38
Answers on page 158

a Write down the electron configurations of the first four elements in Group VII using the s, p, d notation.

b How does the electron configuration of fluorine differ from that of the other members of the group?

c Write down the electron configurations of the fluoride and chloride ions. What is the oxidation state in each ion?

We now consider the trends in atomic and ionic radii for Group VII.

6.2 Atomic and ionic radii

In the first unit of this volume, the s-Block Elements, you learned that atomic and ionic sizes influence the chemical properties of the elements and their compounds. This applies to all elements, not just those of the s-block.

Study the table on the next page and answer the questions which follow.

Table 6
Atomic and ionic radii of the halogens

	Fluorine	Chlorine	Bromine	Iodine
Atomic (covalent) radius/nm	0.071	0.099	0.114	0.133
Ionic radius of X^-/nm	0.133	0.180	0.195	0.215

EXERCISE 39
Answers on page 158

a Explain why the atomic radius increases down the group.
b Why is the ionic radius so much greater than the covalent radius in each case?

In the next exercise, you compare the atomic and ionic sizes of the halogens and the s-block elements.

EXERCISE 40
Answers on page 158

The ions F^-, Na^+ and Mg^{2+} are isoelectronic.
a From your data book, write down the radii of the above ions.
b Describe and explain the trend with increasing atomic number.

As you know, the s-block elements are good reducing agents because they lose their outer electrons readily. Evidence for this is obtained from their ionisation energies. On the other hand, the halogen atoms, with seven electrons in their outer shells, have a tendency to attract an electron, which makes them good oxidising agents. An indication of the strength of this attraction is given by values of electron affinity.

6.3 Electron affinity

This term was defined in ILPAC Volume 2, Chemical Energetics.
The next exercise deals with the changes in electron affinity as Group VII is descended. Part **c** is taken from an A-level examination paper.

EXERCISE 41
Answers on page 158

a Using your data book, write down thermochemical equations to represent the electron affinities of Cl, Br and I.
b Describe and explain the trend in **a**.
c The first ionisation energy of gaseous fluoride ions is +350 kJ mol^{-1}. What is the electron affinity of gaseous fluorine atoms? Briefly explain your answer.
d Suggest a reason why the electron affinity of fluorine is anomalous. (Hint: consider the small atomic size of the F atom and the repulsions between the electrons in the outer shell of the atom.)

As you know, electron affinity is related to electronegativity, which we now discuss.

6.4 Electronegativity

In ILPAC Volume 3, Bonding and Structure, you learned that Group VII contains some of the most electronegative elements in the Periodic Table. The next exercise examines the trend in electronegativity for the halogens.

EXERCISE 42
Answers on page 158

a Using your data book, write down the electronegativities of the first four halogens.
b Describe and explain the group trend.

The reactivity of the halogens is clearly due, in part, to the electron affinities of the atoms. However, chemical reactions usually involve halogen molecules and, in the course of these reactions, halogen–halogen bonds must be broken. We now consider the strength of these bonds.

6.5 Bond dissociation energy

This term (sometimes called bond dissociation enthalpy) was introduced in ILPAC Volume 2, Chemical Energetics. Remember that in the case of diatomic molecules, bond energy term and bond dissociation energy are identical.

The next exercise is about the bond dissociation energies shown in Fig. 15.

Figure 15

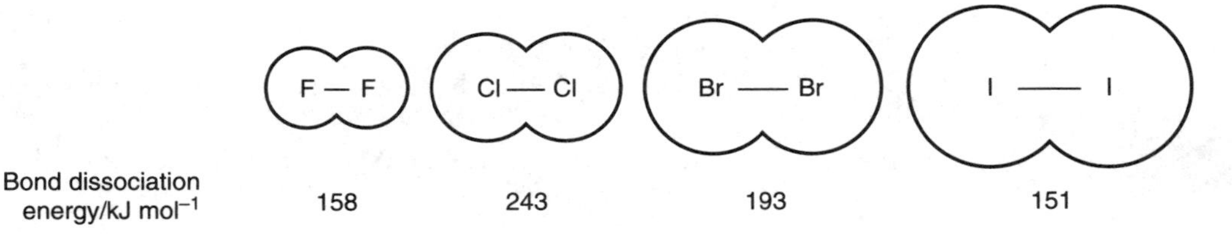

EXERCISE 43
Answers on page 158

a Describe the trend in bond dissociation energy as the group is descended.
b Which halogen molecules are split into atoms most readily and which are split least readily?
c Explain the trend from chlorine to iodine.
d Suggest a reason for the low bond dissociation energy of fluorine. (Hint: consider the small size of the fluorine atoms and repulsions between non-bonding electrons in the molecule.)

Electron affinity values alone might suggest that fluorine would be **less** reactive than chlorine but the high reactivity of fluorine is explained partly in terms of its low bond dissociation energy, which means that little energy is required to break the F—F bond in the initial stages of a reaction. Another factor is the tendency of fluorine to form strong bonds with other elements. We return to the reactivity of the halogens later in this unit.

Clearly, the atomic properties of the halogens illustrate some well-defined group trends, although fluorine is atypical in some respects as we always find for the first element in a group. We now continue the survey of physical properties of the elements by looking at bulk properties.

6.6 Melting points and boiling points

OBJECTIVES

When you have finished this section you should be able to:
- explain the trends in the **melting points** and **boiling points** of Group VII elements;
- state the **appearance** and **physical state** of fluorine;
- compare the **solubilities** of Group VII elements in water and organic solvents.

In the following exercise, you investigate the trends in melting and boiling points for Group VII.

EXERCISE 44
Answers on page 159

a Write down the melting points and boiling points of fluorine, chlorine, bromine and iodine.*
b What is the trend in each of these properties?
c From your data in **a**, give the physical state of each halogen at room temperature and pressure.

*Iodine sublimes if a small amount of it is heated in an open container. However, its melting point can be obtained if a large quantity is gently heated.

Melting points and boiling points depend on the strengths of intermolecular forces. In ILPAC Volume 3, Bonding and Structure, you learned that van der Waals forces operate between all molecules. In the next exercise, you explain the trends in melting points and boiling points by considering van der Waals forces.

EXERCISE 45
Answers on page 159

a How are the strengths of van der Waals forces affected by the number of electrons in a molecule? Explain your answer.
b What is the group trend in strength of van der Waals forces between molecules of the halogen elements?
c Explain why iodine is a solid whereas chlorine is a gas.

The names of some of the halogens are derived from their appearance, which we consider in the next section.

6.7 Appearance of the halogens

Check that you really know what the elements look like by doing the next exercise. You may find it helpful to watch the first part of the ILPAC video programme 'The Halogens', if it is available.

EXERCISE 46
Answers on page 159

Copy and complete Table 7.

Table 7

Name of element	Formula	Colour and physical state at room temperature and pressure
Fluorine		
Chlorine		
Bromine		
Iodine		

The name 'chlorine' comes from the Greek '*chloros*' meaning light green; 'bromine' comes from the Greek '*bromos*' meaning stench; 'iodine' comes from the Greek '*iodos*' meaning violet-like.

Because the halogens are covalent substances, they tend to dissolve in organic non-polar solvents. In certain organic solvents, bromine and iodine produce solutions with characteristic colours and this can help in their identification.

6.8 The solubilities of the halogens

The halogens, like most covalent substances, are not very soluble in water (see Table 8).

Table 8

Halogen	Solubility at 0°C /g per 100 g of water
Fluorine F_2	–
Chlorine Cl_2	1.46 (about 30% reacts)
Bromine Br_2	4.17 (very little reacts)
Iodine I_2	0.016 (very little reacts)

The variation in solubility is such that chlorine and bromine are often described as moderately soluble in water and iodine as sparingly (slightly) soluble in water.

EXERCISE 47
Answer on page 159

Why do you think no value for solubility is assigned to fluorine in Table 8?

Deciding whether a substance dissolves with or without reaction is not always a very easy matter. We will discuss the **reactions** of the halogens with water later in this unit.

Aqueous solutions of chlorine and bromine are often used in the laboratory and referred to as **chlorine water** and **bromine water**. Iodine is only slightly soluble in water so an indirect method is used to produce iodine solution. Find out from your textbooks how iodine solution is made so that you can do the next exercise.

EXERCISE 48
Answers on page 159

How is aqueous iodine solution made in the laboratory? Include any relevant equation(s).

In the following experiment, you investigate the solubility of the halogens in various organic solvents. It is a short qualitative experiment and should not take you more than 30 minutes.

EXPERIMENT 4 The solubility of the halogens in organic solvents

Aim

The purpose of this experiment is to discover whether each of the halogens chlorine, bromine and iodine is:

a soluble in organic solvents,
b more soluble in organic solvents than in water,
c the same colour in organic solvents as it is in water.

Introduction

After mixing aqueous solutions of the halogens separately with Volasil 244,* ethoxyethane, $CH_3CH_2OCH_2CH_3$, and cyclohexane, $(CH_2)_6$, you decide whether each halogen moves out of the aqueous solution into the solvent. If it does, you can compare its colour in the aqueous layer with that in the organic layer – these colours are useful in identifying the halogens.

*Volasil 244 is a cyclic organosilicone, octamethylcyclotetrasiloxane. Its molecule has alternating silicon and oxygen atoms in a ring structure with methyl groups attached to the silicon atoms. You will **not** be expected to remember its full name or structure! Indeed, the phrase 'inert solvent' is adequate in most contexts. We have included it here, and subsequently, because it is more environmentally friendly than most organic solvents and is safer to use, although it is flammable.

Requirements

- safety spectacles
- 3 test-tubes, each fitted with a bung
- test-tube rack
- 6 dropping pipettes approximately graduated for 1 cm^3
- Volasil 244 (octamethylcyclotetrasiloxane)($(CH_3)_2 SiO)_4$
- ethoxyethane (diethyl ether), $CH_3CH_2OCH_2CH_3$
- cyclohexane, $(CH_2)_6$
- chlorine water, Cl_2 (aq)
- bromine water, Br_2 (aq)
- iodine solution, 0.01 M I_2 (in KI (aq))
- 3 labelled bottles for organic residues

HAZARD WARNING

- This experiment should be performed in a **fume cupboard** since all the halogen vapours are **toxic** and the organic vapours are dangerous to inhale. If a fume cupboard is not available then **the laboratory must be well ventilated.**
- Check that no flames are close to where you are working because ethoxyethane and cyclohexane are extremely flammable.

Procedure

1. In a copy of Results Table 5 note the colour of each aqueous halogen solution provided.
2. Into each of three test-tubes in turn put about 1 cm^3 of a different aqueous halogen solution.
3. To each tube add about 1 cm^3 of Volasil 244 and note whether the organic liquid becomes the upper or lower layer. How can you tell?
4. Cork and shake each tube, allow the layers to separate, and note the colour of each layer.
5. Repeat steps 2, 3 and 4 with the other two solvents.
6. Pour residues into the labelled bottles provided, **not** down the sink.

Results Table 5

	Nature of each layer	Chlorine water	Bromine water	Iodine solution
Colour of aqueous solution				
Colour of each layer after shaking with Volasil 244	Upper layer *organic/aqueous			
	Lower layer *organic/aqueous			
Colour of each layer after shaking with ethoxyethane	Upper layer *organic/aqueous			
	Lower layer *organic/aqueous			
Colour of each layer after shaking with cyclohexane	Upper layer *organic/aqueous			
	Lower layer *organic/aqueous			

*Delete organic or aqueous as appropriate.

(Specimen results on page 160.)

Questions
Answers on page 160

1. Do you think the halogens are more soluble in the organic solvents than in water? Explain your answer.
2. Which of the three halogens has a significantly different colour in the organic layer from its colour in the aqueous layer? (Specify the organic solvents in your answer.)
3. How would you distinguish, other than by smell, between a dilute aqueous iodine solution and a fairly concentrated solution of bromine water?

You will use aqueous solutions of the halogens as convenient sources of the Group VII elements in other experiments in this unit. If a halogen solution is produced during a chemical reaction, you now know how to use an organic solvent to help in its identification.

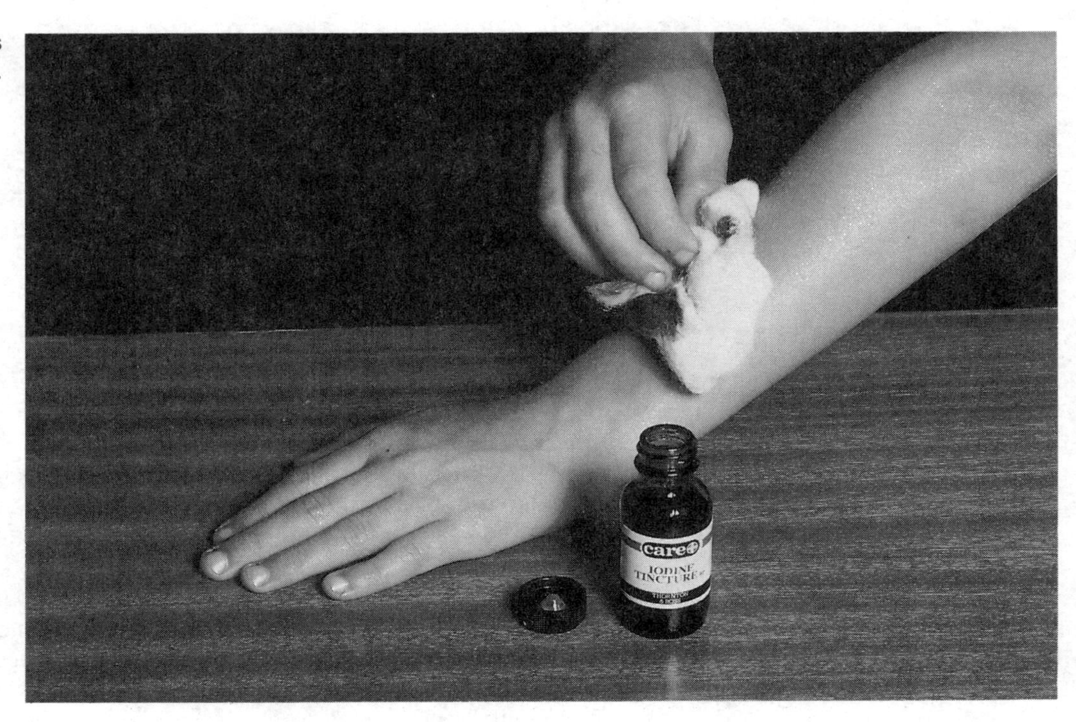

Tincture of iodine used as a mild antiseptic.

The solubility of the halogens in water and organic solvents has some useful applications, e.g. chlorine is used as a germicide in the treatment of drinking water. The toxic nature of chlorine requires very careful control of its use and its corrosive nature makes such control difficult in unskilled hands: for this reason, safer alternatives have been introduced in recent years for the treatment of swimming pool water. Iodine dissolved in ethanol, commonly called 'tincture of iodine', is used as a mild antiseptic.

We now go on to consider the chemical properties of the halogens, and you apply your knowledge of their electron affinities and bond dissociation energies to help you explain the reactivity of the elements.

CHAPTER 7

CHEMICAL PROPERTIES

Electron affinity values indicate that all the Group VII elements have a great tendency to attract electrons, but that this tendency decreases as the group is descended from chlorine onwards. This suggests that the halogens are reactive elements, but we have already shown that bond dissociation energies must also be considered in order to account fully for the group trend in reactivity. In particular, fluorine is much more reactive than chlorine despite its smaller affinity for electrons, and reacts vigorously with nearly all other substances.

In the following section, we discuss the reactivity of the halogens towards other elements.

OBJECTIVES

When you have finished this chapter you should be able to:

- describe how the halogens react with hydrogen, the noble gases and selected **metals** and **non-metals**;
- quote experimental evidence to show that the **reactivity of the halogens** decreases as the group is descended.

Hydrogen is a reactive element, so it is not surprising that it will react with all the halogens. Although the products of each of these hydrogen/halogen reactions are similar, there are striking differences in the rates of reaction.

7.1 Reactions with hydrogen

If the ILPAC video programme 'The Halogens' is available, you should view now any sections you have not already seen.

Read about the reactions between the halogens and hydrogen in your textbook(s), paying particular attention to the experimental conditions used and the vigour of each reaction, so that you can do the following exercises.

EXERCISE 49
Answers on page 160

a Write a general equation for the reaction between a halogen (X) and hydrogen.
b What is the trend in reactivity towards hydrogen as the halogen group is descended?
c If a polythene bag is filled with a 50 : 50 mixture of hydrogen and chlorine and exposed to ultraviolet light or bright sunlight, an explosion occurs. Explain how the light-source initiates the reaction.
d What conditions are required for hydrogen to react with
i) fluorine,
ii) bromine,
iii) iodine?

In the next exercise you discover how the great reactivity of fluorine is attributable in part to the low dissociation energy of the F—F bond, and in part to the fact that the bonds formed between F and other elements are very strong.

EXERCISE 50
Answers on page 160

a Calculate $\Delta H^\ominus$ for the following reactions from bond energy terms. Draw energy level diagrams in your answer.
i) $H_2(g) + F_2(g) \rightarrow 2HF(g)$
ii) $H_2(g) + Cl_2(g) \rightarrow 2HCl(g)$
b Which of the two reactions above is energetically more feasible?
c What two factors contribute to the high negative value of $\Delta H^\ominus$ for the H_2/F_2 reaction?

Fluorine is so reactive that it is known to react with at least three noble gases, krypton, Kr, xenon, Xe, and radon, Rn.

7.2 Reactions with the noble gases

Fluorine is the only member of the halogens to react with the noble gases. For instance, three fluorides of xenon have been obtained by direct synthesis. These compounds, xenon difluoride, XeF_2, xenon tetrafluoride, XeF_4, and xenon hexafluoride, XeF_6, are all colourless crystalline compounds.

The following exercise is about the noble gas compounds of fluorine.

EXERCISE 51
Answers on page 161

a XeF_4 can be made by heating a mixture of xenon and fluorine in a nickel vessel at 400°C for one hour followed by rapid cooling of the mixture.
 i) Write down the equation for the reaction.
 ii) What is the oxidation number of xenon in XeF_4?

b What is the oxidation number of the noble gas in each of the following compounds?
 i) XeF_2, ii) XeF_6,
 iii) KrF_2, iv) KrF_4.

c Why do you think modern textbooks have stopped referring to the noble gases as the inert gases?

The last exercise shows that fluorine can bring out high oxidation states of the noble gases. In fact, it tends to produce the highest possible oxidation states with all the elements with which it reacts. This is mainly because fluorine forms very strong bonds with other elements: the energy released more than compensates for the energy required to partially remove extra electrons to make more bonds. Another factor is the small size of the fluorine atom, which makes it possible to fit larger numbers of fluorine atoms around another atom.

The next section deals with the reactions of the halogens with other elements.

7.3 Reactions with selected metals and non-metals

We have chosen sulphur and phosphorus for our non-metals because they are convenient solids to study and show variable oxidation states. In our choices of metals we have taken sodium as an example of an s-block element and iron as an example of a transition element. Similar reactions occur with other metals and non-metals.

Table 9 gives you some factual information about the reactions of the halogens with these elements; you complete it in the next exercise.

Table 9

Reactant	Fluorine	Chlorine	Bromine	Iodine
Sulphur powder	Ignites spontaneously to form SF_6	Reacts if heated to form S_2Cl_2		No reaction
Red phosphorus	Ignites spontaneously to form ____		Reacts spontaneously to form PBr_3	Solid spontaneously forms PI_3
Iron filings	Ignites if warmed to form ____		Reacts if heated to form $FeBr_3$	Reacts if heated to form FeI_2
Sodium	Reacts explosively to form ____		Continues to burn in vapour to form ____	Continues to burn in vapour to form____

EXERCISE 52
Answers on page 161

a Complete a copy of Table 9, including the formulae of the products.
b An extremely violent reaction occurs if sodium and solid iodine are heated together (you must not, under any circumstances, attempt this) whereas a much slower reaction occurs if burning sodium is lowered into iodine vapour. Suggest an explanation.
c Comment on the oxidation numbers of the other elements in the products formed by fluorine and iodine.

We now go on to consider the reactions of the halogens with some compounds.

7.4 Reactions with water and alkalis

OBJECTIVES

When you have finished this section, you should be able to:

- describe the reactions between the halogens and **water**;
- describe the reactions between the Group VII elements and **alkalis**;
- explain the meaning of the term **disproportionation**;
- place the **oxo-anions** BrO^-, ClO^- and IO^- in order of stability.

We mentioned reactions of halogens with water when we discussed solubility. We now consider these reactions in detail.

Read about the reactions of the halogens with water in your textbook(s) to help you with the following exercises.

EXERCISE 53
Answers on page 161

a If wet blue litmus paper is placed in a gas jar of chlorine it first turns red then white. Explain this with the aid of an equation.
b A rapid reaction occurs between fluorine and water. Give a balanced equation for this reaction.
c If chlorine water is exposed to bright sunlight, it decomposes slowly to give similar products to the reaction in **b** above. Write down the equation for this decomposition.
d How would you expect bromine and iodine to react with water, if at all? Give equation(s) in your answer.

Look up **disproportionation** in your textbook(s) to help you do the next exercise.

EXERCISE 54
Answers on page 162

Consider the reaction between chlorine and water.

$$Cl_2\,(g) + H_2O\,(l) \rightarrow HClO\,(aq) + HCl\,(aq)$$

a Write down the oxidation number of chlorine wherever it appears in the equation.
b Explain the meaning of the term 'disproportionation' using the above reaction as an example.
c Would you class the reactions between fluorine and water and between bromine and water as disproportionation reactions? Explain your answer.

The reactions between the halogens and water are affected by the pH and the temperature of the water. In the next section we consider the reactions between the halogens and dilute alkalis at different temperatures.

You start with a practical investigation of the reactions of bromine water and iodine solution with dilute sodium hydroxide. The experiment is very short and can be completed in about 20 minutes.

EXPERIMENT 5 The action of dilute alkali on the halogens

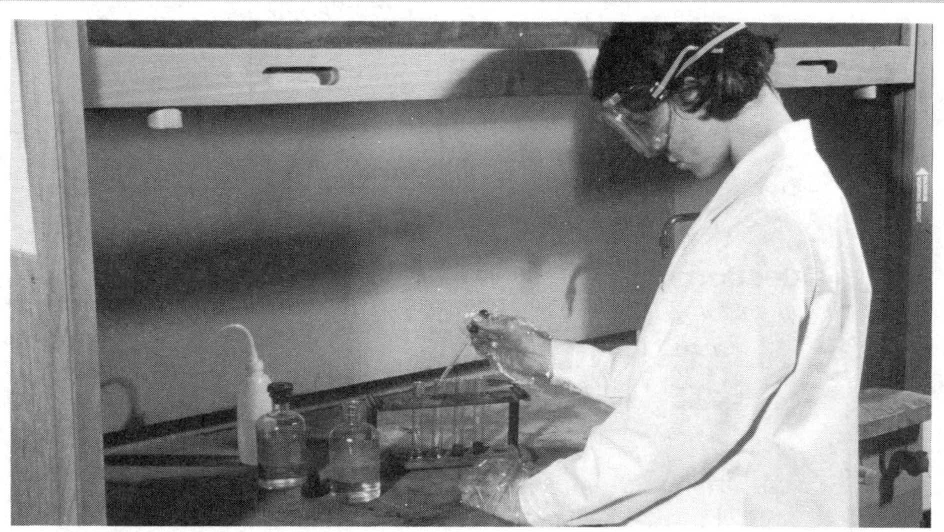

Aim The purpose of this experiment is to show that observable reactions occur between dilute sodium hydroxide and aqueous solutions of bromine and iodine and, furthermore, that these reactions are reversible.

Introduction You add dilute sodium hydroxide dropwise to bromine water and iodine solution in turn. A significant change in colour in either halogen solution indicates that a reaction has occurred. If you suspect that the change in colour is only due to a dilution effect, you should set up a control experiment, where you add the same number of drops of distilled water to the halogen solution.

To determine whether the reaction is reversible, you acidify the alkaline halogen solution and see if the original halogen colour reappears.

Requirements

- safety spectacles
- 5 test-tubes
- 1 test-tube rack
- 4 teat pipettes
- bromine water, Br_2 (aq)
- iodine solution, 0.01 M I_2 (in KI (aq))
- sulphuric acid, 1 M H_2SO_4
- sodium hydroxide solution, 2 M NaOH
- distilled water

HAZARD WARNING

Bromine water is **toxic** and corrosive. The vapour is extremely irritant to the eyes, lungs and skin. Therefore you **must**:

- **avoid contact with skin;**
- **avoid inhaling the vapour.**

Procedure

1. Place about 2 cm^3 of bromine water in a test-tube and note the colour of the solution.
2. Add dilute sodium hydroxide, drop by drop, and note any change of colour in the bromine solution.
3. Now add dilute sulphuric acid to the solution from step 2, and note if the colour returns when the acid is in excess.
4. Repeat the procedure using iodine solution instead of bromine water.
5. Record your results in a copy of Results Table 6.

Results Table 6

Aqueous halogen	Original colour	Colour after adding NaOH (aq)	Colour after adding H_2SO_4 (aq)
Bromine water			
Iodine solution			

(Specimen results on page 162.)

Questions

Answers on page 162

1. Write equations for the reactions of bromine and iodine with dilute sodium hydroxide at room temperature. Use your textbook(s) as necessary.
2. Which of the above reactions would you class as disproportionation reactions?
3. Are these reactions reversible? Explain your answer.
4. How does chlorine differ from bromine and iodine in its reaction with cold dilute sodium hydroxide? Suggest a reason.

You have probably already discovered in your reading that the temperature determines which products are formed in the reactions between halogens and alkalis. The facts are summarised in Table 10, which you should study before doing the next exercise.

Table 10
Reactions of halogens with sodium hydroxide

Halogen	Temperature/°C	Predominant oxo-anion product*
Cl_2	20	ClO^-
	70	ClO_3^-
Br_2	0	BrO^-
	20	BrO_3^-
I_2	0	IO_3^-

*Halide ions and water are also formed but are omitted from the table.

EXERCISE 55

Answers on page 162

a Name the two oxo-anions of chlorine shown in Table 10 and write an equation to show how one is converted to the other in aqueous solution by heating.
b Write an equation to show the reaction between chlorine and dilute sodium hydroxide at 70°C.
c Place the following ions in order of ease of disproportionation at room temperature: BrO^-, ClO^-, IO^-. Explain your answer.
d Draw dot-and-cross diagrams for the oxo-anions ClO^- and ClO_3^-.

In your reading you may have come across references to the reaction of chlorine with **concentrated** sodium hydroxide solution at 70°C. The effect of increasing the concentration is similar to that of raising the temperature, i.e. to increase the proportion of ClO_3^- in the product.

In the first unit of this volume, you learned that the s-block elements are reducing agents because of their tendency to lose electrons. You also learned that metallic character is linked to this tendency to lose electrons. Since the halogens tend to be electron acceptors in their reactions, they can behave as oxidising agents.

In the next chapter we discuss the trends in oxidising ability of the halogens and consider the emergence of slight metallic character in iodine.

GENERAL PROPERTIES RELATED TO ELECTRON TRANSFER

OBJECTIVES

When you have finished this chapter you should be able to:

- state and explain the order of **oxidising ability** for the halogens;
- describe an experiment which illustrates this order;
- account for the **slight metallic character** of iodine.

In the next exercise, you investigate some other halogen reactions, including the iodine–thiosulphate reaction which you met in The Mole unit of ILPAC Volume 1.

EXERCISE 56

Answers on page 162

Study the equations below and answer the questions which follow.

i) $H_2S\ (aq) + Br_2\ (aq) \rightarrow 2HBr\ (aq) + S\ (s)$

ii) $Al\ (s) + 1\tfrac{1}{2}I_2\ (s) \rightarrow AlI_3\ (s)$

iii) $Cl_2\ (g) + H_2O\ (l) \rightarrow HCl\ (aq) + HClO\ (aq)$

iv) $2Na_2S_2O_3\ (aq) + I_2\ (aq) \rightarrow Na_2S_4O_6\ (aq) + 2NaI\ (aq)$

a Write down the oxidation number for each atom appearing in the above equations.
b For each redox reaction, state which species is oxidised and which is reduced.

All the halogen reactions which you have considered so far are redox reactions (i.e. oxidation and reduction reactions). In most of these reactions, the halogen oxidises the substances with which it reacts. You will not be surprised, therefore, that the order of oxidising ability is the same as the order of reactivity.

In the next exercise, we ask you to predict whether certain halogen–halide reactions occur. Following that is an experiment to test your predictions.

EXERCISE 57

Answers on page 163

Use the order of oxidising ability of the halogens (i.e. $F_2 > Cl_2 > Br_2 > I_2$) to predict whether the following reactions occur:

a $Cl_2\ (aq) + 2KBr\ (aq) \rightarrow Br_2\ (aq) + 2KCl\ (aq)$
b $I_2\ (aq) + 2Cl^-\ (aq) \rightarrow Cl_2\ (aq) + 2I^-\ (aq)$
c $Br_2\ (aq) + 2KI\ (aq) \rightarrow I_2\ (aq) + 2KBr\ (aq)$
d $Cl_2\ (aq) + 2I^-\ (aq) \rightarrow I_2\ (aq) + 2Cl^-\ (aq)$
e $Br_2\ (aq) + 2NaCl\ (aq) \rightarrow Cl_2\ (aq) + 2NaBr\ (aq)$.

EXPERIMENT 6 Halogen–halide reactions in aqueous solution

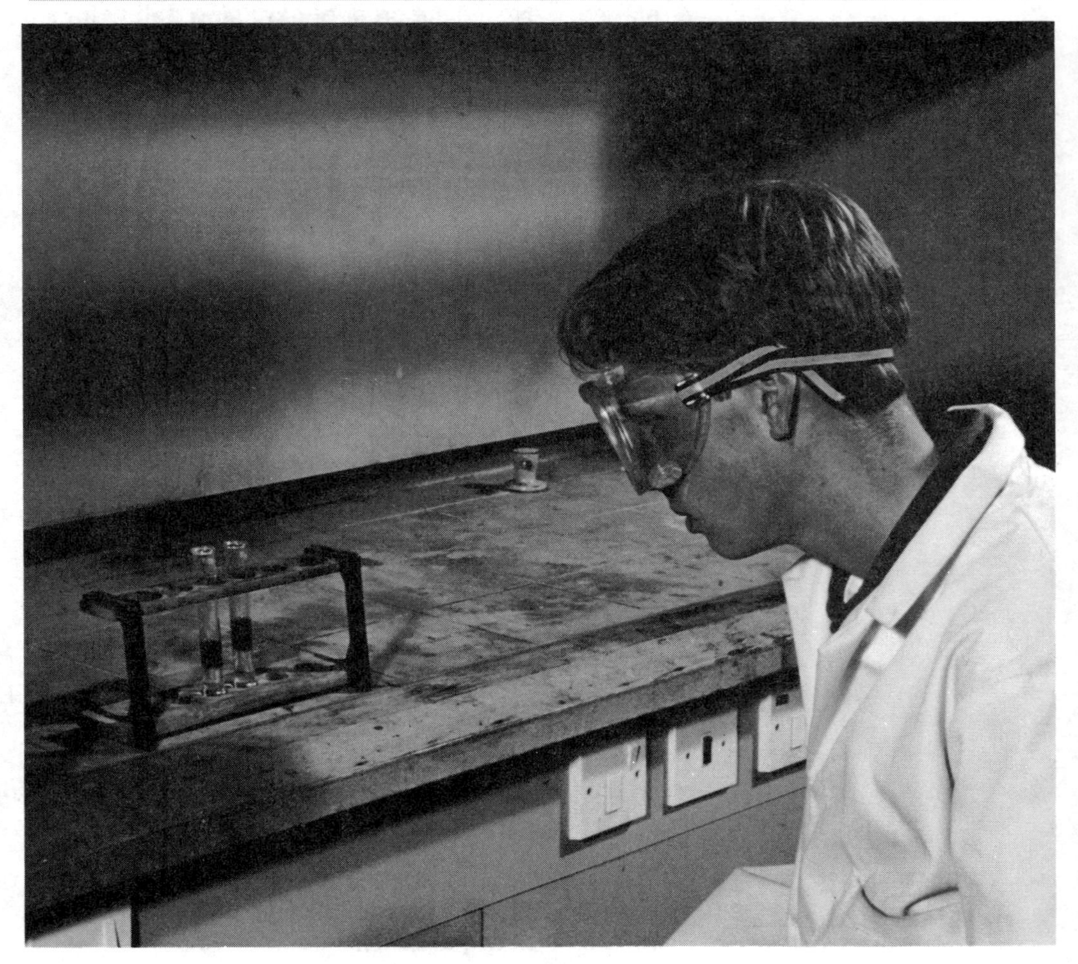

Aim

The purpose of this experiment is to investigate the order of oxidising ability of the halogens Cl_2, Br_2 and I_2 in aqueous solution.

Introduction

You mix each of the aqueous solutions with halide ion solutions, Cl^- (aq), Br^- (aq), and I^- (aq) in turn, and see whether a reaction takes place. The addition of Volasil 244 to the halogen–halide mixture enables you to recognise the halogen molecules present. The halogen which oxidises most of the other halide ions will clearly be the strongest oxidising agent.

Requirements

- safety spectacles
- 6 test-tubes fitted with corks
- test-tube rack
- 7 dropping pipettes
- bromine water, Br_2 (aq)
- chlorine water, Cl_2 (aq)
- iodine solution, I_2 (in KI (aq))
- potassium bromide solution, KBr
- potassium chloride solution, KCl
- potassium iodide solution, KI
- Volasil 244
- bottle for residues

HAZARD WARNING

Halogen vapours must not be inhaled. If a fume cupboard is not available then:
- the laboratory must be **well ventilated** and reagent bottles and test-tubes stoppered as much as possible;
- keep Volasil 244 **away** from flames.

Procedure

1. Reaction (if any) of iodide with chlorine and bromine.
   a To each of two test-tubes add about 1 cm^3 of potassium iodide solution.
   b To one of these tubes, add about the same volume of chlorine water, and to the other add the same volume of bromine water.
   c Cork and shake the tubes and note the colour change – if any.
   d To each tube add about 1 cm^3 of hexane, cork and shake, allow to settle, and note the colour of each layer. The relative volumes of the two layers will tell you which is aqueous and which is organic.
   e Decide which reactions have taken place, and complete a copy of Results Table 7.
2. Reaction (if any) of bromide with chlorine and iodine.
   Repeat the above steps, 1**a**–**e**, using potassium bromide instead of potassium iodide.
3. Reaction (if any) of chloride with bromine and iodine.
   Repeat steps 1**a**–**e** using potassium chloride instead of potassium iodide.

Results Table 7

		Chlorine water	**Bromine water**	**Iodine solution**
1. Initial colour				
2. Colour after shaking with KI solution				
Colour of each layer after shaking with hexane	Upper			
	Lower			
Conclusion				
3. Colour after shaking with KBr solution				
Colour of each layer after shaking with hexane	Upper			
	Lower			
Conclusion				
4. Colour after shaking with KCl solution				
Colour of each layer after shaking with hexane	Upper			
	Lower			
Conclusion				

(Specimen results on page 163.)

Questions

Answers on page 163

1. **a** Does I_2 (aq) oxidise Cl^- (aq) and Br^- (aq)?
   b Does Br_2 (aq) oxidise Cl^- (aq) and I^- (aq)?
   c Does Cl_2 (aq) oxidise Br^- (aq) and I^- (aq)?
   d Were your predictions in Exercise 57 correct?
2. Write ionic equations for the reactions taking place.

8.1 Hydration energy (enthalpy change of hydration)

In Exercise 50, you discovered that bond energies are very important in reflecting the order of reactivity of the halogens in gaseous reactions. In aqueous reactions we also need to consider the formation of hydrated ions when explaining the order of oxidising ability. We need, therefore, to consider the enthalpy change for the half-reaction:

$$\tfrac{1}{2}X_2 \text{ (standard state)} + e^- \rightarrow X^- \text{(aq)} \qquad \text{where X = a halogen}$$

The factors which contribute to this enthalpy change are shown in the following energy-level diagram (not drawn to scale).

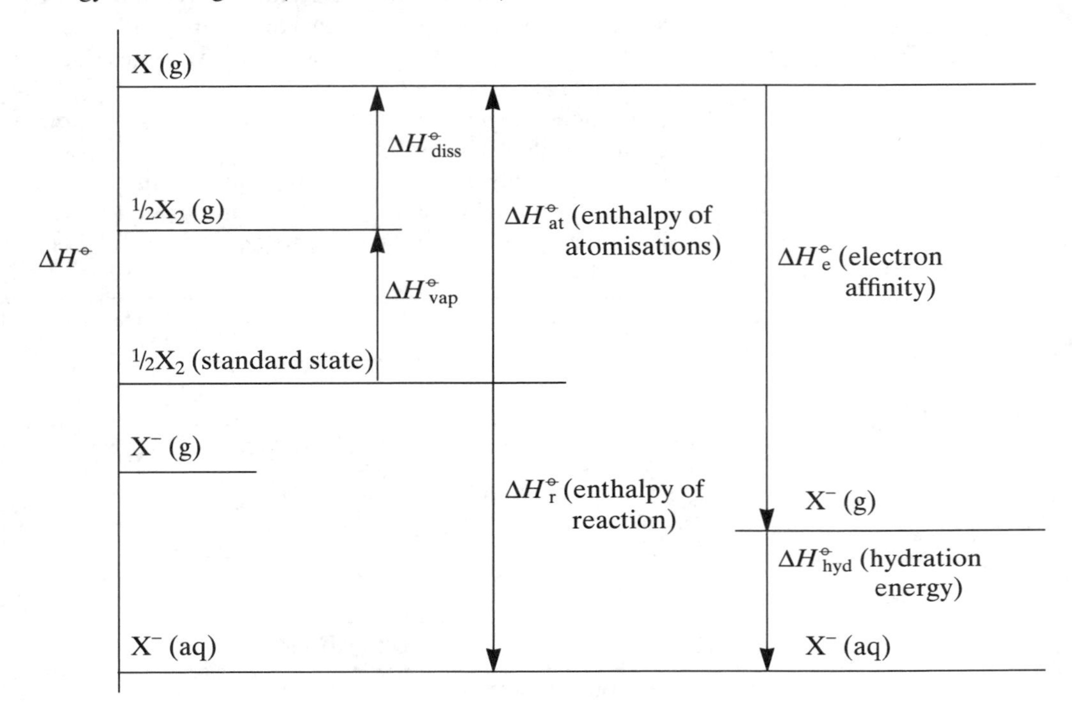

In the next exercise you use this energy-level diagram to calculate the enthalpy change for the formation of aqueous ions for each halogen.

EXERCISE 58
Answers on page 163

a Using your data book, complete Table 11 and calculate $\Delta H^{\ominus}_{r}$ for each halogen.
b Explain the order of oxidising ability in terms of $\Delta H^{\ominus}_{r}$.
c Which energy factor is mainly responsible for this order?

Table 11

	F	Cl	Br	I
$\Delta H^{\ominus}_{at}$/kJ mol^{-1}				
$\Delta H^{\ominus}_{e}$/kJ mol^{-1}				
$\Delta H^{\ominus}_{hyd}$/kJ mol^{-1} (for X^-)	–506	–364	–335	–293
$\Delta H^{\ominus}_{r}$/kJ mol^{-1}				

For the s-block elements you learned that metallic character increased as electronegativity decreased and reducing ability increased. In the next exercise you apply these ideas to the halogens.

EXERCISE 59
Answers on page 164

a Do you expect any metallic character to appear as the group is descended? Explain your answer.

b Do you think the physical appearance of the halogens supports your answer above? Explain.

At this stage you should realise that even though iodine is a non-metal, it does show signs of metallic character. In fact, it is electropositive enough to produce I^+ ions in certain reactions. You will consider the formation of I^+ ions later in this unit.

You have now completed Part A of this unit and to consolidate what you have learned, we suggest you answer the following Teacher-marked Exercise. Before you attempt the question, look back through your notes and then make a rough plan of the points you think should be included in your answer. Spend about 40 minutes planning and writing your answer.

EXERCISE
Teacher-marked

A

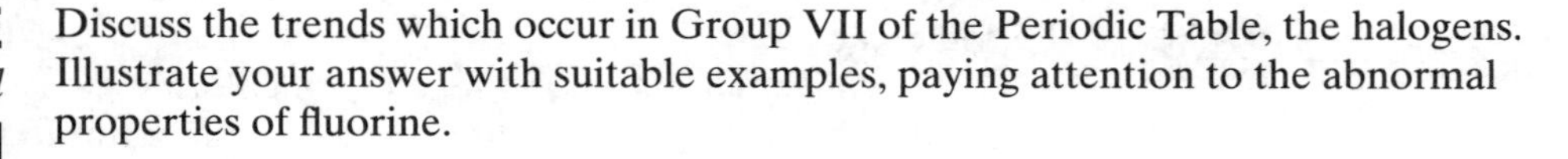

Discuss the trends which occur in Group VII of the Periodic Table, the halogens. Illustrate your answer with suitable examples, paying attention to the abnormal properties of fluorine.

Part A test

To find out how well you have learned the material in Part A, try the test which follows. Read the notes below before starting.

1. You should spend about 60 minutes on this test.
2. Hand your answers to your teacher for marking.

1. Explain each of the following facts.
   a Iodine is far more soluble in potassium iodide solution than it is in water. (2)
   b Chlorine is more electronegative than iodine. (2)
   c The boiling points of the halogens increase as the group is descended. (2)
   d The bond dissociation energy of fluorine is less than that of chlorine. (2)

2. This question concerns the elements from fluorine to iodine in Group VII of the Periodic Table.
   a i) Give an equation for the reaction of chlorine with aqueous bromide ions.
   ii) Use the reaction in i) above to explain the terms **oxidation** and **reduction**.
   iii) Explain briefly why chlorine is a stronger oxidising agent than bromine. (5)
   b When chlorine reacts with cold aqueous sodium hydroxide disproportionation occurs.
   i) Write an ionic equation for this reaction, and explain the term **disproportionation**.
   ii) Give an equation to show the effect of heating the mixture. (5)
   c Explain why xenon forms compounds with fluorine but not with chlorine. (2)

3. This question concerns the elements chlorine, bromine and iodine.
   a Give the electronic configurations of the chlorine atom and bromide ion.

	1s	2s	2p	3s	3p	3d	4s	4p
Cl								
Br^-								

(2)

   b On (copies of) the axes below, indicate approximately the variation of:
   i) bond dissociation energy with atomic number,

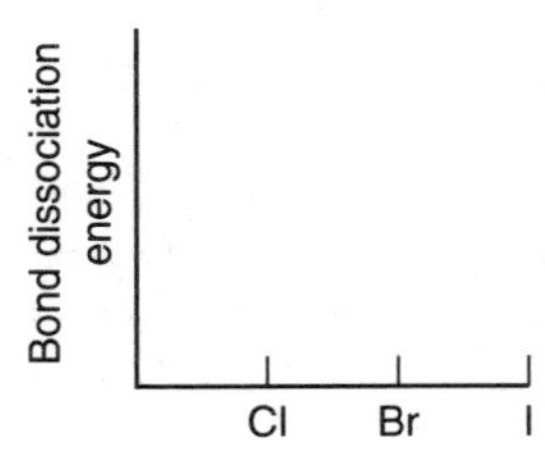

   ii) ionic radius with atomic number.

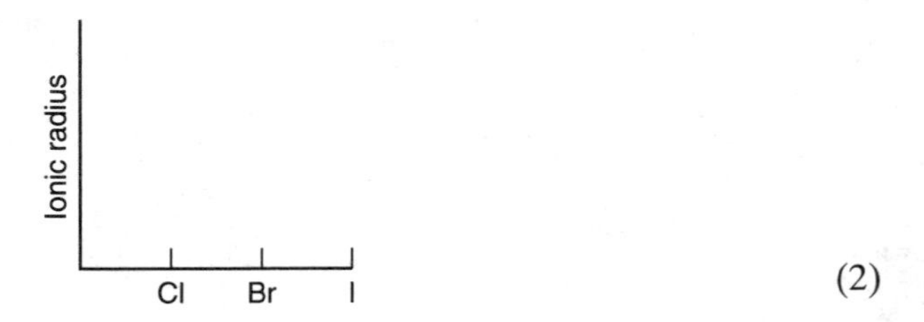

   c Compare the reactions, if any, of chlorine and of iodine with water. (2)

d The following reaction takes place on warming:

$$3Br_2\ (l) + 6OH^-\ (aq) \rightarrow 5Br^-\ (aq) + BrO_3^-\ (aq) + 3H_2O\ (l)$$

i) Give the oxidation number of bromine in BrO_3^- and explain your reasoning.
ii) What is the name given to this type of reaction?
iii) Suggest the shape of BrO_3^- and explain your reasoning. (4)

e Use the following data to determine the enthalpy change for the reaction:

$$\tfrac{1}{2}I_2\ (s) \rightarrow I^-\ (aq)$$

All steps in your calculation must be clearly shown.

$I_2\ (s) \rightarrow I_2\ (g)$ $\Delta H = 30\ \text{kJ mol}^{-1}$
$\tfrac{1}{2}I_2\ (g) \rightarrow I\ (g)$ $\Delta H = 76\ \text{kJ mol}^{-1}$
$I\ (g) \rightarrow I^-\ (g)$ $\Delta H = -297\ \text{kJ mol}^{-1}$
$I^-\ (g) \rightarrow I^-\ (aq)$ $\Delta H = -305\ \text{kJ mol}^{-1}$ (3)

(Total: 33 marks)

HALOGEN COMPOUNDS

Part B is concerned mainly with halogen compounds. A large variety of halogen compounds exist because most of the halogens can have several oxidation states. We begin by considering binary compounds, where one of the two elements is a halogen in the –I oxidation state; such compounds are called halides.

We deal with two categories of halides: the hydrogen halides and the metal halides.

CHAPTER 9

THE HYDROGEN HALIDES

OBJECTIVES

When you have finished this chapter you should be able to:

- state and explain the trends in the following properties of the hydrogen halides:
  - **a** melting point,
  - **b** boiling point,
  - **c** bond dissociation energy,
  - **d** enthalpy of formation;
- explain the trend in **thermal stability** of the hydrogen halides by reference to bond dissociation energies and enthalpies of formation;
- describe the **solubility/reactivity** of the hydrogen halides in water.

Scan those sections of your textbook(s) which deal with the hydrogen halides so that you know where to look for information to help you with the exercises.

Earlier in this unit, you learned that the hydrogen halides can be made by reacting the halogens directly with hydrogen under certain conditions. You now go on to study some of their important physical and chemical properties.

9.1 Melting points and boiling points

In the next exercise, you relate these properties to the strengths of intermolecular forces, as you have done before for other compounds.

EXERCISE 60

Answers on page 164

a Complete a copy of Table 12 below, using your data book.
b What is the trend in boiling point with increasing molar mass?
c Do the melting points follow a similar trend?
d Explain the trend in boiling points from hydrogen chloride to hydrogen iodide in terms of the strengths of van der Waals forces.

Table 12

	Formula	Molar mass /g mol^{-1}	Melting point/K	Boiling point/K	Physical state at s.t.p.*
Hydrogen fluoride					
Hydrogen chloride					
Hydrogen bromide					
Hydrogen iodide					

*Standard temperature and pressure.

It is clear from the last exercise that the properties of hydrogen fluoride are anomalous. The reason for the high boiling point of hydrogen fluoride was discussed in ILPAC Volume 3, Bonding and Structure. Refer back to that unit, if you need to, before going on to the next exercise, which is concerned with the anomalous properties of hydrogen fluoride.

EXERCISE 61
Answers on page 164

With the aid of a labelled diagram, explain why HF is a liquid at standard temperature and pressure whereas all the other hydrogen halides are gases.

The next section concerns the thermal stability of the hydrogen halides.

9.2 Thermal stability

In the next exercise, you predict the trend in thermal stability of the hydrogen halides by considering their bond dissociation energies and enthalpies of formation.

EXERCISE 62
Answers on page 164

Study the following data and answer the questions below.

	H—F	H—Cl	H—Br	H—I
Enthalpy of formation /kJ mol^{-1}	–269	–92.3	–36.2	+25.9
Bond dissociation energy/kJ mol^{-1}	+562	+431	+366	+299

a Identify and explain the trend in bond dissociation energy.
b If a hot wire is placed in a test-tube of colourless gaseous hydrogen iodide, violet fumes appear. Nothing happens if this is repeated with the gases hydrogen bromide and hydrogen chloride.
i) Write an equation for the decomposition of hydrogen iodide.
ii) Interpret the observations in **b** in terms of the data given above.

In the absence of water, the hydrogen halides have no effect on dry blue litmus paper, whereas they turn **wet** blue litmus paper red. In the following section, we discuss the reactions between the hydrogen halides and water.

9.3 Reaction of the hydrogen halides with water

In your pre-A-level work, you have probably encountered the 'fountain experiment' which shows the high solubility of hydrogen chloride in water. If you have never seen this done, you should ask your teacher for a demonstration.

All the hydrogen halide are extremely soluble in water to the extent that approximately 500 dm^3 of hydrogen halide will 'dissolve' in 1 dm^3 of ice-cold water. The resulting solutions are strongly acidic (apart from HF (aq)) because of the reaction with water to form hydrogen ions, i.e.

$$HX\,(g) + aq \rightarrow H^+\,(aq) + X^-\,(aq) \qquad \text{where X = a halogen}$$

or, more precisely,

$$HX\,(g) + H_2O\,(l) \rightarrow \underset{\text{hydronium ion}}{H_3O^+\,(aq)} + X^-\,(aq)$$

(see the Acids and Bases unit in ILPAC Volume 7).

Read about the acidic properties of the hydrogen halide solutions, paying particular attention to the anomalous properties of hydrogen fluoride in water. Then you should be able to do the following exercises.

EXERCISE 63
Answers on page 164

a What names are given to the acids formed by dissolving the hydrogen halides in water?
b Why is HF (aq) a weak acid in dilute solution whereas the others are strong?
c Amongst the three strong acids, HCl (aq), HBr (aq) and HI (aq), there are small differences in acid strength. State and explain the trend which exists.

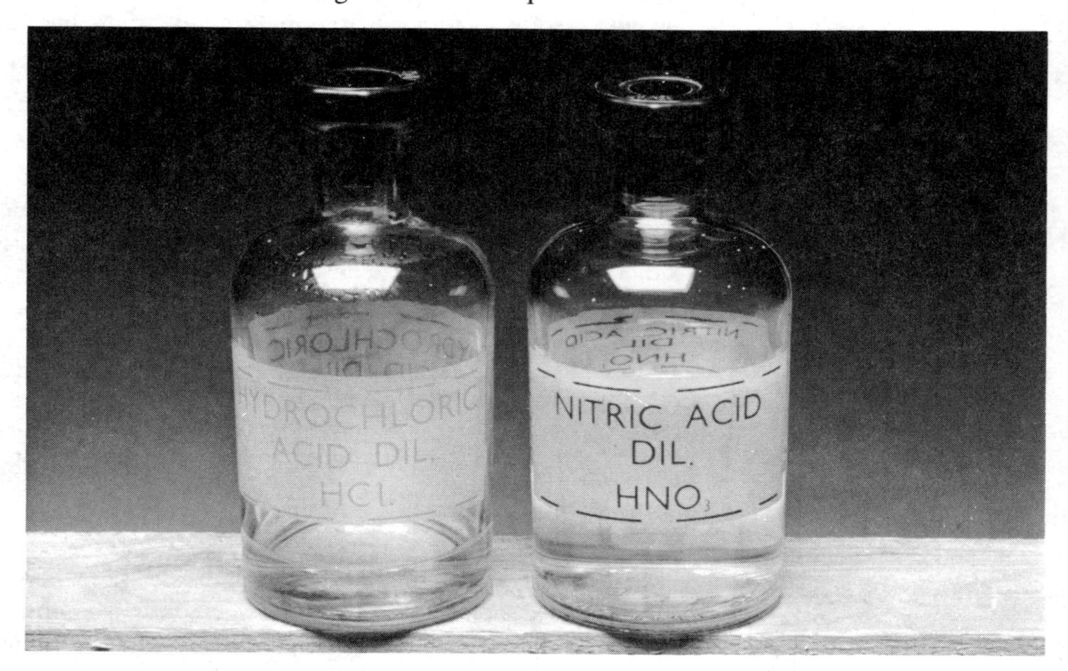

Concentrated hydrofluoric acid attacks glass and is sometimes used to etch patterns or letters on pieces of glassware.

You may have some reagent bottles in your laboratory like those in the photograph. The name-labels were made by etching, with hydrofluoric acid, the glass surrounding the letters, which were protected by a layer of wax or plastic.

The next exercise is taken from an A-level question.

EXERCISE 64
Answer on page 165

Comment on the following statement.

The hydrides of chlorine, bromine and iodine dissolved in water are strong acids and each forms only one potassium salt; hydrogen fluoride forms a weaker acid, and forms both potassium fluoride and potassium hydrogendifluoride (KHF_2).

To consolidate your knowledge so far in Part B, attempt the following Teacher-marked Exercise, which is taken from an A-level paper. In examination conditions, you might spend about 40 minutes planning and writing your answer.

EXERCISE
Teacher-marked

a Illustrate the trends in the chemical properties of the halogens F, Cl, Br and I by considering how these elements react with i) metals, ii) hydrogen, iii) aqueous sodium hydroxide.
b Discuss the bonding in hydrogen fluoride and explain how this accounts for one physical property and one chemical property of this hydride which may be described as 'abnormal'.

Having considered the hydrogen halides, we now move on to the metal halides.

CHAPTER 10

METAL HALIDES

In this chapter we deal mainly with the s-block halides, because they show typical halide reactions. The properties of these halides (with the exception of fluorides) can be easily demonstrated in the laboratory.

OBJECTIVES

When you have finished this chapter you should be able to:

- state and explain the effects of **oxidising and non-oxidising acids** on solid metal halides;
- describe the reactions between **aqueous halide compounds** and the following reagents:
  a silver nitrate solution,
  b lead(II) nitrate solution,
  c acidified hydrogen peroxide solution.

We start with an experiment to show the effects of two acids on the s-block halides.

EXPERIMENT 7 Reactions of solid halides

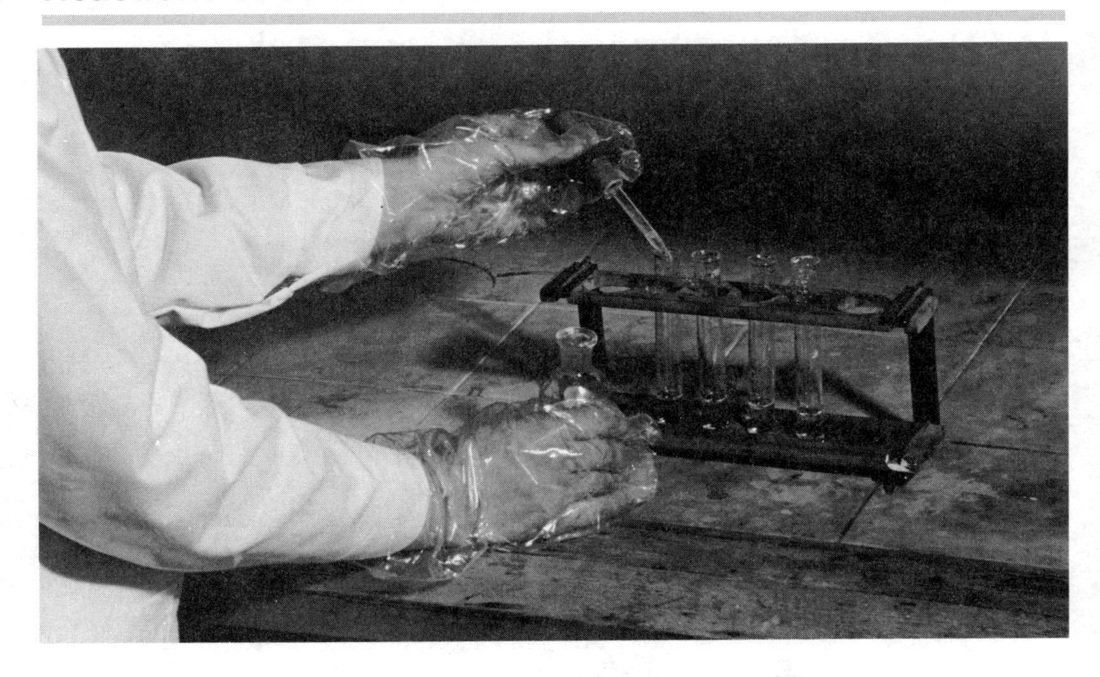

Aim The purpose of this experiment is to study the effect of an oxidising acid (concentrated sulphuric acid) and a non-oxidising acid (phosphoric(V) acid) on three solid potassium halides: potassium chloride, potassium bromide and potassium iodide.

Introduction In this experiment, you mix separate samples of crystalline potassium chloride, potassium bromide and potassium iodide with the following reagents in turn:

a H_2SO_4 (l) and MnO_2 (s)
b H_2SO_4 (l) alone
c H_3PO_4 (l).

Possible products include the halogens, the hydrogen halides, sulphur dioxide (SO_2) and hydrogen sulphide (H_2S). You already know how to recognise the halogens. Tests to recognise the other products are as follows:

Hydrogen halides Hold a moist stopper from a bottle of ammonia solution near the source of the gas. Dense white fumes indicate the presence of a hydrogen halide (or other strongly acidic gas).

Sulphur dioxide Hold a strip of filter paper soaked in acidified potassium dichromate(VI) solution near the source of the gas. A colour change from orange to green indicates the presence of sulphur dioxide (or other strongly reducing gas).
Hydrogen sulphide The 'bad egg' smell is very characteristic, but take care – the gas is very toxic. Hold a strip of filter paper soaked in lead ethanoate (acetate) solution near the source of the gas. A silver black colour indicates the presence of hydrogen sulphide.

Requirements

- safety spectacles
- access to fume cupboard
- 12 test-tubes in rack
- spatula
- potassium bromide, solid, KBr
- potassium chloride, solid, KCl
- potassium iodide, solid, KI
- manganese(IV) oxide, MnO_2
- glass stirring rod
- sulphuric acid, concentrated, H_2SO_4
- phosphoric(V) acid, 100%, H_3PO_4
- test-tube holder
- Bunsen burner and bench mat
- distilled water
- 3 dropping pipettes
- ammonia solution, 2 M NH_3
- lead(II) ethanoate solution, $(CH_3COO)_2Pb$
- potassium dichromate(VI) solution, $K_2Cr_2O_7$
- strips of filter paper
- starch solution
- Volasil 244

HAZARD WARNING

Concentrated sulphuric acid is very corrosive and reacts violently with water. Phosphoric(V) acid and potassium dichromate are also very corrosive. Therefore, you **must**:

- **avoid contact with skin**; if contact does occur, wash immediately under a cold tap with **plenty** of water;
- dispose of **cold** residues containing concentrated sulphuric acid by pouring **slowly** into plenty of water.

The halogens, hydrogen halides, sulphur dioxide and hydrogen sulphide are toxic. Therefore you **must:**

- **carry out these experiments in a fume cupboard.**

Hexane is very flammable.

- **Keep hexane stoppered and away from flames.**

Procedure

1. Reaction with H_2SO_4 and MnO_2.
   - **a** Into three separate test-tubes, place enough potassium chloride, potassium bromide and potassium iodide to half-fill the rounded part at the bottom.
   - **b** To the contents of each test-tube, add a roughly equal quantity of manganese(IV) oxide, and mix the solids together with a stirring rod.

   - **c** Hold the tube in a fume cupboard, with its mouth pointed away from you, and cautiously add ten drops of concentrated sulphuric acid, shaking the tube gently after the addition of each drop.

   - **d** Note whether any reaction occurs, and confirm any suspected products by appropriate tests. Complete a larger copy of Results Table 8.
   - **e** If no reaction seems to occur, warm the test-tube carefully.

2. Reaction with H_2SO_4.
   Repeat the above procedure without using manganese(IV) oxide.
3. Reaction with H_3PO_4.
   Repeat the above procedure, using phosphoric(V) acid alone in place of sulphuric acid, i.e. without using manganese(IV) oxide.

Results Table 8

Test	Chloride	Bromide	Iodide
1. **Action of conc. H_2SO_4 and MnO_2** Observations Suspected product(s) Confirmatory tests			
2. **Action of conc. H_2SO_4** Observations Suspected product(s) Confirmatory tests			
3. **Action of H_3PO_4** Observations Suspected product(s) Confirmatory tests			

(Specimen results on page 165.)

Questions

Answers on page 166

1. In many of the reactions you may have detected mixtures of the halogens and the hydrogen halides. In such cases, you should assume that at least two reactions are occurring. With this in mind and with the aid of textbooks, complete and balance the following equations:
   a $KCl (s) + H_2SO_4 (l) \rightarrow$
   b $KCl (s) + H_3PO_4 (l) \rightarrow$
   c $KBr (s) + H_2SO_4 (l) \rightarrow$
   $HBr (g) + H_2SO_4 (l) \rightarrow$
   d $KBr (s) + H_3PO_4 (l) \rightarrow$
   e $KI (s) + H_2SO_4 (l) \rightarrow$
   $HI (g) + H_2SO_4 (l) \rightarrow$
   f $KI (s) + H_3PO_4 (l) \rightarrow$

   (We have used the formula H_3PO_4 (l) rather than H_3PO_4 (s) because the solid melts before reaction occurs.)
2. Manganese(IV) oxide is a strong oxidising agent capable of oxidising all the hydrogen halides (except HF) to the halogens. In the light of this statement, explain the reactions between potassium chloride and concentrated sulphuric acid, with and without manganese(IV) oxide.
3. Why does the addition of manganese(IV) oxide appear to have little effect on the reaction between potassium iodide and concentrated sulphuric acid?

Now attempt the next two exercises which are taken from A-level papers.

EXERCISE 65

Answers on page 166

List the hydrogen halides in order of decreasing ease of oxidation by concentrated sulphuric acid. Explain the sequence using bond energy terms.

EXERCISE 66

Answers on page 166

A sodium halide reacts with cold concentrated sulphuric acid to give colourless fumes. On warming the mixture, brown fumes are obtained.

i) Name the halide ion in the salt.
ii) Write the equation for the reaction which gives colourless fumes.
iii) Write the equation for the reaction which gives brown fumes, and state why the brown fumes are formed.

Use your results from Experiment 7 to help you with the next exercise. You may also need guidance from your textbook(s).

EXERCISE 67

Answers on page 166

Outline the laboratory preparation of each of the four hydrogen halides, HF, HCl, HBr and HI.

In the next experiment, you study some reactions of the halide ions in aqueous solution.

EXPERIMENT 8 Reaction of halides in solution

Aim

The purpose of this experiment is to find out whether the ions Cl^-, Br^- and I^- react in solution with certain reagents and, where they do react, what products are formed.

Introduction

In this experiment, you add various reagents to separate samples of solutions containing Cl^-, Br^- and I^- ions. In many of the reactions, precipitates are formed. Where you are asked to add another reagent to excess, you should look carefully to see if any of the precipitate dissolves.

Requirements

- safety spectacles
- 18 test-tubes, 9 with corks
- 3 test-tube racks
- 8 dropping pipettes
- potassium bromide solution, 0.1 M KBr
- potassium chloride solution, 0.1 M KCl
- potassium iodide solution, 0.1 M KI
- silver nitrate solution, 0.02 M $AgNO_3$
- nitric acid, dilute, 2 M HNO_3
- ammonia solution, 5 M NH_3
- lead(II) nitrate solution, 0.1 M $Pb(NO_3)_2$
- hydrogen peroxide solution, H_2O_2, 20 volume
- starch solution
- sulphuric acid, dilute, 1 M H_2SO_4
- Volasil 244

HAZARD WARNING **Keep Volasil 244 well stoppered and away from flames.**

Silver nitrate is toxic and corrosive. Lead nitrate is toxic.

Ammonia solution and hydrogen peroxide are corrosive substances.

Procedure

Add the following reagents to 1 cm^3 of the chloride, bromide and iodide solutions in turn, and record your observations in a copy of Results Table 9.

1. Add approximately 1 cm^3 of silver nitrate solution and shake gently. Note what happens. Move the three tubes to a dark cupboard, leave them there until the end of the lesson and note their appearance again.
2. Add silver nitrate solution as in (1). Leave these tubes in their racks until the end of the lesson, noting their appearance every 10–15 minutes.
3. Add approximately 1 cm^3 of silver nitrate solution followed by excess (e.g. 5 cm^3) dilute nitric acid. Cork the test-tube and shake vigorously.
4. Add approximately 1 cm^3 silver nitrate solution followed by excess (e.g. 5 cm^3) ammonia solution. Cork the test-tube and shake.
5. Add approximately 1 cm^3 lead(II) nitrate solution.
6. Add approximately 1 cm^3 of hydrogen peroxide solution followed by approximately 1 cm^3 of dilute sulphuric acid. Cork these tubes and allow them to stand. Add any further reagent(s) which you think will help you to decide what has happened.

Results Table 9

Test	Chloride	Bromide	Iodide
Action of $AgNO_3$ (aq)			
Effect of standing in **a** dark **b** light			
Action of $AgNO_3$ (aq) followed by dilute HNO_3 (aq)			
Action of $AgNO_3$ (aq) followed by NH_3 (aq)			
Action of $Pb(NO_3)_2$ (aq)			
Action of H_2O_2 (aq) and dilute H_2SO_4 (aq)			

(Specimen results on page 167.)

Questions

Answers on page 167

1. Write ionic equations for the reactions between each of the three halide solutions and
   a silver nitrate solution,
   b lead(II) nitrate solution.
2. What chemical tests would you perform in order to distinguish between
   a Cl^- (aq) and Br^- (aq),
   b Br^- (aq) and I^- (aq)?

3. **a** Write an ionic equation for the reaction between an aqueous iodide and acidified hydrogen peroxide.
   b Why do you think no reaction occurs between acidified hydrogen peroxide and the other halide ions?
4. Suggest a reason for the darkening effect of light on the silver chloride and silver bromide precipitates.

By consulting your textbook(s) and using the knowledge you have already gained about the halogens, you should be able to answer the following A-level questions.

EXERCISE 68

Answers on page 167

Describe the observations which can be noted in each of the following experiments, and write equations:

a potassium manganate(VII) (permanganate) crystals are mixed with concentrated hydrochloric acid;

b aqueous potassium chloride and aqueous silver nitrate are mixed and concentrated aqueous ammonia is then added;

c aqueous bromine (i.e. a dilute solution) is mixed with an excess of potassium iodide solution, and aqueous sodium thiosulphate, $Na_2S_2O_3$, is then added.

During your study of The Mole unit in ILPAC Volume 1, you carried out a titration involving the oxidation of the thiosulphate ion, $S_2O_3^{2-}$, by iodine solution. You may need to refer back to that experiment when you do the next exercise.

EXERCISE 69

Answers on page 168

a Describe, with full practical instructions, how you would determine the concentration (g dm^{-3}) of a solution of hydrogen peroxide using the quantitative reactions:

$$H_2O_2 + 2H^+ + 2I^- \rightarrow I_2 + 2H_2O$$

$$I_2 + 2S_2O_3^{2-} \rightarrow 2I^- + S_4O_6^{2-}$$

The usual titrimetric (volumetric) apparatus is available together with aqueous solutions of potassium iodide, sulphuric acid, starch and 0.10 M sodium thiosulphate, ($Na_2S_2O_3$).

b Show how you would calculate the result from the experimental data in **a**. (H = 1, O = 16.)

In the s-Block Elements unit of this volume, you learned that the s-block elements show only one oxidation state in all their compounds. By contrast, the halogens (with the exception of fluorine) show several oxidation states, which we illustrate by considering some oxides and oxoacids (oxyacids).

CHAPTER 11

OXIDES AND OXOACIDS OF THE HALOGENS

OBJECTIVES

When you have finished this chapter you should be able to:

- list the range of **oxidation numbers** displayed by the halogens in their compounds;
- compare the **oxidising powers** of the **halogen oxoacid** salts (sometimes called the **halates**);
- compare the **acid strengths** of the **oxoacids of chlorine**.

We begin this chapter with the various oxides formed by the halogens.

11.1 Halogen oxides

None of the halogens reacts directly with oxygen. However, many different oxides can be formed by indirect means, though they are mostly unstable, some explosively so. The halogen oxides are relatively unimportant but they do illustrate an important characteristic of the halogens – the wide range of oxidation states. They are also of some interest as the anhydrides of the halogen oxoacids, which are more stable, important and useful.

EXERCISE 70

Answers on page 168

a Complete a copy of the oxidation number chart (Table 13) to show the oxidation state of the halogen in each of the following oxides: F_2O_2, F_2O, Cl_2O, ClO_2, Cl_2O_6, Cl_2O_7, Br_2O, BrO_2, BrO_3, I_2O_4, I_2O_5 and I_2O_7.

Table 13

	F	Cl	Br	I
+VII				
+VI			BrO_3	
+V				
+IV			BrO_2	
+III				
+II				
+I			Br_2O	
0				
–I				

b Use a table of electronegativity values to deduce the nature of the bonds in the above compounds.

c Why is the maximum oxidation state +VII?

d In which of the above compounds does oxygen not have an oxidation state of –II?

e Why do you think that F_2O_2 and F_2O are sometimes referred to as fluorides of oxygen rather than oxides of fluorine, and given the formulae O_2F_2 and OF_2?

f Would you expect the oxides of the halogens to be basic or acidic (think of the more familiar oxides of other non-metals)? What, therefore, would you expect to be the reaction of Cl_2O_7 with water?

The next exercise is taken from an A-level question. You should be able to answer it by recalling what you learned in ILPAC Volume 3, Bonding and Structure, about shapes of molecules.

EXERCISE 71
Answers on page 169

Suggest a structure for F_2O, giving a bond diagram and predicting the shape of the molecule.

In the next section, we consider some of the oxoacids and their salts.

11.2 Oxoacids and their salts

We shall deal mainly with the oxoacids of chlorine. You have already met chloric(I) acid (hypochlorous acid), HClO, as a product of the reaction between chlorine and water.

The next exercise is concerned with the names, formulae and acid strengths of the oxoacids. Some of the information you require is given in Table 14, but you may also need to refer to your textbook(s).

Table 14
Oxoacids of chlorine

Formula	IUPAC name	Old name	Acid strength	Oxidation state of halogen	Name and formula of anion
	chloric(I) acid	hypochlorous acid		+I	ClO^- chlorate(I)
$HClO_2$		chlorous acid	weak		ClO_2^- chlorate(III)
	chloric(V) acid	chloric acid			
$HClO_4$		perchloric acid*	very strong		

*Perchloric acid is explosive when it comes into contact with organic matter. It is also one of the strongest acids known.

EXERCISE 72
Answers on page 170

a Complete a copy of Table 14.
b Draw dot-and-cross diagrams for each anion shown in Table 14. (Hint: dative covalent bonds are involved in three of the anions.)
c Write down the name and formula of the sodium salt of each of the acids listed in the table.
d Chlorine(I) oxide, Cl_2O, reacts with water to produce chloric(I) acid, HClO. State the name and formula of the acid produced when chlorine(VII) oxide reacts with water.

In the last exercise you learned that the acid strength of the oxoacids increases as the oxidation number of the halogen increases. Now you consider reasons for this variation.

A strong acid is one which is largely ionised in aqueous solution, whereas a weak acid remains mostly in molecular form. If we represent an acid by the general formula HA, we can represent the ionisation by the equation:

$$HA\,(aq) \rightleftharpoons H^+\,(aq) + A^-\,(aq)$$

The concentration of hydrogen ions in the solution depends on the strength of the parent acid. For example, $HClO_4$ is a strong acid and exists in solution mainly as ions, H^+ (aq) and ClO_4^- (aq); but HClO is a weak acid and exists in solution mainly as HClO molecules, with very few hydrogen ions.

In the following Revealing Exercise, you explore the reasons for the relative strengths of the oxoacids of chlorine. A fuller treatment will be found in the Acids and Bases unit of ILPAC Volume 7.

EXERCISE
Revealing

Q1. Draw dot-and-cross diagrams to represent **a** HClO, **b** $HClO_2$, **c** $HClO_3$ and **d** $HClO_4$. (Hint: there are some dative bonds.)

A1

a

```
   ••   xx
 : Cl x O • H
   ••   ••
```

b

```
  xx   ••   xx
 x O  •Cl • O x H
  xx   ••   xx
```

c

```
     xx
    x O x
     ••   xx
   : Cl x O x H
     ••   xx

    x O x
     xx
```

d

```
        xx
       x O x
    xx   ••   xx
   x O  •Cl x O x H
    xx   ••   xx
       x O x
        xx
```

Q2 Which of the atoms, O and Cl, is the more electronegative?

A2 Oxygen (O = 3.5, Cl = 3.0). You are not expected to memorise electronegativity values but you should be aware of this relative order by memorising the trends in the Periodic Table.

Q3 Are the electrons in the dative covalent bonds drawn more towards the oxygen atoms or the chlorine atoms? (Indicate the polarity of the bond.)

A3 The bonding pairs are closer to the oxygen atoms. As a result, each chlorine atom has slightly positive charge.

Q4 How does the slight positive charge on the chlorine vary as the number of oxygen atoms increases?

A4 The slight positive charge on the chlorine increases as the number of oxygen atoms attached to it increases.

Q5 What effect does this positive charge have on the electrons in the Cl—OH bond?

A5 Electrons are pulled towards the chlorine to reduce its positive charge.

Q6 Consider the dot-and-cross diagrams you drew for HClO and $HClO_2$. How does the shift of electrons in the Cl—OH bond affect the distribution of electrons in the O—H bond in each molecule?

A6 In both cases, the electrons in the O—H bond are drawn nearer to the oxygen atoms, but this effect will be more marked in $HClO_2$.

Q7 Considering the same argument for all the acids, which of the four is likely to release hydrogen ions most readily?

A7 $HClO_4$ has three polar O—Cl bonds, each drawing electrons away from the chlorine atom. This effect is transmitted to the O—H bond and makes the release of H^+ ions easiest for this acid.

Fluorine does not form stable oxoacids because its electronegativity is too high to allow its non-bonding electrons to form dative covalent bonds with oxygen atoms. Bromine and iodine do form stable aqueous oxoacids in the +I and +V oxidation states.

In the next exercise you compare some of the oxoacids of chlorine, bromine and iodine.

EXERCISE 73
Answers on page 170

Place the following weak acids in order of increasing acid strength.

a HBrO, HClO, HIO.

b HIO, HIO_3.

Explain your answers.

Iodic(I) acid (hypoiodous acid) is such a weak acid that it can behave as an amphoteric substance. The next exercise is concerned with this point.

EXERCISE 74
Answers on page 171

Iodic(I) acid can ionise in aqueous solutions to form hydrogen ions or hydroxide ions.

a Write equations to represent the two possible ionisations.

b How does this illustrate a degree of metallic character in iodine?

You should not be surprised to find that the oxoacids and their salts are useful oxidising agents, particularly those with higher oxidation numbers. This is illustrated by the reactions between the oxoacid(V) salts and acidified iodide ions but the equations for them are not easy to balance by trial and error. In the next section, we show you how a knowledge of oxidation numbers can be used to balance equations.

11.3 Balancing redox equations

OBJECTIVES

When you have finished this section you should be able to:

- write **balanced equations for redox reactions;**
- describe how the equation for the **iodate(V)/iodide reaction** can be confirmed by experiment.

The following Worked Example shows you how to balance a fairly cumbersome redox equation by two different methods.

WORKED EXAMPLE

Balance the following redox equation:

$$ClO_3^- (aq) + I^- (aq) + H^+ (aq) \rightarrow I_2 (aq) + Cl^- (aq) + H_2O (l)$$

Solution

1. Identify which species is oxidised and which is reduced. This can be done by looking at oxidation numbers.

$$\overset{+5}{Cl}O_3 (aq) + \overset{-1}{I^-} (aq) + H^+ (aq) \rightarrow \overset{0}{I_2} (aq) + \overset{-1}{Cl^-} (aq) + H_2O (l)$$

$\therefore$ the species oxidised is I^-, [Ox(I) $-1 \rightarrow 0$]
and the species reduced is ClO_3^- [Ox(Cl) $+5 \rightarrow -1$]

2. Construct two balanced half-equations, one representing oxidation and one representing reduction.
   a Balance the elements in each half-equation: if necessary, include H^+, OH^- and H_2O, as appropriate.

Oxidation $2I^- (aq) \rightarrow I_2 (aq)$

Reduction $ClO_3^- (aq) \rightarrow Cl^- (aq)$

The three oxygen atoms become incorporated in water molecules, i.e.

$$ClO_3^- (aq) \rightarrow Cl^- (aq) + 3H_2O (l)$$

Since the reaction occurs in an acid medium, include H^+ ions to balance the hydrogen in the water molecules, i.e.

$$ClO_3^- (aq) + 6H^+ (aq) \rightarrow Cl^- (aq) + 3H_2O (l)$$

b Balance the charge in each half-equation. This can be done either by looking at the change in oxidation number or by balancing the charges on the ions.

Oxidation number method

$$2I^- (aq) \rightarrow I_2 (aq)$$

Ox(I) changes from –1 to 0, i.e. each I atom loses one electron. Since there are two iodide ions, two electrons must be released in forming each iodine molecule

Balancing charge method

$$2I^- (aq) \rightarrow I_2 (aq)$$

Count the charges on each side of the half-equations:

2 negative charges → zero charge

Therefore, two electrons must be released from two iodide ions in order to form an iodine molecule

$$2I^- (aq) \rightarrow I_2 (aq) + 2e^-$$

Similarly, for

$$ClO_3^- (aq) + 6H^+ (aq) \rightarrow Cl^- (aq) + 3H_2O (l)$$

Ox(Cl) changes from +5 to –1, i.e. 6 units. Therefore, for each ClO_3^- ion reduced, 6 electrons are required.

Similarly, for

$$ClO_3^- (aq) + 6H^+ (aq) \rightarrow Cl^- (aq) + 3H_2O (l)$$

5 positive charges → 1 negative (6 – 1) Therefore, 6 electrons are needed for each ClO_3^- ion reduced.

$$ClO_3^- (aq) + 6H^+ (aq) + 6e^- \rightarrow Cl^- (aq) + 3H_2O (l)$$

3. Scale the half-equations up or down, so that the number of electrons required by one half-equation is the same as the number provided by the other.

$$ClO_3^- (aq) + 6H^+ (aq) + 6e^- \rightarrow Cl^- (aq) + 3H_2O (l)$$

$$2I^- (aq) \rightarrow I_2 (aq) + 2e^- \text{ (multiply this equation by 3)}$$

$$6I^- (aq) \rightarrow 3I_2 (aq) + 6e^-$$

4. Combine the two half-equations by adding the left sides together and the right sides together.

$$ClO_3^- (aq) + 6H^+ (aq) + 6I^- (aq) \rightarrow 3I_2 (aq) + Cl^- (aq) + 3H_2O (l)$$

Decide which of the two methods you prefer and attempt the next exercise. We use the balancing charge method in the answers, but you should be aware of both methods.

EXERCISE 75

Answers on page 171

Balance the following equations.

a IO_3^- (aq) + I^- (aq) + H^+ (aq) → I_2 (aq) + H_2O (l)

b $S_2O_3^{2-}$ (aq) + I_2 (aq) → I^- (aq) + $S_4O_6^{2-}$ (aq)

You can now check the equation for the iodate(V)/iodide reaction experimentally.

EXPERIMENT 9 Balancing a redox reaction

Aim

The purpose of this experiment is to calculate the amount of iodide ions which react with each mole of iodate(V) ions in aqueous solution.

Requirements

- safety spectacles
- 2 measuring cylinders, 10 cm^3
- potassium iodide solution, ~ 1 M KI
- 2 conical flasks, 250 cm^3
- hydrochloric acid, ~ 2 M HCl
- 2 burettes, stands and filter funnels
- 1 white tile
- potassium iodate solution, 0.10 M KIO_3
- sodium thiosulphate solution, 0.10 M $Na_2S_2O_3$
- starch solution, 0.2%
- wash-bottle of distilled water

Procedure

1. Use a measuring cylinder to pour about 10 cm^3 of potassium iodide solution into a 250 cm^3 conical flask.
2. To the solution in the conical flask add about 10 cm^3 of dilute hydrochloric acid.
3. From a burette, add precisely 5.0 cm^3 of 0.10 M potassium iodate solution to the acidified iodide solution.
4. Titrate the iodine formed against 0.10 M potassium thiosulphate solution. When the colour of the iodine has nearly gone, add 1–2 cm^3 of starch solution and continue the addition of thiosulphate solution drop by drop until the blue colour disappears.
5. Record your burette readings in a copy of Results Table 10.
6. Repeat steps 1 to 5 as a check on your accuracy.

Results Table 10

Solution in flask					mol dm^{-3}	cm^3
Solution in burette					mol dm^{-3}	
Indicator						
		Trial	1	2	3	4
Burette readings	Final					
	Initial					
Volume used/cm^3						
Mean titre/cm^3						

(Specimen results on page 171.)

Calculations

Specimen results and calculations on page 171

1. Calculate the amount of sodium thiosulphate present in the volume of solution run out from the burette.
2. Calculate the amount of iodine **atoms** which must have reacted with the amount of $S_2O_3^{2-}$ (aq) calculated in step 1. Use the equation:

$$S_2O_3^{2-}(aq) + I_2(aq) \rightarrow 2I^-(aq) + S_4O_6^{2-}(aq)$$

3. Calculate the amount of iodine **atoms** present in 5.0 cm^3 of 0.10 M KIO_3.
4. Subtract the value obtained in step 3 from the value obtained in step 2 to obtain the amount of iodine atoms which originated from the potassium iodide.
5. State the amount of iodide ions which reacts with each mole of iodate ions, and check your result with the equation you wrote for Exercise 75**a**.

You should now be able to attempt the next exercise.

EXERCISE 76

Answers on page 171

a What mass of potassium iodate(V) (KIO_3) would be required to make 250 cm^3 of a solution containing one-sixtieth of a mole per dm^3?

b When 25.0 cm^3 of the solution of potassium iodate(V) of the concentration in **a** was added to excess of acidified potassium iodide solution, the iodine liberated reacted with 20.0 cm^3 of a solution of sodium thiosulphate. Calculate the concentration of the thiosulphate solution in moles per dm^3.

$$IO_3^- + 5I^- + 6H^+ \rightarrow 3I_2 + 3H_2O$$

$$I_2 + 2S_2O_3^{2-} \rightarrow 2I^- + S_4O_6^{2-}$$

c State how you would use the iodate(V)/iodide reaction and a standard solution of sodium thiosulphate to find the concentration of a solution of hydrochloric acid.

d 50 cm^3 of a solution containing 0.10 mol dm^{-3} of bromine (Br_2) was added to 10 cm^3 of a 0.10 mol dm^{-3} sodium thiosulphate solution. Excess potassium iodide was then added to the solution; the bromine which was left over from the first reaction liberated enough iodine to react with exactly 20 cm^3 of the same thiosulphate solution.

i) What is the apparent oxidation number of S in the thiosulphate ion ($S_2O_3^{2-}$)?

ii) From the figures given, calculate the number of moles of bromine which reacted directly with one mole of thiosulphate.

iii) To what oxidation number of the S did the bromine oxidise the thiosulphate?

iv) Derive the equation for the reaction between bromine molecules and thiosulphate ions.

We complete this section on the oxoacid salts by briefly considering some of their uses.

11.4 Uses of the salts of the halogen oxoacids

OBJECTIVE

When you have finished this section you should be able to:

- state some important **uses of the salts of halogen oxoacids.**

Read about the uses of the salts of the halogen oxoacids so that you can answer the questions in the following exercise.

EXERCISE 77

Answers on page 173

a Name a salt of a halogen oxoacid which is used for each of the following:

i) a bleach,

ii) a weed-killer (shown in use in the photograph below),

iii) a disinfectant,

iv) a primary standard in volumetric analysis,

v) an ingredient in explosives,

vi) an improving agent in flour.

b Explain the first of the hazard warnings on the bleach label shown below.

Figure 16
Some uses of salts of halogen oxoacids.

SODIUM HYPOCHLORITE

IRRITANT

CONTACT WITH ACID LIBERATES A TOXIC GAS IRRITATING TO EYES AND SKIN

KEEP OUT OF REACH OF CHILDREN

AVOID CONTACT WITH EYES

NOT TO BE TAKEN

BEWARE OF GASES

STORE UPRIGHT IN A COOL PLACE

DO NOT USE WITH ANY OTHER TOILET CLEANER

DO NOT USE FOR WOOLLENS, RAYONS, WAFFLE, EVERGLAZE, SEERSUCKER, PIQUE, SILK OR DRIP-DRY MATERIALS

DO NOT POUR DIRECTLY ONTO CLOTHING

We complete Part B of this unit by asking you to identify, by experiment, some inorganic substances which you have studied in this unit. You will find the two experiments in Chapter 12 particularly important if you are taking a practical examination at the end of your A-level course; both experiments are taken from past practical examination papers.

IDENTIFICATION OF UNKNOWN SUBSTANCES

OBJECTIVES

When you have finished this chapter you should be able to:
- test and **identify common gases**;
- **identify**, as far as possible, some unknown **inorganic substances**.

Some examining boards set observation and deduction exercises in the practical examination. In these exercises you are usually told which tests to carry out on the unknown substances. You may be allowed to use any books to help you make your deductions (inferences) during the examination, but check the requirements of your particular syllabus with your teacher.

In any case, practical books are useful in your preparation for practical examinations. Look for a book which indicates the reaction(s) which may occur if a certain reagent is added to the substance being tested.

The table which follows illustrates the type of information you are likely to find in such a book. It shows the observations and inferences which can be made if silver nitrate solution is added to a test solution. You can match the observations you make with one of those in the book and make your inferences accordingly.

Table 15
Reactions with silver nitrate solution.
Add the reagent dropwise to the test solution, observe, then add excess and warm

Observation	Inference	
	Ion(s) probably present	**Probable reaction**
1. PRECIPITATE FORMED		
a White, curdy, turning buff of heating	CO_3^{2-}, HCO_3^-	Ag_2CO_3 pptd $\rightarrow Ag_2O$
White, curdy, turning purplish grey on standing in bright light; insoluble in dil. HNO_3	Cl^-	AgCl pptd
b Cream (pale, sometimes almost white)	Br^-	AgBr pptd
Cream (deep, sometimes almost yellow) *(N.B. Ag_3PO_4 is soluble in both NH_3 (aq) soln. and dil. HNO_3; AgI is insoluble in these reagents)*	PO_4^{3-}, I^-	Ag_3PO_4,AgI pptd respectively
c Red from yellow soln. from orange soln.	CrO_4^{2-} $Cr_2O_7^{2-}$	Ag_2CrO_4 pptd
d Greyish-brown *(N.B. If NH_3 (aq) soln. is used the initial ppt is transient – dissolving in the excess NH_3 (aq) forming complexion $Ag(NH_3)_2^+$)*	OH^-	Ag_2O pptd (AgOH unstable)
e Black *(N.B. If Ag is pptd this is sometimes brownish and sometimes in the form of a mirror)*	S^{2-} Fe^{2+} SnO_2^{2-}	Ag_2S pptd Ag pptd in redox reactions $Fe^{2+} + Ag^+ \rightleftharpoons Ag + Fe^{3+}$ $SnO_2^{2-} + 2OH^- + 2Ag^+ \rightleftharpoons SnO_3^{2-} + 2Ag + H_2O$
2. CRYSTALLINE GROWTH OF SILVER SLOWLY FORMED	**Redox reaction of displacement type by metal above Ag in E.C.S., e.g.** $Cu + 2Ag^+ \rightarrow Cu^{2+} + Ag$	
3. NO APPARENT REACTION	**No anion present which can give insoluble silver salt by double decomposition. Reducing agents such as Fe^{2+}, SnO_2^{2-}, SO_3^{2-} absent**	

We now present a specimen question with answers to show you how to record your observations and inferences.

Specimen question

You are provided with an s-block metal compound X. Carry out the following tests and record your observations and inferences in the table provided. Identify the anion and cation present.

Table 16

Test	Observation	Inference
1. Transfer about 0.5 g of X to a hard-glass test-tube and heat strongly for a few minutes. Test any gas evolved	An odourless, colourless gas is given off, which turns lime-water milky. A white residue remains	CO_2 is given off. This suggests the presence of a carbonate (probably not Na or K) or a hydrogencarbonate (Na or K)
2. Add dilute HCl (aq) to about 0.5 g of the solid X in a test-tube	An odourless, colourless gas is given off which turns lime-water milky. A clear solution remains at the end	Again CO_2 is given off. This confirms the presence of a carbonate (not Na or K) or a hydrogencarbonate (Na or K)
3. Add 2 drops of $MgSO_4$ (aq) to 1 cm^3 of an aqueous solution of X	A white precipitate is produced. No gas is evolved	Ppt. must be $MgCO_3$ ($Mg(HCO_3)_2$ is soluble). X must be a soluble carbonate, perhaps Li_2CO_3?
4. Carry out a flame test on X	An intense red colour is obtained	Li^+ present. (Not Sr^{2+} – carbonate insoluble)

Conclusion

Anion = carbonate, CO_3^{2-}

Cation = lithium, Li^+

Some further points to consider.

1. You may not be expected to make a **complete** identification of the given substance(s). **Read the question** carefully so that you know precisely what is required.
2. Many marks are awarded for clear and accurate recording of observations. Make sure you do this properly even if you cannot make any inferences from them – many students pass practical examinations without getting 'the right answer'.
3. You may be asked to record your method of carrying out the tests, and perhaps to draw conclusions about the nature of the reactions you observe. Again, **read the question** carefully so that you know precisely what is required.
4. Testing for gases evolved during reactions is an important part of the examination of unknown substances. In the next section we present a simple guide to help you to identify common gases.

12.1 A simple guide to the identification of gases

This guide includes only those gases which you are most likely to meet when carrying out tests on unknown substances.

Before you perform any specific tests on a gas, you should smell it **cautiously** and look carefully for any trace of colour. While you are doing this, test the gas with moist litmus paper or pH paper. (Don't forget that if you heat an unknown with dilute hydrochloric acid you are bound to get an acidic vapour!) These three tests are sufficient to identify some gases and, in any case, serve to narrow the field, as shown in the chart below.

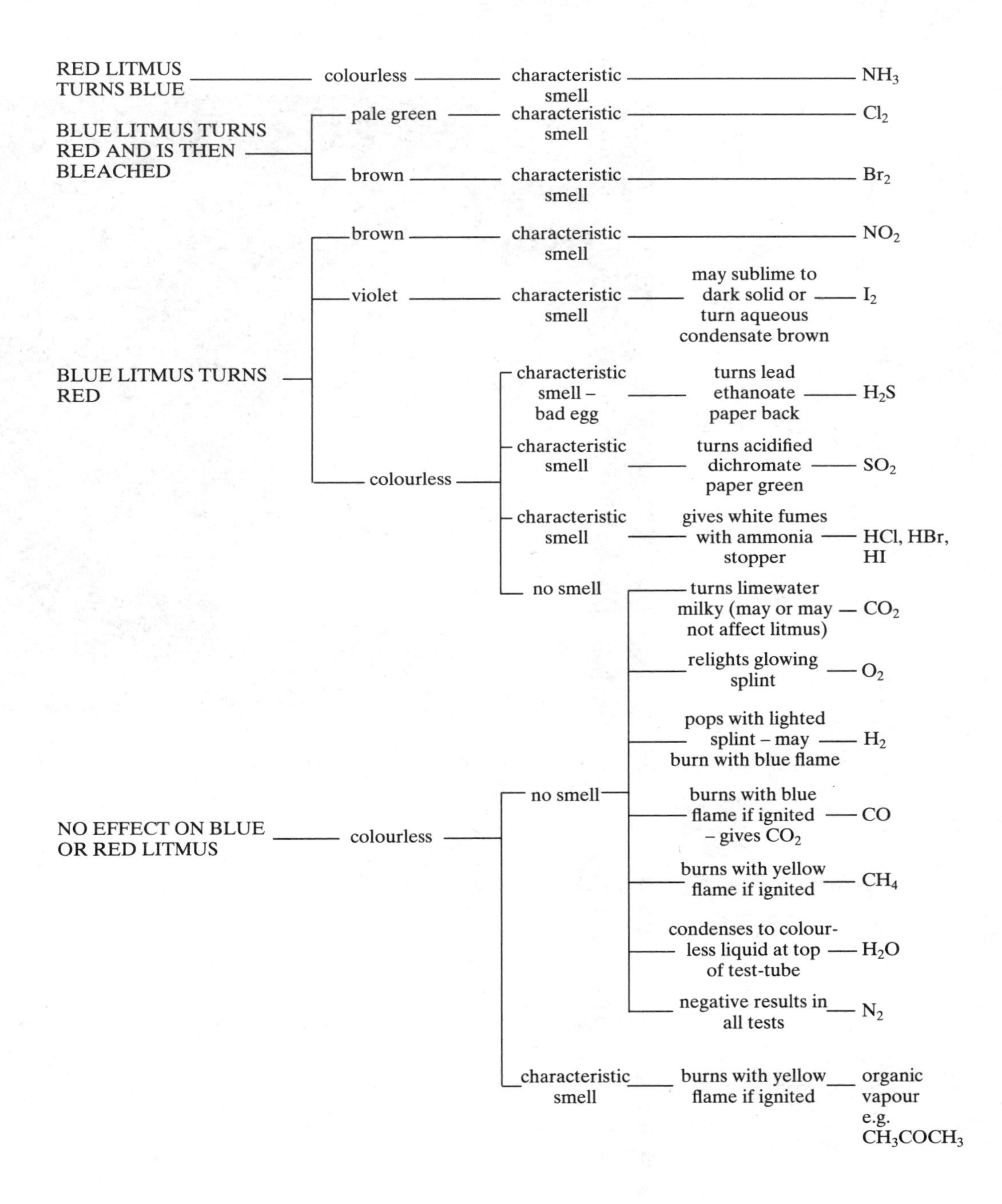

If it is available, view the first part of the ILPAC video programme 'Identifying Unknown Substances'; it will help you to carry out the two 'observation and deduction' experiments which now follow.

Both of the following experiments are taken from practical examination papers. Allow about 30 minutes of laboratory time for Experiment 10 and about 90 minutes for Experiment 11.

EXPERIMENT 10 Observation and deduction exercise

Aim

The purpose of this experiment is to give you some practice in the investigation of unknown substances.

Introduction

The procedure below is taken from an A-level practical examination paper; read it carefully and report fully.

Requirements

- safety spectacles
- 5 test-tubes in rack
- test-tube holder
- alkali metal salt, F
- spatula
- Bunsen burner and bench mat
- red and blue litmus papers
- wood splints
- wash-bottle of distilled water
- silver nitrate solution, 0.02 M $AgNO_3$
- nitric acid, dilute, 2 M HNO_3
- chlorine water, Cl_2 (aq)
- lead(II) ethanoate solution, 0.1 M $(CH_3CO_2)_2Pb$
- other chemicals, for testing gases, are available from your teacher

Procedure

You are provided with an alkali metal salt, F. Carry out the following tests and record your observations and inferences in (larger copies of) Results Tables 11 and 12 provided. Then answer the question which follows the tables.

Results Table 11

Test	Observations	Inferences
a Heat approximately 0.1 g of F in a Pyrex tube, at first gently and then more strongly, until the change is complete. Cool and keep the residue. Test any gases evolved		
b Make an aqueous solution of the residue from **a** and carry out the following tests on portions: i) Add aqueous silver nitrate followed by dilute nitric acid. ii) Add aqueous chlorine.  iii) Add aqueous lead(II) ethanoate (lead acetate)		

Now answer the following question.

For a non-metal in F, give two substances or ions involved in the reactions in **a** and **b** which contain the non-metal and in which the non-metal has different oxidation numbers. Write your answer in Results Table 12.

Results Table 12

Substance provided	Name of non-metal	Name and formula of substance/ion	Oxidation number
F			

We do not give specimen results since this experiment may be used for assessment.

EXPERIMENT 11 Observation and deduction exercise

Aim

The purpose of this experiment is to give you some practice in the investigation of unknown substances.

Introduction

The procedure below is taken from an A-level practical examination paper; read it carefully and report fully.

Requirements

- safety spectacles
- 5 test-tubes in rack
- test-tube holder
- potassium salts, D and E
- spatula
- Bunsen burner and bench mat
- red and blue litmus papers
- wood splints
- sulphuric acid, concentrated, H_2SO_4
- potassium manganate(VII) (permanganate) solution, 0.01 M $KMnO_4$
- sulphuric acid, dilute, 1 M H_2SO_4
- wash-bottle of distilled water
- other chemicals, for testing gases, are available from your teacher

HAZARD WARNING

Concentrated sulphuric acid is very corrosive and reacts violently with water. Therefore, you **must**:

- **avoid contact with skin**; if contact does occur, wash immediately under a cold tap with **plenty** of water;
- dispose of **cold** residues by pouring **slowly** into plenty of water.

Procedure

You are provided with potassium salts, D and E. Test each salt in turn, as follows:

a Heat a portion until any reaction ceases. Test any gases evolved.
b Allow the residue from **a** to cool; then cautiously add a few drops of concentrated sulphuric acid.
c Add a fresh portion of each salt to a few drops of aqueous potassium manganate(VII) previously acidified with twice its volume of dilute sulphuric acid, and warm.
d Now make aqueous solutions of D and E and mix the two solutions.
e Acidify the mixture from **d** with dilute sulphuric acid.

Carefully observe what happens and report fully.

What tentative inferences do you draw from these experiments?

Carry out and report on **two** further experiments which test your inferences. These experiments can be on D, E or on the products of the above reactions.

Full credit will not be given unless your answer discloses the method (including the scale of your experiments), careful observations, and some comment on the types of chemical reactions involved.

The record of your work must be made in the form of three tables.

Results Table 13
Tests with unknown substance D

Test	Method	Observations	Inferences
a Heat			
b Concentrated sulphuric acid on cold residue from **a**			
c Acidified potassium manganate(VII) (permanganate) and warm			

(Specimen results on page 173.)

Results Table 14
Tests with unknown substance E

Test	Method	Observations	Inferences
a Heat			
b Concentrated sulphuric acid on cold residue from **a**			
c Acidified potassium manganate(VII) (permanganate) and warm			
d Mix aqueous solutions of D and E			
e Dilute sulphuric acid with mixture from **d**			

(Specimen results on page 174.)

Results Table 15
Experiments to test inferences

Inference tested	Test and observations	Conclusion

(Specimen results on page 175.)

End-of-unit test

To find out how well you have learned the material in this unit, try the test which follows. Read the notes below before starting.
1. You should spend about 60 minutes on this test.
2. Hand your answers to your teacher for marking.

1. When 240 cm^3 of a gaseous oxide of chlorine (measured at room temperature and atmospheric pressure) was dissolved in 400 cm^3 of water, a 0.05 mol dm^{-3} solution of an acid $HClO_4$ was obtained. (1 mol of any gas occupies a volume of 24 dm^3 at room temperature and atmospheric pressure.)
   The molecular formula of the oxide
   A is Cl_2O,
   B is Cl_2O_3,
   C is Cl_2O_5,
   D is Cl_2O_7,
   E cannot be deduced from the information given. (1)

2. Which one of the following is true?
   A HCl (aq) is a weaker acid than HF (aq).
   B HCl has a lower boiling point than HF.
   C Cl_2 has a lower boiling point than F_2.
   D Cl_2 is a stronger oxidising agent than F_2.
   E Cl is more than electronegative than F. (1)

3. Which of the following sets of data concerning an anion of formula BrO_n^- is correct?

	Value of *n*	Oxidation number of the bromine
A	0	+1
B	1	0
C	1	+3
D	3	+3
E	3	+5

(1)

4. In the qualitative test for a halide ion in aqueous solution, dilute nitric acid is added prior to the addition of silver nitrate. Which one of the following is the correct reason for the addition of nitric acid?
   A It prevents the precipitation of silver salts other than halides.
   B It prevents the silver nitrate being precipitated.
   C Silver halides require an acidic solution for precipitation.
   D It increases the concentration of nitrate ions.
   E It lowers the solubility of silver nitrate. (1)

5. Which anions containing chlorine are formed when an excess of chlorine is passed into hot, concentrated, aqueous potassium hydroxide?
   A ClO_3^-, ClO_4^-,
   B ClO^-, ClO_3^-,
   C Cl^-, ClO_3^-,
   D Cl^-, ClO_4^-,
   E Cl^-, ClO^-. (1)

6. The reaction between sodium iodide and concentrated phosphoric acid produces hydrogen iodide but no iodine. The reaction of sodium iodide with concentrated sulphuric acid produces mainly iodine. The difference in product occurs because, in comparison with sulphuric acid, phosphoric acid is
   A the stronger acid, B the weaker acid,
   C the stronger oxidising agent, D the weaker oxidising agent,
   E the stronger reducing agent. (1)

In Questions 7 to 10, one or more than one of the suggested responses may be correct. Answer as follows:

A if **1**, **2** and **3** are correct,
B if **1** and **2** only are correct,
C if **2** and **3** only are correct,
D if **1** only is correct,
E if **3** only is correct.

Directions summarised				
A	B	C	D	E
1, 2, 3	**1, 2**	**2, 3**	**1**	**3**
correct	only	only	only	only

7. Which of the following properties of the halogens become less endothermic down Group VII from Cl to I?
1 First ionisation energy.
2 The bond enthalpy of breaking of X—X, where X is Cl, Br or I.
3 Standard enthalpy of formation of the element at 298 K. (1)

8. Which of the following ions can disproportionate in aqueous solution?
1 ClO^-,
2 ClO_4^-,
3 Cl^-. (1)

9. Which of the following properties of the elements increase(s) down Group VII?
1 electronegativity,
2 ability to oxidise a given reducing agent,
3 boiling point. (1)

10. The trends in some properties of the hydrogen halides, HX, are shown below. Which trend(s) occur(s) as you go down the halogen group?
1 They become stronger reducing agents.
2 The bond dissociation energy of H—X decreases.
3 The boiling points decrease in a regular manner. (1)

11. **a** The boiling points, in kelvins, of the hydrogen halides are given below.

Hydrogen halide	Boiling point/K
HF	293
HCl	188
HBr	206
HI	238

Account for this variation in boiling point. (4)

b Compare and contrast the thermal stabilities of the four hydrogen halides in **a**. (3)

c Aqueous hydrochloric acid is a strong acid which forms one potassium salt, whereas aqueous hydrofluoric acid is a weak acid which forms two potassium salts, KF and KHF_2. Account for the existence of the two potassium salts of hydrofluoric acid. (3)

d Groups of elements in the Periodic Table are said to show an increase in metallic behaviour with increase of atomic number. Give **two** properties of the halogens or their compounds which illustrate this trend. (2)

12. Chlorine disproportionates in water at room temperature according to the following equation

$$Cl_2\ (g) + H_2O\ (l) \rightleftharpoons HClO\ (aq) + HCl\ (aq)$$

a i) Give the names of the anions formed in this reaction, showing the oxidation number of chlorine in each.
ii) What is meant by the term **disproportionates**?
iii) Suggest why the concentration of hydrogen ions in the reaction mixture cannot be determined directly by titration with alkali. (6)

b On boiling the solution, one of the ions undergoes further disproportionation.
i) Which one of the ions disproportionates and why can it alone do so?
ii) Write a balanced equation for the disproportionation reaction. (4)

c When fluorine is bubbled into water at room temperature, oxygen is evolved and a weakly acidic solution results. The reaction below occurs:

$$2F_2\ (g) + 2H_2O\ (l) \rightarrow 4HF\ (aq) + O_2\ (g)$$

i) Suggest two reasons why oxygen is produced in the reaction with fluorine but not with chlorine.
ii) Explain why the resulting solution is **weakly** acidic in terms of the bonding in HF. (4)

d Gaseous hydrogen fluoride may be prepared in the laboratory by heating solid sodium fluoride with concentrated sulphuric acid.
i) Name the products formed when the reaction is repeated using sodium bromide.
ii) Explain any differences between the two reactions. (5)

13. Describe and explain what happens in each of the following experiments. Write balanced equations for the reactions that occur.
i) A mixture of the solids sodium chloride and manganese(IV) oxide is heated with concentrated sulphuric acid.
ii) Aqueous sodium bromide and aqueous silver nitrate are mixed and concentrated aqueous ammonia is then added.
iii) Solid iodine is shaken with aqueous potassium iodide and aqueous sodium thiosulphate(VI) is then added (thiosulphate(VI) = thiosulphate). (15)

14. Iodine dissolves in hot concentrated solutions of sodium hydroxide according to the equation

$$3I_2\ (s) + 6NaOH\ (aq) \rightarrow NaIO_3\ (aq) + 5NaI\ (aq) + 3H_2O\ (l)$$

In one experiment 3.81 g of iodine was dissolved in 4 M sodium hydroxide solution. (Relative atomic masses: H = 1, O = 16, Na = 23, I = 127.)

a How many moles of iodine were used?

b What volume of 4 M sodium hydroxide would be just sufficient to react with the iodine? (4)

(Total: 60 marks)

APPENDIX: The industrial production of chlorine

The production of chlorine is closely linked with the production of sodium hydroxide, which we dealt with in the s-Block Elements unit of this volume. However, it is so important that we include another exercise here. It is based on the following passage from *The Essential Chemical Industry*, produced by the Chemical Industry Education Centre at the University of York. Read the passage and use it to answer the questions.

Chlorine and sodium hydroxide

Chlorine and sodium hydroxide are manufactured together by the electrolysis of sodium chloride. This process is of fundamental importance to the industrial world. The primary raw material is common salt, available worldwide usually in the form of underground deposits of high purity. It is brought to the surface by solution in a pumped high pressure water supply. The chlorine and caustic products are widely used in the production of plastics, solvents, glass, water treatment chemicals, disinfectants and many other products which are essential to modern life.

Chlorine production is often regarded as a measure of the state of development of any particular community and is found to correlate well with other accepted economic yardsticks. Some forty million tonnes/year of production capacity are now installed worldwide.

Figure 17
Uses of chlorine and sodium hydroxide.

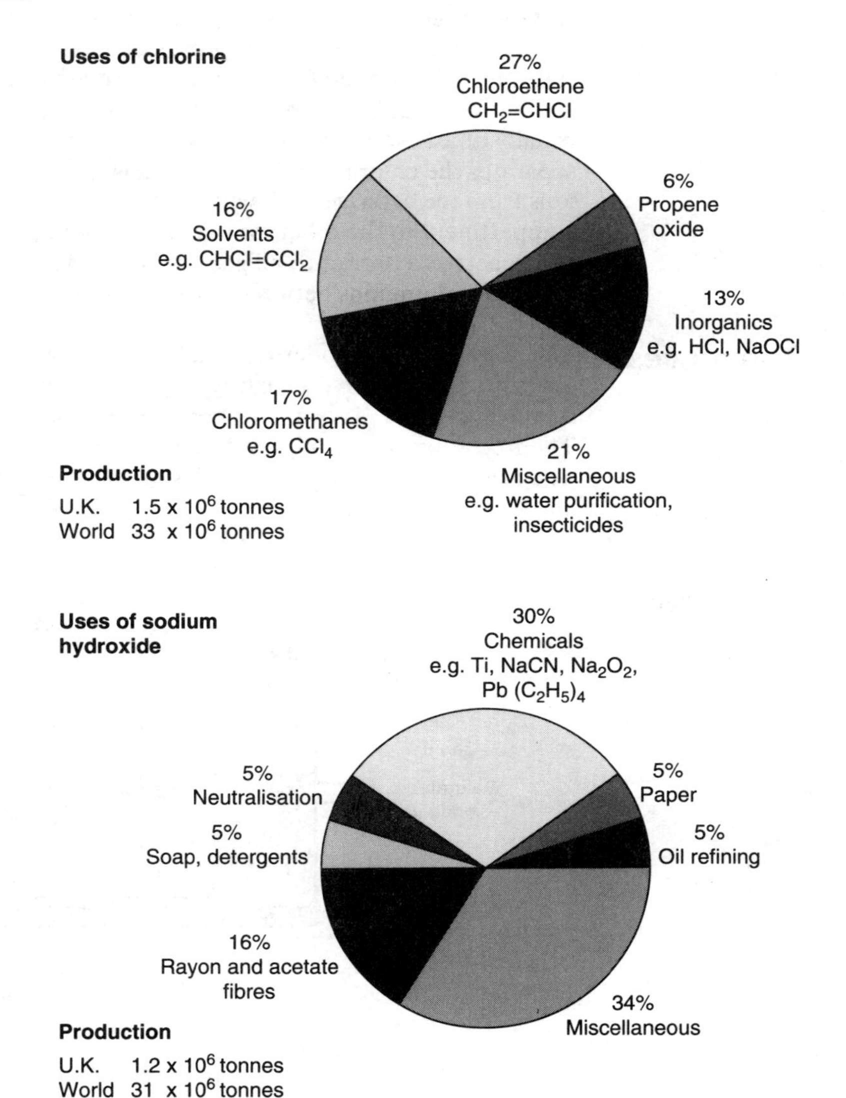

Raw materials

Sodium chloride is located in the U.K. in Cheshire, South Durham and Staffordshire. Brine is removed from underground by pumping and is replaced by fresh water to generate more brine.

This natural brine is purified by precipitating magnesium and other metal ions by adding sodium hydroxide and precipitating sulphate ions using a soluble barium salt. After settling and filtration the brine is conveyed to the cells.

Manufacture

There is no satisfactory alternative to the use of electricity to separate the sodium chloride brine into its constituent components. The process is known as electrolysis and the basic reaction is illustrated below.

Anode $Cl^- \rightarrow Cl + e^-$
$Cl + Cl \rightarrow Cl_2$

Cathode $H_2O + e^- \rightarrow H + OH^-$
$H + H \rightarrow H_2$

The essential requirement for industrial implementation of this process is an economic and effective means of separating the anode and cathode reactions, whilst still allowing them to proceed. This has been achieved historically by the mercury amalgam and diaphragm processes and more recently by the use of ion-exchange membranes.

Key features of these three processes are either a **flowing mercury cathode** which transports the sodium from anode to cathode in the form of a mercury–sodium amalgam and allows complete separation of the two compartments; or a **percolating diaphragm**, usually of asbestos, which allows a through flow of brine from anode to cathode but separates the chlorine and hydrogen gas spaces and prevents back-migration of OH^- ions from the cathode to the anode by virtue of the velocity of liquid flow from one compartment to the other; or the use of a non-permeable **ion-exchange membrane** which acts as a barrier to all gas and liquid flows and allows only the transport of charged sodium ions between compartments.

The process

The Mercury Cell Modern gas-tight rubber or PVC-lined steel cells measure 1.8 m × 15 m and have a slightly sloping base over which flows a thin layer of the mercury cathode. The anodes are titanium plates coated with a rare earth oxide layer. Their position can be adjusted to maintain a very small inter-electrode distance (2 mm). The cells typically operate in series of 100, each cell having a working voltage of 4.5 V and a current of 300 kA.

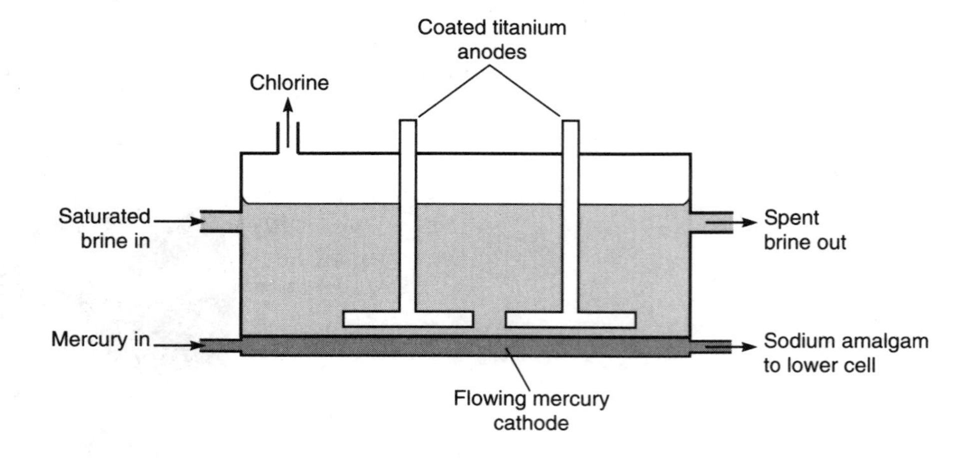

Figure 18
The mercury cell.

Purified, saturated brine (25.5% sodium chloride at 292 K) flows through the cell in the same direction as the mercury. This high concentration ensures the discharge of chloride ions rather than the hydroxide ions which would yield oxygen at the titanium anodes.

$$Cl^- \rightarrow Cl + e^-$$
$$Cl + Cl \rightarrow Cl_2$$

The chlorine is led off as shown in Fig. 18.

At the mercury cathode sodium ions are discharged in preference to hydrogen ions due to the high overvoltage of hydrogen at the mercury electrode.

$$Na^+ + e^- \rightarrow Na$$

A low concentration amalgam, containing approximately 0.3% sodium, is formed which moves on to a decomposer situated below the mercury cell.

The exit brine, normally containing 21% sodium chloride, is freed from chlorine by air blowing or vacuum degassing, resaturated and returned to the cell.

The decomposer is made of steel and contains fixed grids of graphite which float on the flowing amalgam. Alternatively the decomposer is a tower packed with graphite spheres. The grids are cathodic with respect to the amalgam and in the resulting galvanic cell sodium ions pass into solution while hydrogen is discharged at the cathodes.

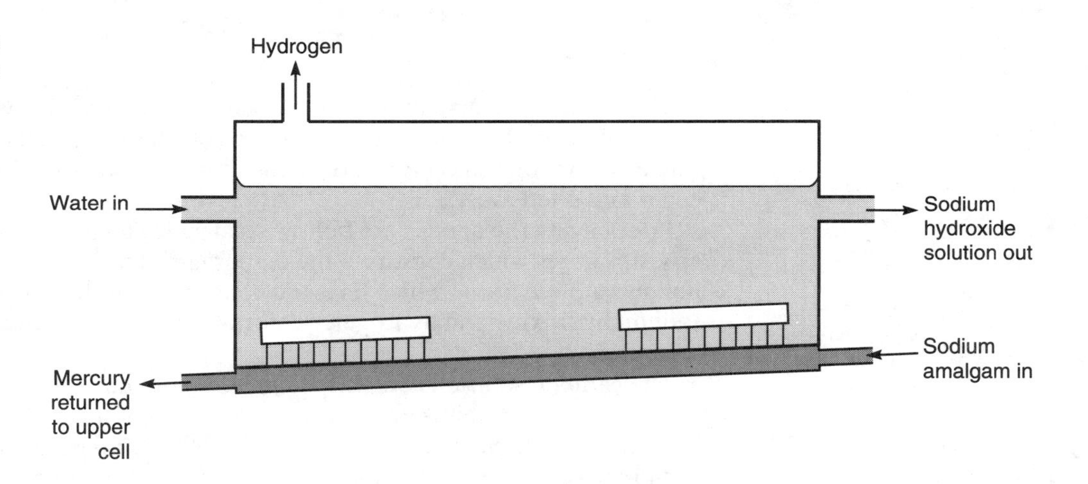

Figure 19 The amalgam decomposer.

Anode $Na \rightarrow Na^+ + e^-$

Cathode $H^+ + e^- \rightarrow H$

$H + H \rightarrow H_2$

The mercury is returned to the electrolysis cell and the hydrogen removed.

Fifty percent sodium hydroxide liquor is produced in the decomposer and most sodium hydroxide sold is in this form. Some is concentrated by evaporation to 75% and then heated to 770–870 K to obtain the solid alkali.

The Diaphragm Cell In the diaphragm cell titanium anodes and steel cathodes are used with a porous asbestos diaphragm to isolate the sodium hydroxide in the cathode compartments.

As the hydrogen ions are discharged, hydroxide ions accumulate in the cathode compartment together with aqueous sodium ions to produce sodium hydroxide at the cathode. The hydrogen and chlorine also formed are pumped off. The electrolyte level is maintained at a higher level in the anode compartment so that the used brine percolates through the diaphragm into the cathode section where it is led away with the sodium hydroxide.

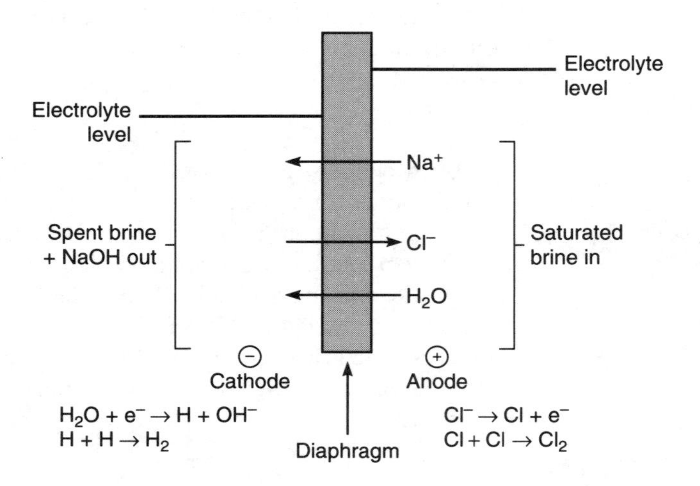

Figure 20
Reactions in the diaphragm cell.

The 'Tank' type diaphragm cell has a conducting metal base, protected from corrosion by a rubber or titanium liner. Mounted on the base are vertical coated titanium anodes. The chlorine formed on the anodes rises through the brine into the space formed by the cover and is led away.

Interleaving the anodes are hollow steel gauze fingers sheathed with a coating of asbestos fibres which constitute the diaphragm. These finger cathodes are connected to a hollow cathode frame which lines the container. Inside this cathode assembly both sodium hydroxide and hydrogen are formed, the two products being piped off separately.

The cathode solution contains about 10% sodium hydroxide and 15% sodium chloride by mass. This is evaporated to one-fifth of its original volume when the much less soluble sodium chloride crystallises to leave a marketable solution containing 50% sodium hydroxide and less than 1% sodium chloride by mass.

Comparison of Mercury and Diaphragm Cells

	Mercury	Diaphragm
Construction costs	Expensive	Relatively cheap
Operation	4.5 V; toxic mercury must be removed from effluent	3.8 V; frequent diaphragm replacement
Product	High purity at required concentration (50%)	Less pure, low concentration, needs evaporation
Overall energy consumption	Similar	

Membrane Cells In these the anode and cathode compartments are completely separated by an ion-permeable membrane rather than an asbestos diaphragm. The membrane is permeable to cations, but not anions; it allows the passage of sodium ions but not that of chloride or hydroxide ions. Sodium ions pass through in hydrated form $(Na{\cdot}xH_2O)^+$, so some water is transferred, but the membrane is impermeable to free water molecules.

The membrane (0.15–0.3 mm thick) is a copolymer of tetrafluorethane and a similar fluorinated monomer.

The advantages of membrane cells are:

- they produce 30–35% sodium hydroxide (possibly 40% with improved membranes) compared with about 10% from diaphragm cells and so concentration costs are much reduced.
- product purity compares favourably with that from mercury cells.
- the mixing of hydrogen gas or hydroxide ions with chlorine is prevented, without the need for the careful control and the constant monitoring required in diaphragm cells.
- membranes do not need frequent cleaning or replacement, giving long-life, low-maintenance cells. They do, however, require a higher brine purity than mercury or diaphragm cells. Cost analyses suggest that membrane cells are more economic than diaphragm cells, especially for smaller plants, where the sodium hydroxide is consumed on-site.

Factors such as capital and energy cost and freedom from environmental concerns all favour the ion-exchange membrane process but its development was not possible until work by DuPont in the U.S.A. in the early 1970s and more recently in Japan resulted in the production of membrane material capable of performing the required function. By comparison, the mercury and diaphragm processes were first operated commercially at the turn of the century and have been subject to continuous development ever since. The ion-exchange membrane process is now the first choice for all new installations and some two million tons/yr capacity have been installed over the last 10 years.

The chlorine–alkali balance

In the last 30 years the growth in demand for chlorine has been rapid, due mainly to the development of chloro-organics such as solvents and plastics. This has resulted in a change in the balance of demand for the two substances. Previously chlorine was in surplus, which led to disposal problems which held up the growth of the chloro-alkali industry. World production was only 1.1×10^6 tonnes of chlorine in 1950.

EXERCISE 78

Answers on page 175

a What is the likely origin of the underground deposits of common salt? (1)

b Write ionic equations for the two processes mentioned for the purification of natural brine. (2)

c The passage states that 'there is no satisfactory alternative to the use of electricity'. Suggest an alternative method for producing chlorine from brine and say why it is not satisfactory for an industrial process. (4)

d The pair of equations given in the text for the production of hydrogen at the cathode is sometimes presented in a different form, i.e. the discharge of the hydrogen ions always present in water. Write an equation for this discharge and show that it achieves the same result as the equations given. (3)

e Explain why it is necessary to separate the anode and cathode reactions, in terms of what would happen (i) to the gaseous products and (ii) to the aqueous products, if the reactions were **not** separated. (4)

f Why is chloroethene so important as a use of chlorine? (1)

g How (in outline) would the 'inorganics' HCl and NaOCl be produced from chlorine? (4)

h The 'high overvoltage' simply means that if the cathode is made of mercury it is more difficult to discharge hydrogen ions than usual, with the result that sodium ions are discharged instead. Compare the half-equations for the discharge of the two cations and, from your knowledge of the chemistry of sodium, explain why you would normally expect hydrogen to be produced rather than sodium. (3)

N.B. Even when mercury is used, the concentration of sodium in it must be kept very low to prevent the discharge of hydrogen.

i What is the essential difference in function between the asbestos diaphragm and the semi-permeable membrane in the two types of cell? (2)

j Several advantages of membrane cells over diaphragm cells are listed but only one disadvantage – what is it? (2)

k Two advantages of mercury cells over diaphragm cells are mentioned: one is partially met by using membrane cells and the other completely met. Explain. (4)

l Freedom from environmental concerns is mentioned as one reason why chlorine and sodium hydroxide are increasingly produced in membrane cells.

i) Comment briefly on the other two reasons. (4)

ii) Suggest one factor of environmental concern for each of the other two processes. (2)

iii) Suggest why, if the case for membrane cells is so strong, mercury cells and diaphragm cells are still widely used. (2)

m If you were a large chemicals manufacturer considering building a new plant to manufacture chlorine and sodium hydroxide by the membrane process, what factors would influence your choice of site? (4)

THE PERIODIC TABLE

INTRODUCTION

The Periodic Table helps you to organise your knowledge and thus makes factual information easier to remember. In the Atomic Structure unit of ILPAC Volume 1 you learned how the Periodic Table is built up and divided into major blocks. In the s-Block Elements and The Halogens units of ILPAC Volume 4 you studied the extreme groups on either side of the Periodic Table with an emphasis on the vertical trends and changes.

In this unit, we look at the Periodic Table with particular reference to the horizontal trends and changes that occur across Periods 2 and 3. We give the symbols of the elements in Periods 2 and 3 in the outline Periodic Table below (Fig. 21)

Figure 21

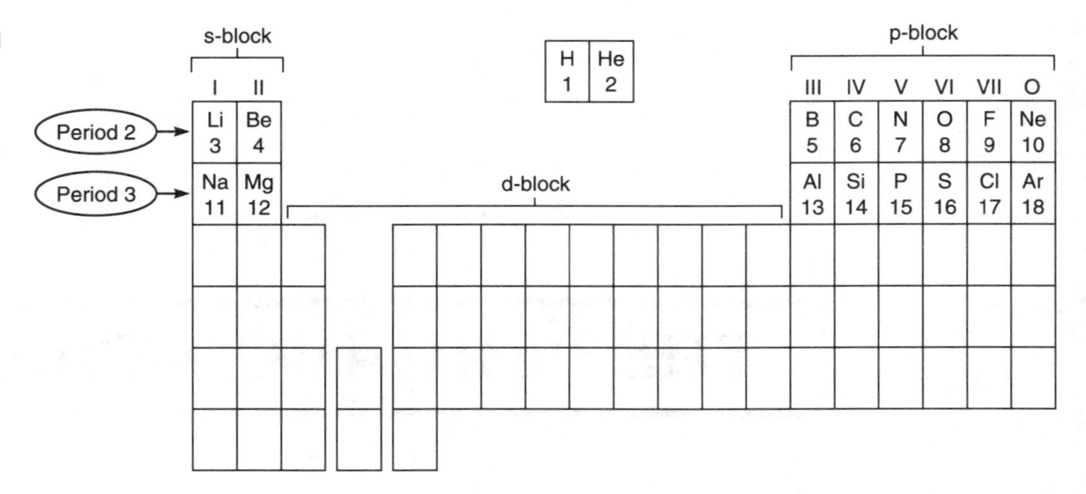

In Part A we look at the elements, concentrating on the main trends in physical properties with increasing atomic number. We relate these to the elements' structures and reach conclusions about the overall changes across a period.

In Part B, we deal with the chlorides, oxides and hydrides of the elements of Periods 2 and 3. There are three experiments in this unit, all in Part B.

There are two ILPAC video programmes designed to accompany this unit. They are not essential, but you should try to see them at the appropriate times if they are available.

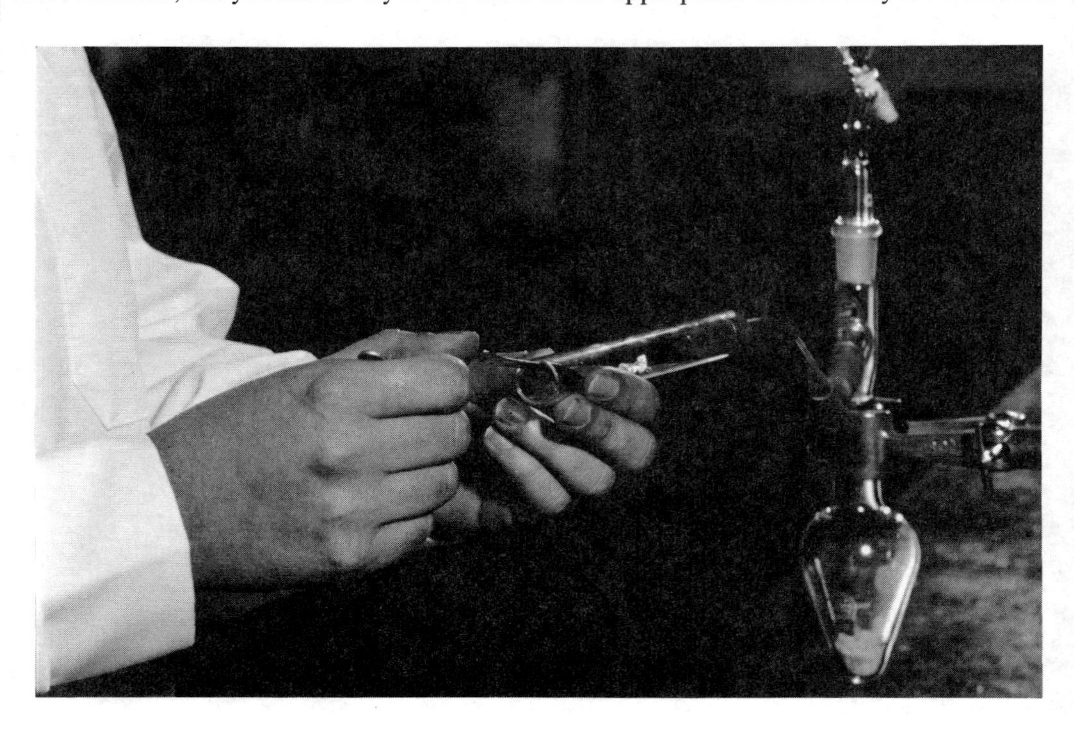

Preparation of aluminium chloride.

Chlorides and oxides.

Pre-knowledge

Before you start work on this unit, you should be able to:

1. Describe the periodic classification of the elements.
2. Divide a Periodic Table into numbered periods and groups.
3. State the names of Groups I, II, VII and O.
4. State the typical properties of **a** metals, and **b** non-metals.
5. Explain what is meant by the following terms:
   a element,
   b compound,
   c direct synthesis,
   d atomic number,
   e covalent bond,
   f ionic bond,
   g molecule,
   h giant structure of atoms or ions,
   i acidic oxide,
   j basic oxide.
6. State the properties of typical covalent and ionic compounds.
7. State the difference between covalent and van der Waals radii.
8. Describe the trends in electronegativity across a period and down a group in the Periodic Table.

Pre-test

To find out whether you are ready to start Part A, try the following test which is based on the pre-knowledge items. You should not spend more than 30 minutes on this test. Hand your answers to your teacher for marking.

1. Using either the group numbers or atomic numbers, identify on the outline Periodic Table below (Fig. 22) the spaces occupied by:
   a the alkali metals, (1)
   b the halogens, (1)
   c the noble gases, (1)
   d carbon, (1)
   e a metal with a coloured ion. (1)

Figure 22

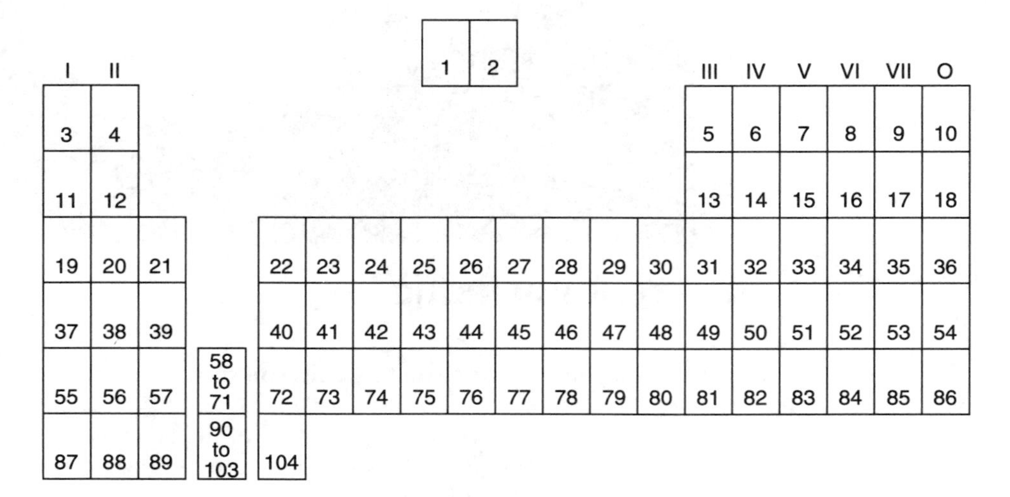

2. Copy and complete the table below, which shows some typical properties of metals and non-metals.

Table 17

Property	Metal	Non-metal
Melting point		
Type of oxide		
Malleability		
Electrical conductivity		

(4)

3. Copy and complete the table below, which shows some typical properties of molecular and ionic compounds.

Table 18

Property	Molecular compound	Ionic compound
Melting point		
Electrical conductivity when molten		
Solubility in hexane		
Solubility in water		

(4)

4. Which of the following substances will have the properties of a typical ionic compound?
   Na NaCl H_2O LiH (2)

5. Write equations summarising the reactions between the following substances. Include the state of each substance in the equation.
   a Zinc and hydrochloric acid. (2)
   b Sodium and chlorine. (2)
   c Sulphur dioxide and water. (2)
   d Sodium oxide (Na_2O) and water. (2)

6. Figure 23 shows two molecules in a sample of solid chlorine. Identify the radii marked as *a* and *b* in the diagram.

Figure 23

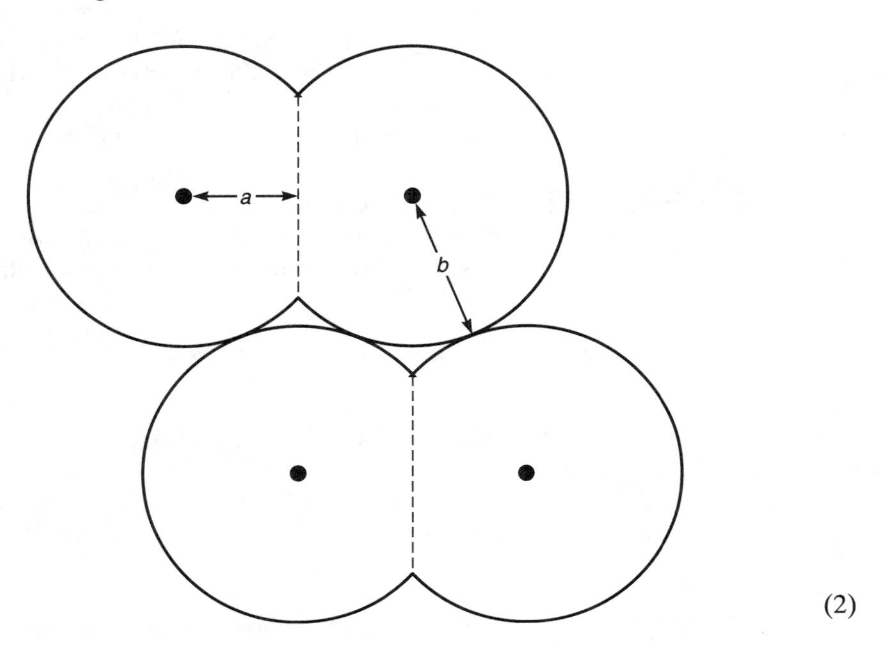

(2)

(Total: 25 marks)

PART A

PERIODICITY

CHAPTER 13

PERIODICITY OF PHYSICAL PROPERTIES

The first part of this unit is concerned with several physical properties. You have already studied the vertical trends in these properties for Groups I, II and VII in the s-Block Elements and The Halogens units of this volume. We now look at the horizontal trends in these properties with increasing atomic number. In doing this we aim to give you an understanding of the term 'periodic' and how to use it.

OBJECTIVE

When you have finished this chapter you should be able to:

- explain the meaning of **periodicity** with reference to **atomic and ionic radius**, first **ionisation energy**, **electron affinity** and **atomic volume**.

The first property we consider is atomic radius.

13.1 Atomic radius

You encountered atomic radius in the Bonding and Structure unit of ILPAC Volume 3 and used it in studying Groups I, II and VII. Here we examine the changes in atomic radius that are apparent over the Periodic Table as a whole, with an emphasis on the horizontal changes.

Figure 24 below shows a graph of atomic (covalent) radius against atomic number for the first 56 elements. Figure 25 opposite gives similar information on the relative sizes of the atoms of the s-, p-, and d-block elements. Study both diagrams and then attempt the exercise which follows.

Figure 24
Change in atomic (covalent) radius with atomic number.

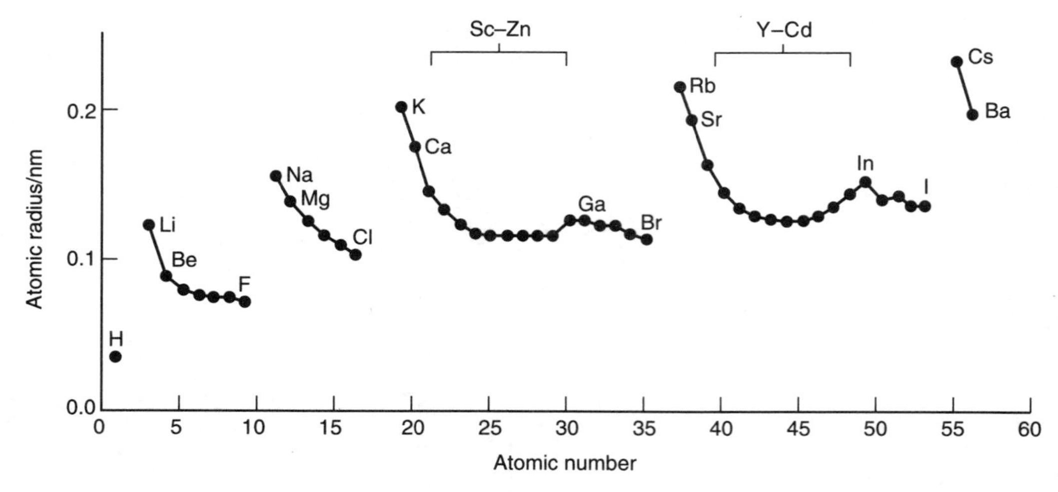

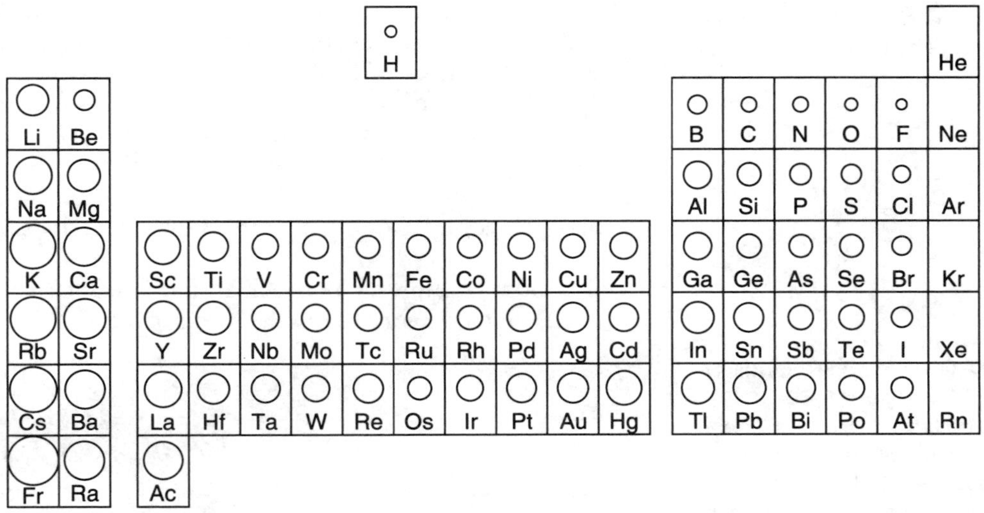

Figure 25
Atomic (covalent) radii of s-, p- and d-block elements.

H He
Li Be B C N O F Ne
Na Mg Al Si P S Cl Ar
K Ca Sc Ti V Cr Mn Fe Co Ni Cu Zn Ga Ge As Se Br Kr
Rb Sr Y Zr Nb Mo Tc Ru Rh Pd Ag Cd In Sn Sb Te I Xe
Cs Ba La Hf Ta W Re Os Ir Pt Au Hg Tl Pb Bi Po At Rn
Fr Ra Ac

EXERCISE 79

Answers on page 176

a Describe the changes in atomic radius across Periods 2 and 3. Is there a recognisable trend?
b Explain the changes in terms of nuclear charge and shielding.
c Identify and state the trend in atomic radius in Groups I, II and VII from Fig. 25. Is the same trend found in Groups III, IV, V and VI?
d What do you notice about the radii of the first and second transition series (Sc–Zn and Y–Cd, in the d-block)?
e Suggest an explanation for the fact that aluminium and gallium in Group III have the same radius.
f We have omitted the noble gases from Figs 24 and 25 as their covalent radii cannot be measured. Use your knowledge of the trends in atomic size so far to predict:
i) the covalent radius of each noble gas compared to other elements in its period;
ii) the trend in covalent radii down the group.

We now go on to show how ionic radii relate to atomic radii for elements in Periods 2 and 3.

13.2 Ionic radius

Table 19 shows the ionic radii of some elements in Periods 2 and 3. Some of the values given are for purely hypothetical ions. The figures in brackets indicate the charge on the ion.

Table 19
Ionic radii/nm (charges in brackets)

Period 2	Li 0.060 (+1)	Be 0.031 (+2)	B 0.020 (+3)	C 0.260 (–4) 0.015 (+4)	N 0.171 (–3)	O 0.140 (–2)	F 0.136 (–1)
Period 3	Na 0.095 (+1)	Mg 0.065 (+2)	Al 0.050 (+3)	Si 0.271 (–4) 0.041 (+4)	P 0.212 (–3)	S 0.184 (–2)	Cl 0.181 (–1)

EXERCISE 80

Answers on page 177

a What is the trend in ionic radius across Periods 2 and 3?
b How does this compare with the change in atomic radius across the same period?
c State four ions given in Table 19 which are purely hypothetical.
d In the s-Block Elements and The Halogens units of ILPAC Volume 4 you studied the trend in ionic radius down Groups I, II and VII. Using the information in the table and additional values from your data book decide whether the same trend occurs in Groups III, V and VI.
e With which noble gases are the ions shown in Periods 2 and 3 isoelectronic?

There is a close relationship between atomic size and first ionisation energy (enthalpy of ionisation), which we consider in the next section.

Johann Wolfgang Döbereiner (1780–1849). The first person to suggest that relative atomic mass could be used as a basis for grouping elements.

13.3 First ionisation energy

Figure 26 shows the first ionisation energies of the elements up to barium in the Periodic Table. Compare it with Fig. 24 and then attempt the exercise which follows.

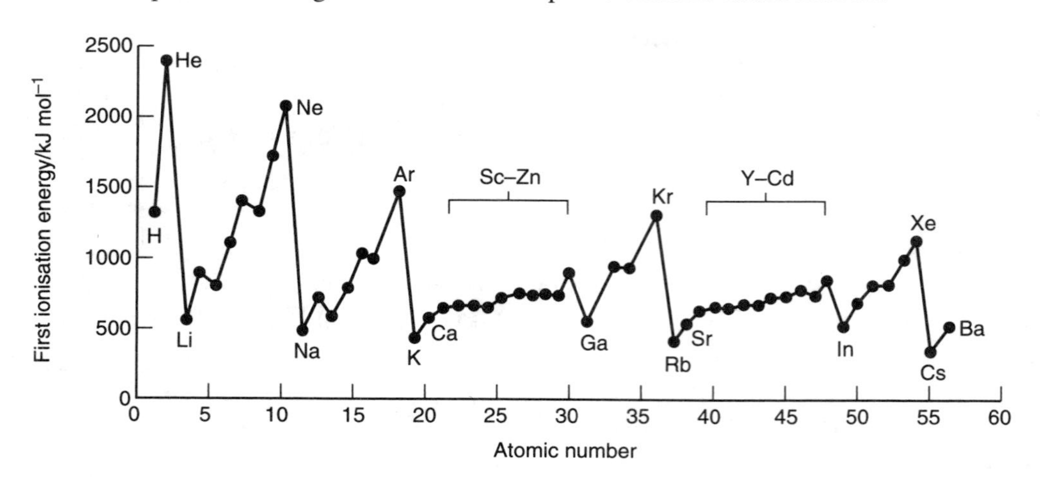

Figure 26
Change in first ionisation energy with atomic number.

EXERCISE 81
Answers on page 177

a Excluding the noble gases, which elements are found at the peaks of the ionisation energy graph?
b Where are these elements found on the atomic radius graph?
c What does this suggest about the relationship between first ionisation energy and atomic radius? Explain your answer.

First ionisation energy is associated with cation formation. We now consider the electron affinities of the elements, which are associated with anion formation.

13.4 Electron affinity

You came across this term in ILPAC Volume 2, Chemical Energetics, and have used some values in your study of Groups I, II and VII. Each value represents the energy change ($\Delta H^\ominus_e$) for the process:

$$X\,(g) + e^- \rightarrow X^-\,(g) \qquad \text{(where X = the symbol of any element)}$$

Table 20 gives values of $\Delta H^\ominus_e$ for Periods 2 and 3, excluding the noble gases. Study the table and then attempt the exercise which follows.

Table 20
Some electron affinities/kJ mol^{-1}

Li –52	Be* +66	B –29	C –120	N –3	O –142	F –348
Na –71	Mg* +67	Al* –26	Si –180	P –70	S –200	Cl –364

(Values of electron affinities can vary considerably according to the source. Values are rarely given for those elements marked *.)

EXERCISE 82
Answers on page 177

a Draw a graph of electron affinity (vertical axis) against atomic number, for the elements lithium to chlorine (excluding the noble gases).
b Does the graph show a repeating pattern between Periods 2 and 3?
c Explain why the electron affinities for beryllium and nitrogen differ from those of the other elements in the period.

Next we consider one of the bulk properties, atomic volume.

13.5 Atomic volume

The atomic volume of an element is the volume occupied by one mole of its atoms. Since density = mass/volume the atomic volume is calculated using the formula:

$$\text{Atomic volume} = \frac{\text{molar mass}}{\text{density}} \quad (\text{usual unit cm}^3\text{ mol}^{-1})$$

When comparing atomic volumes we use densities at 25°C. For an element which is not solid at this temperature, use the density of the liquid form at some specified temperature, usually its boiling point.

Since atomic volume depends on the molar mass of an element, you might expect similarities between graphs of atomic volume and atomic radius with increasing atomic number. You compare these two properties in the next exercise.

Figures 27 and 28 on the next page are graphs of atomic radius and atomic volume against atomic number. Compare the two and then do the exercise which follows.

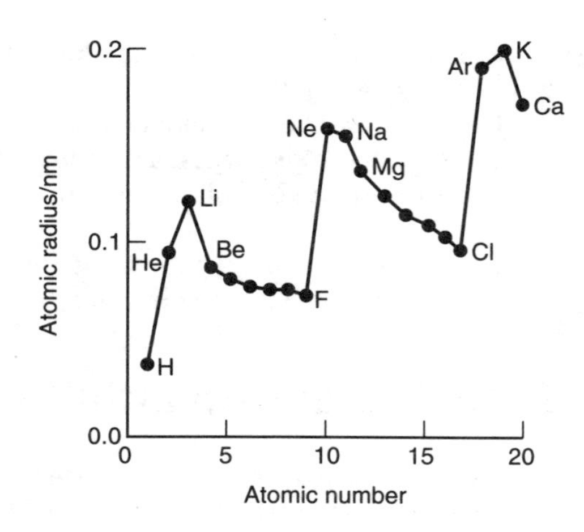

Figure 27
Change in atomic radius with atomic number.

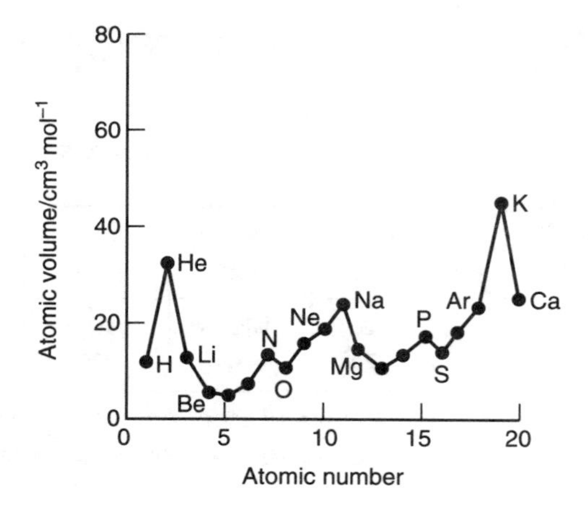

Figure 28
Change in atomic volume with atomic number.

EXERCISE 83
Answers on page 178

a Compare elements between boron and fluorine and between aluminium and chlorine on the two graphs. How does the change in atomic volume compare with the change in atomic radius?

b Suggest a reason for the difference in **a**.

In the last exercise you saw some evidence for structural changes taking place in the p-block elements. We now look for further evidence by examining another bulk property, melting point, and its associated energy change, enthalpy of fusion.

■ 13.6 Melting point and enthalpy of fusion

When a substance melts, its structure breaks down. The temperature at which the change takes place and the energy needed to bring it about (enthalpy of fusion) depend on the type of bonding.

In this section you compare values of these quantities for different elements and use them to explain the changes in bonding and structure which take place along Periods 2 and 3.

OBJECTIVE

When you have finished this section you should be able to:

- explain how the changes in **melting point** and **enthalpy of fusion** across a period are related to changes in structure.

Read about melting point and enthalpy of fusion (molar enthalpy of melting), looking for an explanation of why they change in going across a period. Then attempt the following exercise.

EXERCISE 84
Answers on page 178

a Using values from your data book draw a graph of melting point against atomic number for the first 18 elements.
b Using a different vertical scale, add values of enthalpy of fusion on the same paper.
c Suggest a reason for any similarities in the patterns of the two properties.
d In which group are the elements at the peaks of each graph?
e What does this suggest about the structures of these elements?
f Are these two properties periodic, according to your graph?

You have seen that melting points and enthalpies of fusion are related to bonding and structure. We now consider these properties in more detail.

13.7 Structure and bonding in elements of Periods 2 and 3

In this section you complete a table showing the structures and bonding of elements in Periods 2 and 3.

OBJECTIVE

When you have finished this section you should be able to:
- state the types of **bonding and structure** found in the elements of Periods 2 and 3.

In the next exercise you complete a copy of Table 21 shown on page 112. Small diagrams of the structures for the elements in Periods 2 and 3 are drawn for you. You should be familiar with the terms 'close-packed' and 'body-centred cubic' from ILPAC Volume 3, Bonding and Structure.

EXERCISE 85
Answers on page 179

a Fill in a copy of Table 21, classifying each structure as one of the following:
i) giant molecular (giant atomic), ii) simple molecular,
iii) metallic, iv)atomic (non-metallic).
For iii), specify whether the structure is close-packed (CCP or HCP) or not close-packed (BCC).
b Look back at your graph of melting point against atomic number (Exercise 84). Explain the following by considering differences in structure and/or bond strength.
i) The steady increase in melting point and enthalpy of fusion between lithium and boron and between sodium and aluminium.
ii) The sharp rise in melting point and enthalpy of fusion between boron and carbon and between aluminium and silicon.
iii) The sharp drop in melting point and enthalpy of fusion between carbon and nitrogen and between silicon and phosphorus.
c The enthalpy of fusion of carbon is so high that it cannot be measured with any accuracy. Suggest a reason why the enthalpies of fusion of the elements following it, in Groups V, VI, VII and O, are much lower.
d Would you say, from your completed table, that structure is a periodic property? Explain.

Now that you have classified the elements according to structure we turn to another bulk property, boiling point, and its associated energy change, enthalpy of vaporisation.

Table 21

Element	**Lithium**	**Beryllium**	**Boron**	**Carbon (graphite)**	**Nitrogen**	**Oxygen**	**Fluorine**	**Neon**
Bonding								
Structure								
Type								
Element	**Sodium**	**Magnesium**	**Aluminium**	**Silicon**	**Phosphorus (white)**	**Sulphur**	**Chlorine**	**Argon**
Bonding								
Structure								
Type								

13.8 Boiling point and enthalpy of vaporisation

When a substance boils, the bonds between its particles are completely broken. In comparing boiling points of different elements we get an idea of the forces between their particles in the liquid state. These forces vary between different structural types as we show in this section.

OBJECTIVE

When you have finished this section you should be able to:

- explain, in structural terms, why the **difference between melting point and boiling point** is greater for **metals** than for **non-metals.**

Read about boiling point and enthalpy of vaporisation. Look for an explanation of the differences between melting point and boiling point in metals and non-metals.

In Fig. 29 we have superimposed the boiling points and melting points of the first 18 elements. (Some of the boiling points are uncertain.) This will enable you to make direct comparisons in the next exercise.

Figure 29

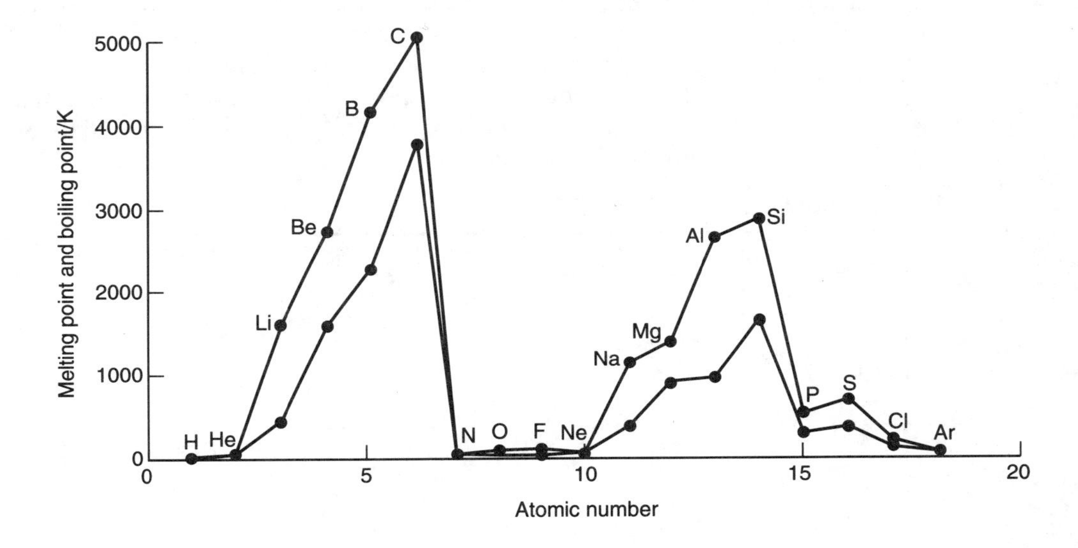

EXERCISE 86
Answers on page 180

Study Fig. 29 and answer the following questions.

a Explain why there is generally a greater difference between melting and boiling temperatures for metals than for non-metals.

b Identify the places in Periods 2 and 3 where the sharpest changes in melting point and boiling point take place.

c Do the changes you have pointed out in **b** correspond to structural changes? Give details.

d If you plotted enthalpy of vaporisation values on the same graph, how would the general shape compare with the shape of the boiling point plot?

e Explain why enthalpy of vaporisation values are greater than enthalpy of fusion values.

Now that you have surveyed the main physical properties of the elements in Periods 2 and 3 we consider, briefly, their chemical properties.

PERIODICITY OF CHEMICAL PROPERTIES

Since chemical properties of elements are related to their atomic structure you might expect a periodic relationship in chemical properties. In this section we consider certain reactions of elements in Periods 2 and 3 to decide whether this is the case.

OBJECTIVES

When you have finished this chapter you should be able to:

- describe the reactions of elements in Periods 2 and 3 with **oxygen, hydrogen, water, dilute acids** and **magnesium**;
- state the **trends in reactivity** across Periods 2 and 3 in terms of **oxidising** and **reducing power**.

Start by reading about the reactions of elements in Periods 2 and 3 bearing in mind the reactions stated in the first objective above. If possible, choose a textbook which has a section on **chemical periodicity**. If not, you will need to look up the reactions separately. Remember that you are looking for general patterns here, rather than a mass of detail. The next exercise is designed to help you organise the information from your reading.

EXERCISE 87

Answers on page 181

Complete a copy of Table 22, which appears below, to show:

a the ease of reaction (state whether the reaction is violent, very vigorous, vigorous, slow, very slow or whether there is no reaction);

b the compounds formed for elements in Period 3.

Note that you have already studied the reactions of sodium, magnesium and chlorine. When you are completing the table you should find that you can predict many of the others. We have filled in some of the spaces already, as a guide.

Table 22

		Na	Mg	Al	Si	P (white)	S	Cl	Ar
Dry O_2 and heat	A			Vigorous at first					
	B			Al_2O_3 on surface					
Dry Cl_2 and heat	A					Slow	Slow		
	B						SCl_2 and S_2Cl_2		
Dry H_2 and heat	A	Very vigorous		No reaction	No reaction	No reaction	Very slow		
	B	NaH		–	–	–			
Cold H_2O	A							Slow	
	B							HClO (aq)	
Cold dilute HCl	A			Vigorous if oxide layer removed.		No reaction	No reaction	No reaction	
	B			$AlCl_3$		–	–	–	
Mg and heat	A	No reaction		No reaction	Slow	Vigorous			
	B	–		–	Mg_2Si	Mg_3P_2			

A = Ease of reaction: violent, very vigorous, vigorous, slow, very slow, no reaction.
B = Main product (compound of given element).

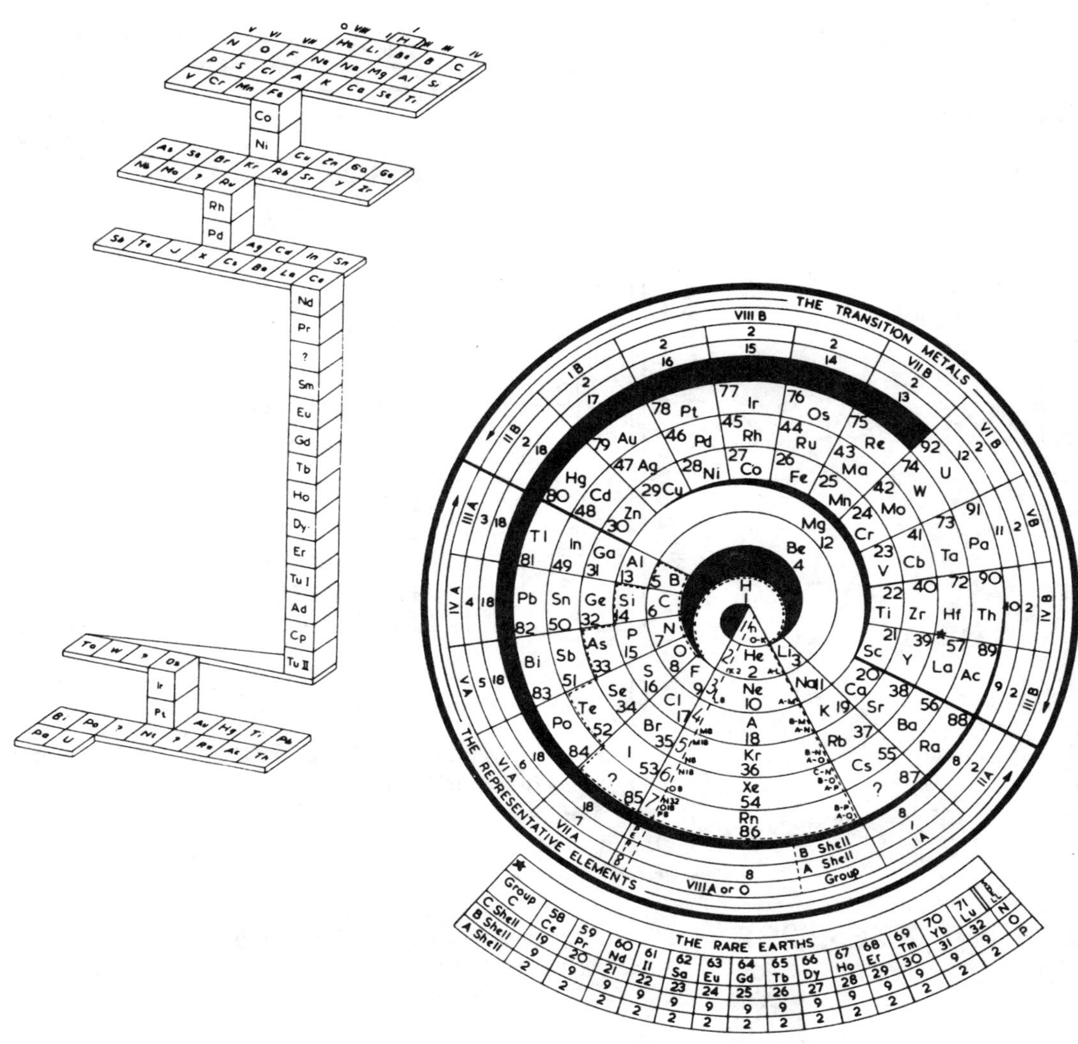

Some unusual forms of the Periodic Table.

Now use your copy of Table 22 to answer the next exercise.

EXERCISE 88

Answers on page 181

a How does the reactivity with oxygen, chlorine and hydrogen change in going across the period?

b Explain the changes in **a** in terms of reducing power of the elements.

c What is the trend in reactivity with magnesium across the period? How does this compare with the trend you identified in **a**?

d Explain this trend in terms of oxidising power.

e Using the final two reactions in Table 22 decide at what point the elements in Period 3 change from being typical metals to typical non-metals.

f Would you expect similar reactions in Period 2? State any general differences.

In the last exercise you found that elements' reducing power decreases in going across a period, while their oxidising power increases. These two trends are important in describing elements' reactivity. We use them to classify elements as metals (electron donors with considerable reducing power) and non-metals (electron acceptors with considerable oxidising power).

Between the two extremes it is not easy to classify elements as metals or non-metals. Elements which show both metallic and non-metallic properties are called metalloids.

Figure 30 is an outline Periodic Table showing the approximate division between metals and non-metals. Metalloids appear near the diagonal 'staircase'.

Figure 30

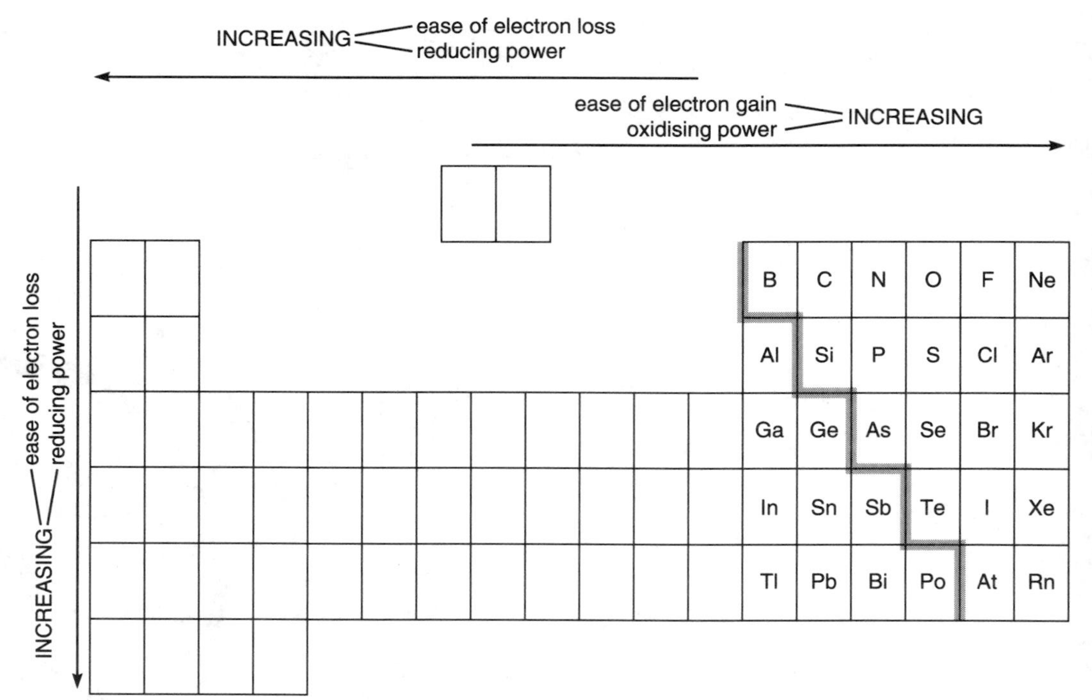

To consolidate your ideas so far, try the following Teacher-marked Exercise. Before you start this question, you should look through the notes you have made throughout Part A. You may also want to re-read your notes from the s-Block Elements and The Halogens units. Since this is an essay-style question, you should make a plan before you start writing.

EXERCISE

Teacher-marked

Define the terms covalent and ionic radius.

Give an account of the trends in the atomic radius of the elements both along a period and down the groups of the Periodic Table. Show how these trends help to explain the changes in chemical properties of the elements.

Dmitri Ivanovich Mendeleev (1839–1907) published the forerunner of the modern Periodic Table in 1869.

Extract from a book (published 1884) written by John Newlands, in which he claims to be the discoverer of the Periodic Table.

> Having been the first to publish the existence of the periodic law more than nineteen years ago, I feel, under existing circumstances, compelled to assert my priority in this matter.
>
> That both D. Mendelejeff and Lothar Meyer have done a good deal to develop the periodic law is admitted, but this admission by no means assumes that either of these eminent chemists was the first discoverer of the law in question. As a matter of simple justice, and in the interest of all true workers in science, both theoretical and practical, it is right that the originator of any proposal or discovery should have the credit of his labour.

Part A test

To find out how well you have learned the material in Part A, try the test which follows. Read the notes below before starting.

1. You should spend about 90 minutes on this test.
2. When you have finished, hand your answers to your teacher for marking.

Questions 1–4 concern the following graphs showing how certain physical properties of elements vary either across a period or down a group of the Periodic Table:

Figure 31

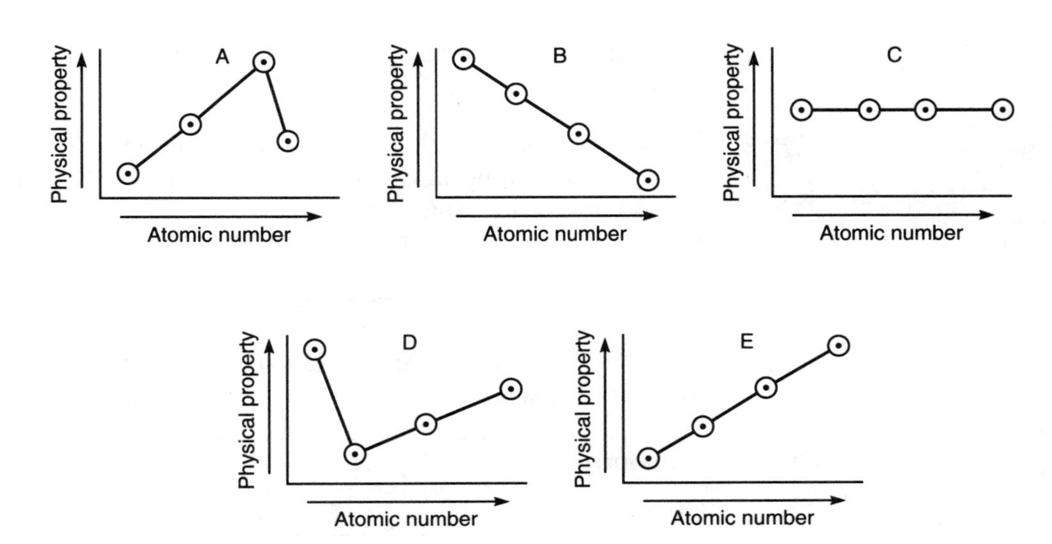

Select from A to E, the graph which would best represent the

1. electronegativities of C, N, O and F, (1)
2. first ionisation energies of Li, Na, K and Rb, (1)
3. number of electrons in Ne, Na^+, Mg^{2+} and Al^{3+}, (1)
4. ionic radii of Li, Na, K and Rb. (1)

In Questions 5–8 inclusive, one, or more than one, of the suggested responses may be correct. Answer as follows:

A if **1**, **2** and **3** are correct,
B if **1** and **2** only are correct,
C if **2** and **3** only are correct,
D if **1** only is correct,
E if **3** only is correct.

Directions summarised				
A	B	C	D	E
1, 2, 3	**1, 2**	**2, 3**	**1**	**3**
correct	only	only	only	only

5. Along which of these series do the melting points of the elements rise?
   1 Be, B, C.
   2 Na, Mg, Al.
   3 Si, P, S. (1)

6. Which of the following physical properties of the elements when plotted against the atomic number will give Group I elements on the peaks?
   1 Standard enthalpy of formation of atoms.
   2 Second ionisation energy.
   3 Atomic volume of the solid element. (1)

7. A graph of the periodic variation of a property with atomic number was constructed for the first twenty elements of the Periodic Table. This exhibited maxima at atomic numbers 6 and 14 and minima at atomic numbers 2, 10 and 18.
   The property plotted could be the
   1 melting point;
   2 first ionisation energy;
   3 atomic volume. (1)

8. Which of the following statements is/are true?
   1 The electronegativity of the alkali metals decreases with increase in atomic number of the metal.
   2 Beryllium and aluminium have similar electronegativities.
   3 In a given short period of the Periodic Table, the electronegativity of the elements decreases from left to right. (1)

Question 9 consists of an incomplete statement followed by five suggested answers. Select the best answer.

Table 23

Element	***M***	***N***	***O***	***P***	***Q***	***R***	***S***	***T***
Atomic number	Z	Z+1	Z+2	Z+3	Z+4	Z+5	Z+6	Z+7
Molar enthalpy of vaporisation /kJ mol^{-1}	2.8	3.4	3.3	1.8	89	129	294	377
Boiling point/K	73	93	83	23	1163	1373	2673	2973

9. The data in Table 23 refer to eight elements, lettered *M* to *T* (these letters are **not** chemical symbols).
   From these data, it can be deduced that:
   A *T* is in the same group of the Periodic Table as helium;
   B *S* has a giant structure;
   C *N* is a metallic element;
   D the elements are all in the same period of the Periodic Table;
   E *M* is a Group I element in the Periodic Table. (1)

10. Which of the following properties does **not** show periodicity when the values for successive elements in the Periodic Table are plotted against atomic number?
    A Atomic volume.
    B Enthalpy of vaporisation.
    C Melting point.
    D Atomicity.
    E Ionisation energy. (1)

11. This question concerns the elements Na to Cl in the third period of the Periodic Table.
    a State and explain the trend in atomic radii across the period. (3)
    b i) Explain why the first ionisation energy of aluminium is less than that of magnesium.
    ii) Explain why the first ionisation energy of sulphur is less than that of phosphorus. (4)
    c State which element in the third period forms the following.
    i) Chlorides XCl_3 and XCl_5.
    ii) Oxides X_2O_7 and X_2O.
    iii) Oxides XO_2 and XO_3. (3)

12. **a** i) Explain the term **electronegativity**.
    ii) How do the electronegativities of the elements change along the short period lithium to fluorine, and how do you account for this change? (4)
    b i) Define the term **electron affinity**.
    ii) Which of the elements Cl, I has the smaller numerical value of electron affinity and why? (4)

13.

Figure 32

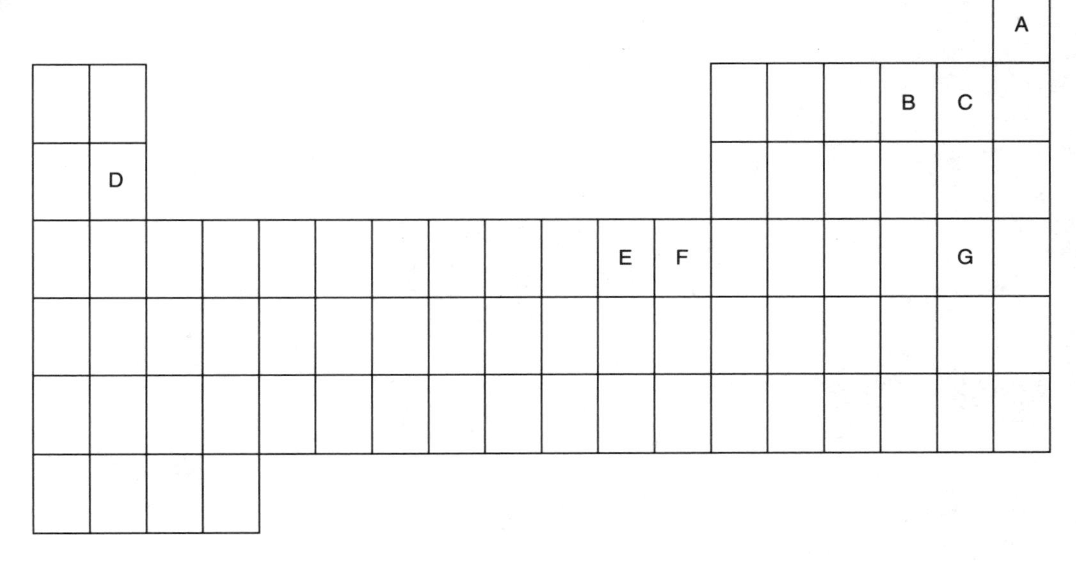

Figure 32 shows in outline the Periodic Table, omitting the lanthanides and actinides. You should answer the following questions by using the letters A to G as appropriate, and **not** by the usual symbols which you think represent the elements.

a Select from the elements A to G:
i) an element which is liquid at ordinary temperature,
ii) **three** elements which are gaseous at ordinary temperature,
iii) **three** elements which are good electrical conductors,
iv) the element whose first four ionisation energies are 740, 1500, 7700, and 10 500 kJ mol^{-1},
v) the element with electron configuration $1s^2\ 2s^2\ 2p^5$. (7)

b Select from the elements A to G:
i) **one** element which occurs in nature as its carbonate,
ii) **two** elements which can occur uncombined. (3)

14. Account for the variation in the radii of the following ions.

Ion	Na^+	Mg^{2+}	Al^{3+}	Si^{4-}	P^{3-}	S^{2-}	Cl^-
Radius/nm	0.095	0.065	0.050	0.271	0.212	0.184	0.181

(4)

What would you predict about the size of
a the K^+ ion,
b the Si^{4+} ion?
Give your reasons. (4)

15. Consider the elements of the second period of the Periodic Table (lithium to neon).
Explain the variations in the first ionisation energies of these elements including particular reference to a comparison of the first ionisation energies of the following pairs of atoms: beryllium and boron; nitrogen and oxygen. (4)

(Total: 50 marks)

COMPOUNDS OF PERIODS 2 AND 3

CHAPTER 15

COMPOUNDS OF ELEMENTS IN PERIODS 2 AND 3

In Part A you studied the elements in Periods 2 and 3. You examined key physical and chemical properties and built up a picture of the Periodic Table as a whole. In Part B you use this knowledge as a basis for studying three important groups of compounds, the chlorides, oxides and hydrides of these elements. We begin with a survey of their formulae.

15.1 Periodicity of formulae of Period 2 and 3 oxides, chlorides and hydrides

In the s-Block Elements and The Halogens units of this volume you learned that Groups I and II show oxidation states of +1 and +2 respectively in all their compounds, and that Group VII elements show a range of oxidation states in their compounds. In this section you extend your knowledge to include the other members of Periods 2 and 3.

First, you predict the formulae of the other members of Periods 2 and 3 and decide whether there is a periodic pattern.

OBJECTIVES

When you have finished this section, you should be able to:

- state the formulae of the oxides, chlorides and hydrides of the elements in Periods 2 and 3;
- identify the **periodic pattern** in the **formulae of oxides, chlorides** and **hydrides**.

Start by reading about the compounds of the elements in Periods 2 and 3 in a textbook. Look for a chapter on periodicity which will help you to do the next exercise.

EXERCISE 89
Answers on page 182

a Complete copies of Tables 24–26 on the next page with the formulae of the oxides, chlorides and hydrides respectively.
b Describe the pattern shown by each group of compounds. Would you say it is periodic in each case? Explain.
c Explain why phosphorus, sulphur and chlorine in Period 3 show several oxidation states in their oxides and chlorides.

Table 24

General formula and ratio O/X		Formulae of oxides in Groups of Period 2							Formulae of oxides in Groups of Period 3						
		1	2	3	4	5	6	7	1	2	3	4	5	6	7
X_2O_7	3.5														
XO_3	3.0														
X_2O_5	2.5														
XO_2	2.0														
X_2O_3	1.5														
XO	1.0														
X_2O	0.5														

Table 25

General formula and ratio Cl/X		Formulae of chlorides in Groups of Period 2							Formulae of chlorides in Groups of Period 3						
		1	2	3	4	5	6	7	1	2	3	4	5	6	7
XCl_5	5														
XCl_4	4														
XCl_3	3														
XCl_2	2														
XCl	1														

Table 26

General formula and ratio H/X		Formulae of hydrides in Groups of Period 2							Formulae of hydrides in Groups of Period 3						
		1	2	3	4	5	6	7	1	2	3	4	5	6	7
XH_4	4														
XH_3	3														
XH_2	2														
XH	1														

Having considered the formulae of oxides, chlorides and hydrides, you can now compare the oxidation states of the elements in each compound. You do this in the next exercise.

EXERCISE 90

Answers on page 183

a Make a copy of the oxidation number chart shown in Fig. 33 and insert symbols at the appropriate places for the oxidation numbers of the elements in Periods 2 and 3. (Ignore the hydrides of C and Si except for CH_4 and SiH_4 since the presence of C—C and Si—Si bonds gives confusing oxidation numbers.)

We have inserted three symbols as a guide, using × for oxides, ○ for hydrides, and □ for chlorides.

Figure 33

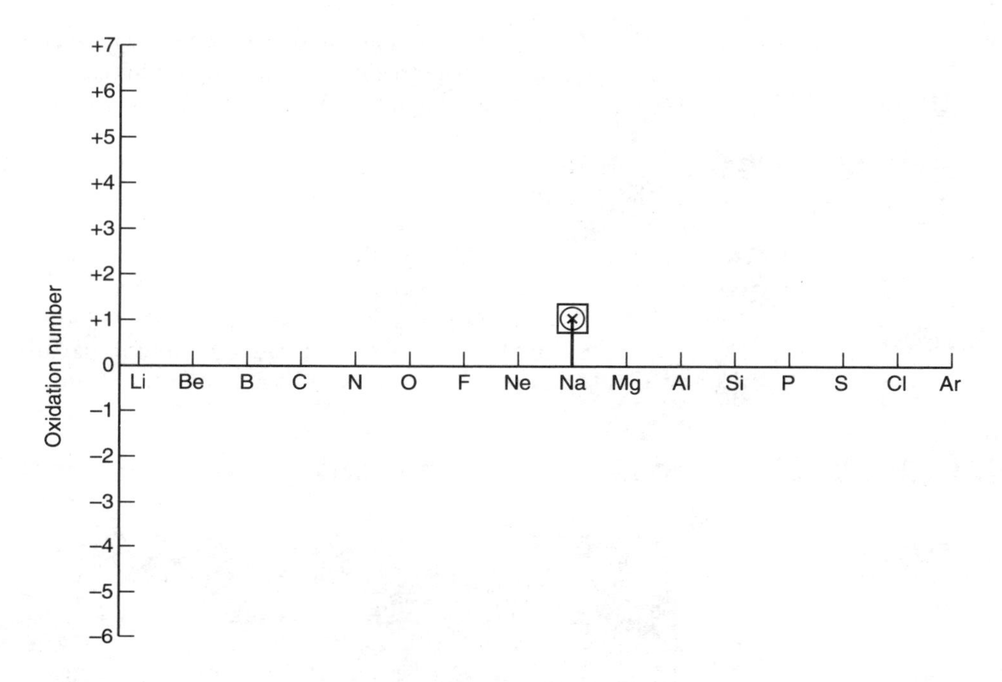

b As you noticed in part **a**, many of the elements show more than one oxidation state in their compounds. How do you account for the fact that phosphorus, sulphur and chlorine show their highest oxidation states in oxides or chlorides but not hydrides? (Hint: compare the electronegativities of O, Cl and H.)

We now consider the physical and chemical properties of the oxides, chlorides and hydrides. We start with the chlorides.

CHAPTER 16

CHLORIDES OF THE ELEMENTS IN PERIODS 2 AND 3

In this chapter you use electronegativity values to predict the bond type in the chlorides of the elements in Period 3. You then test these predictions by experiment.

OBJECTIVES

When you have finished this chapter you should be able to:

- explain the variation in **bonding and structure** which is evident in the chlorides of Periods 2 and 3;
- identify a **periodic pattern** in the **hydrolysis** of Period 2 and 3 chlorides;
- write **equations** for the **hydrolysis** reactions shown by Period 2 and 3 chlorides.

In ILPAC Volume 3, Bonding and Structure, you learned that differences in electronegativity values between elements in a compound can be used as a rough guide to identify the type of bonding found between them. You use this idea again in the next exercise.

EXERCISE 91

Answers on page 184

Use electronegativity values from your data book to identify the trend in bond character in the chlorides of Period 3.

Now test your predictions by doing Experiment 12, in which you examine the chlorides of the elements in Period 3.

There is an ILPAC video programme entitled 'Chlorides and Oxides' which covers similar ground to the experiment you are about to perform. Ask your teacher if it is available and whether you should watch it at this point.

EXPERIMENT 12 Investigating the properties of Period 3 chlorides

Aim

The purpose of this experiment is to study the chlorides of Period 3 elements and classify them according to structural type and bonding.

Introduction

You first examine the appearance of each compound and then you find out whether it dissolves in water and/or hexane. If it does dissolve you may detect a temperature change. In general, a small temperature change indicates a physical process and a large one a chemical process. This will help you to distinguish between the physical process of dissolving and the chemical one of hydrolysis when you add these substances to water.

You also determine any pH changes that take place when you mix the chlorides with water. A decrease in pH indicates that hydrolysis has taken place.

Finally, you consider physical data for each compound and reach a conclusion about its bonding and structure.

Requirements

- safety spectacles
- protective gloves
- access to fume cupboard
- 14 test-tubes (6 must be dry)
- test-tube rack
- 2 measuring cylinders, 10 cm^3 (1 must be dry)
- distilled water
- thermometer, 0–100°C
- spatula
- universal indicator solution and colour chart
- pH paper to cover the range 1–7
- ammonia solution, 2 M NH_3
- sodium chloride, NaCl
- magnesium chloride, $MgCl_2$
- aluminium chloride, $AlCl_3$ (anhydrous if possible)
- 4 teat-pipettes
- silicon tetrachloride, $SiCl_4$
- phosphorus trichloride, PCl_3
- disulphur dichloride, S_2Cl_2
- cyclohexane, C_6H_{12}
- organic residues bottle

HAZARD WARNING

Many of the chlorides in this experiment react vigorously with water. $SiCl_4$, PCl_3 and S_2Cl_2 are corrosive and harmful. Therefore you **must:**

- **do this experiment in a fume cupboard;**
- **keep stoppers on bottles as much as possible;**
- **wear gloves and safety spectacles.**

Old stock of silicon tetrachloride often has hydrogen chloride trapped at the neck of the bottle. Ensure the bottle has been checked by your teacher before you attempt to open it.

Cyclohexane is very flammable. Therefore you **must:**

- **keep the stopper on the bottle as much as possible;**
- **keep the bottle away from flames.**

Procedure

A. **Appearance**

Examine the chloride samples provided and, in a larger copy of Results Table 16, note for each:

a whether it is solid, liquid or gaseous,

b its colour (if any).

B. **On mixing with water**

1. Set up seven test-tubes, side by side.
2. Into each test-tube pour about 5 cm^3 of distilled water.
3. In the first test-tube place a thermometer.
   - **a** Note the temperature.
   - **b** Add half a spatula-tip of sodium chloride and very carefully stir with the thermometer.
   - **c** Note, after about one minute, i) the temperature, ii) whether the solid has dissolved and iii) anything else you see. For example, is gas evolved at any time? If so, is the gas acidic? Can you identify it using a simple test?

d Add 2–4 drops of universal indicator solution, or use a piece of pH paper, compare the colour with the chart provided, and note the pH indicated.

4. Repeat (but with more care!) the above steps 3**a**–**d** using, in turn, magnesium chloride, aluminium chloride, silicon tetrachloride (2 drops), phosphorus trichloride (2 drops), and disulphur dichloride (2 drops).
5. Measure the pH of the water in the seventh test-tube by adding 2–4 drops of universal indicator solution or by using pH paper, for comparison with the above.

C. **On mixing with cyclohexane**

1. Set up another six test-tubes, side by side. These must be dry.
2. Into each test-tube pour about 5 cm^3 of cyclohexane.
3. In the first test-tube place a thermometer.
   a Note the temperature.
   b Add half a spatula-tip of sodium chloride and stir very carefully with the thermometer.
   c Note, after about one minute, i) the temperature, ii) whether the solid dissolves and iii) anything else you see.
   (Dispose of cyclohexane by pouring into the residue bottle provided.)

4. Repeat the above steps 3**a**–**c** using, in turn, magnesium chloride, aluminium chloride, silicon tetrachloride (2 drops), phosphorus trichloride (2 drops), and disulphur dichloride (2 drops).

Results Table 15

	NaCl	$MgCl_2$	$AlCl_3$	$SiCl_4$	PCl_3	S_2Cl_2
Appearance						
On mixing with water Initial temperature Final temperature Does it dissolve? pH of solution Other observation(s) (if any)						
On mixing with hexane Initial temperature Final temperature Does it dissolve? Other observation(s) (if any)						

(Specimen results on page 184)

Questions

Answers on page 185

1. Complete a copy of Table 27 on the next page using your experimental results and your data book. Then decide on the structure of these chlorides and the bonding found in them and fill in the last part of your table.

2. In the experiment you discovered that some of the chlorides are hydrolysed by water. Look up the equations for these reactions in your textbook(s). In the case of S_2Cl_2 you may find that most books do not give an equation for its hydrolysis. This is because a mixture of products is obtained. We suggest the following equation:

$$2S_2Cl_2\,(l) + 2H_2O\,(l) \rightarrow SO_2\,(aq) + 3S\,(s) + 4HCl\,(aq)$$

3. Compare your conclusions from this experiment with the predictions you made in Exercise 91. Did the experiment confirm your predictions?

Table 27
Properties of chlorides of Period 3

Formula of chloride	**NaCl**	**$MgCl_2$**	**$AlCl_3$**	**$SiCl_4$**	**PCl_3**	**S_2Cl_2**	**Cl_2**
Melting point/°C							
Boiling point/°C							
Physical state at r.t.p.*							
$\Delta H_f^\ominus$/kJ mol^{-1}							
$\Delta H_f^\ominus$ per mole of Cl/kJ mol^{-1}							
Conductivity of liquid							
Action of water							
pH of aqueous solution							
Solubility in hexane							
Structure							
Bonding							

* r.t.p. = room temperature and pressure (i.e. 20°C and 1 atm).

You have seen how the physical and chemical properties of the chlorides change in going across Period 3. You should now be able to make some predictions about the chlorides of the elements in Period 2. Bear in mind that the first three elements in Period 2 resemble those **diagonally** below them.

You make these predictions in the next exercise.

EXERCISE 92

Answers on page 186

a Complete a larger copy of Table 28. Some of the table has been filled in for you.
b Using your textbook(s) if necessary, write an equation for the reaction of each chloride which is hydrolysed by water.

Table 28

Formula of chloride	**LiCl**	**$BeCl_2$**	**BCl_3**	**CCl_4**	**NCl_3**	**OCl_2**	**FCl**
State at r.t.p.							
Conductivity of liquid							
Action of water		Reacts					
Structure		Chain polymer					
Bonding							

From what you know about s-block compounds you might expect that calcium chloride would be resistant to hydrolysis. This is not the case, however, as the next exercise shows.

EXERCISE 93
Answer on page 186

Calcium chloride hydrolyses **slightly** as shown by the equation:

$$CaCl_2\,(s) + H_2O\,(l) \rightleftharpoons CaO\,(s) + 2HCl\,(g)$$

This indicates some degree of covalent character. Suggest an explanation for this using your knowledge of polarising powers of cations and the polarisability of anions from the s-Block Elements unit of this volume.

We now briefly consider the anhydrous chlorides of Group II elements.

■ 16.1 Anhydrous chlorides of Group II elements

OBJECTIVE

When you have finished this section, you should be able to:

- explain why the chlorides of certain Group II elements cannot be obtained simply by heating the hydrated salts.

Find out from your textbook(s) why a sample of hydrated magnesium chloride cannot be made anhydrous directly by heating it. Read about the indirect method of making the anhydrous salt. This will enable you to do the next exercise.

EXERCISE 94
Answers on page 186

The salt $MgCl_2{\cdot}6H_2O$ when heated alone does not yield anhydrous $MgCl_2$. Anhydrous $MgCl_2$ can, however, be obtained by heating the salt in a stream of hydrogen chloride gas. Explain.

Now attempt the next exercise, again using your knowledge of polarising power from the s-Block Elements unit of this volume.

EXERCISE 95
Answers on page 186

Beryllium(II) chloride hydrolyses with complete removal of chlorine, but magnesium(II) chloride forms an oxychloride on hydrolysis. Explain.

You should now be able to answer the following A-level question.

EXERCISE 96
Answers on page 187

a Copy and complete Table 29.

Table 29

Element	Formula of chloride	Physical state of chloride at s.t.p.	Type of bonding found in chloride
Hydrogen			
Barium			
Nitrogen			
Silicon			

b Give the equations describing the reaction of the chlorides of hydrogen and silicon with water.
i) chloride of hydrogen, ii) chloride of silicon.

We end the work on chlorides by considering methods of preparing them. The methods used depend on the physical states of the elements and on the nature of the chlorides formed. This section draws on ideas both from your pre-A-level course and from the work you have just done on chlorides.

■ 16.2 Methods of preparing chlorides in Period 3

We focus on the preparation of aluminium chloride, $AlCl_3$, which you carry out in Experiment 13. You then suggest adaptations of this method, or alternative methods, for preparing other chlorides.

OBJECTIVES

When you have finished this section you should be able to:

- prepare a sample of a solid covalent chloride, e.g. aluminium chloride;
- describe the apparatus suitable for **preparing a solid covalent chloride**;
- explain how the apparatus for preparing a solid chloride needs to be modified for preparing a liquid or gaseous chloride;
- calculate the **percentage yield** of a product.

In the next experiment you prepare a sample of aluminium chloride. You use a known amount of aluminium and weigh your product at the end. You then calculate the theoretical mass of aluminium chloride from the chemical equation and compare this with the actual mass. This enables you to obtain the percentage yield of the product.

We briefly consider the method for such a calculation in the following Worked Example. This will enable you to calculate your percentage yield at the end of the experiment.

WORKED EXAMPLE

In an experiment to prepare anhydrous aluminium chloride, 0.80 g of aluminium foil was heated in a stream of dry chlorine. This gave 2.38 g of product. What is the percentage yield of $AlCl_3$?

Solution

1. Write the equation for this reaction:

$$Al\ (s) + 1\tfrac{1}{2}Cl_2\ (g) \rightarrow AlCl_3\ (s)$$

2. Use the equation to calculate the mass of aluminium chloride that is formed from 0.80 g of aluminium.

1 mol of Al produces 1 mol of $AlCl_3$
i.e. 27 g of Al produces 133.5 g of $AlCl_3$

$$\therefore\ 1.0 \text{ g of Al produces } \frac{133.5 \text{ g}}{27} \text{ of } AlCl_3$$

$$\therefore\ 0.80 \text{ g of Al produces } \frac{133.5 \text{ g}}{27} \times 0.80 = 4.0 \text{ g of } AlCl_3$$

3. Express the actual mass formed in the experiment as a percentage of the theoretical mass.

$$\%\ \text{yield} = \frac{\text{actual mass of product}}{\text{theoretical mass of product}} \times 100$$

$$\therefore\ \%\ \text{yield} = \frac{2.38 \text{ g}}{4.0 \text{ g}} \times 100 = \mathbf{60\%}$$

You need to use expensive ground-glass-joint apparatus in this experiment. If you have not already used this apparatus in the Functional Groups unit of ILPAC Volume 8 ask your teacher for advice; or, if it is available, watch the ILPAC video programme 'Organic Techniques I'. Alternatively, you could watch the complete experiment on the ILPAC video programme 'Preparation of Aluminium Chloride' either as an introduction or, if your teacher prefers, instead of carrying it out yourself.

EXPERIMENT 13 Preparing anhydrous aluminium chloride

Aim In this experiment you gain experience in setting up an assembly of glassware in order to carry out an inorganic synthesis. You also calculate the percentage yield of your product.

Introduction You prepare chlorine by adding concentrated hydrochloric acid to potassium manganate(VII), dry it using anhydrous calcium chloride and then pass it over heated aluminium foil in a combustion tube. When the reaction is complete you weigh your collected product and calculate the percentage yield.

Requirements

- safety spectacles
- access to fume cupboard
- forceps
- glass rod
- calcium chloride, anhydrous, $CaCl_2$
- long spatula
- combustion tube
- ceramic wool
- bung fitted with a short piece of glass tubing
- access to a balance capable of weighing to within 0.01 g
- aluminium foil, Al
- absorption tube
- soda lime
- receiver bottle with two holed bung (connected to absorption and combustion tubes)
- ruler
- rubber tubing for connections
- 3 clamps, bosses and stands
- potassium manganate(VII), $KMnO_4$
- pear-shaped flask with ground-glass joint, 50 cm^3
- ground-glass adapter with T-connection

- cylindrical funnel with ground-glass joint
- hydrochloric acid, concentrated, HCl
- Bunsen burner
- specimen tube with lid
- labels
- access to a desiccator

HAZARD WARNING

Chlorine is a toxic gas. Therefore you must:

- **do the experiment at the fume cupboard.**

Concentrated hydrochloric acid is a corrosive liquid, and its vapour is harmful to eyes, lungs and skin. Therefore you **must**:

- **wear gloves;**
- **wear safety spectacles;**
- **keep the hydrochloric acid in a fume cupboard;**
- **keep the stopper on the bottle as much as possible.**

Procedure

There are several steps in assembling the apparatus for this experiment. The diagram below (Fig. 34) gives you an idea of what you are aiming for. Details of the separate stages are given at appropriate points in the procedure.

Figure 34 Preparation of aluminium chloride.

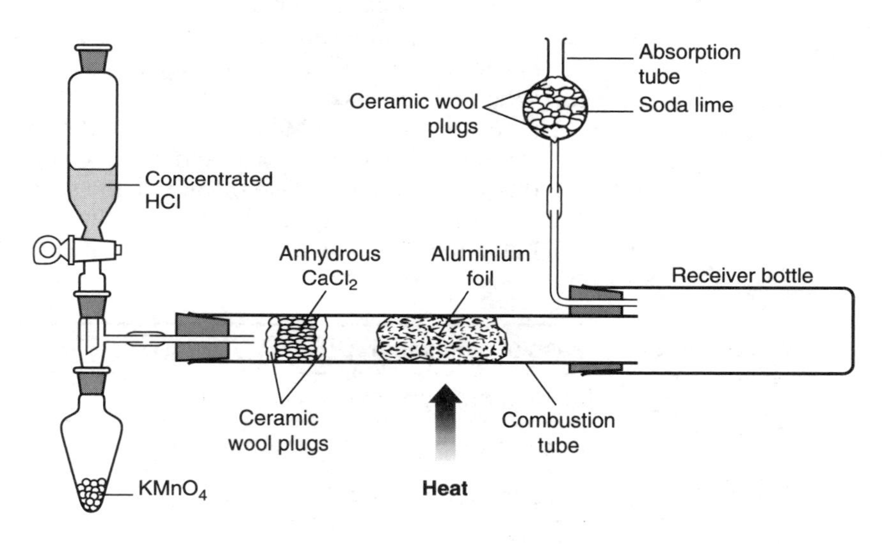

1. Using forceps and a glass rod, put some granular anhydrous calcium chloride between two loose plugs of ceramic wool near the entrance of the combustion tube. (Make sure that the calcium chloride fills the cross-section of the tube without preventing the free flow of chlorine.) Attach the bung fitted with glass tubing at the entrance of the combustion tube.
2. Weigh about 0.25 g of aluminium foil, crumple it loosely, and put it in the combustion tube as shown in Fig. 35.

Figure 35

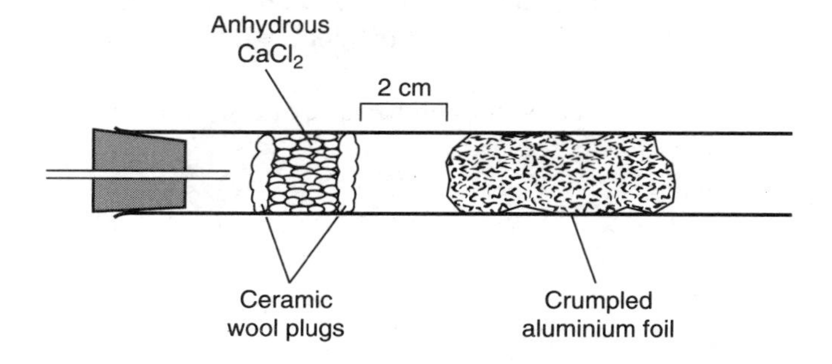

3. Loosely pack the absorption tube as follows:
   a Using forceps, push in a plug of ceramic wool.
   b Fill with soda-lime.
   c Using forceps again, close with a second plug of ceramic wool. Both plugs must be loose to avoid blockage.
4. Fit the combustion tube and absorption tube to the receiver bottle as shown in Fig. 34. Clamp the apparatus so that the combustion tube is about 15 cm above the base of the fume cupboard.

5. Weigh about 5 g of potassium manganate(VII) and place it in the pear-shaped flask.
6. Fit the pear-shaped flask with the adapter and dropping funnel. Then clamp the flask and connect it to the combustion tube, as shown in Fig. 34.

You are now ready to start the preparation.

7. Get your teacher to check the apparatus.
8. Make sure that the tap of the dropping funnel is closed.
9. Pour 10 cm^3 of concentrated hydrochloric acid into the dropping funnel.

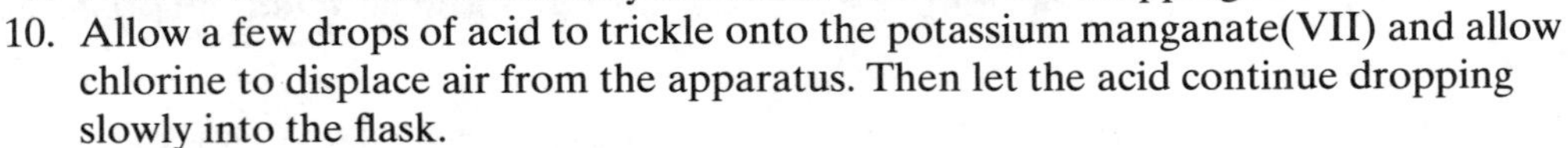

10. Allow a few drops of acid to trickle onto the potassium manganate(VII) and allow chlorine to displace air from the apparatus. Then let the acid continue dropping slowly into the flask.
11. Heat the aluminium gently near the calcium chloride until a bright glow shows that the chloride is reacting exothermically with the aluminium. If the glow is very bright, remove the heat until it subsides.
12. Continue heating, all around the tube, moving the flame slowly towards the receiver bottle, until reaction is complete.
13. When reaction is complete, stop the trickle of acid and let the combustion tube cool (about 10 minutes). Meanwhile weigh the empty specimen tube and top.
14. Remove the receiver bottle and, using your spatula, quickly scrape the product into the specimen tube. Place the top on the specimen tube and weigh it.
15. Record your results in a copy of Results Table 17.
16. Label the specimen tube with your name and the name of the product and store it in a desiccator.

Results Table 17

Mass of aluminium	g
Mass of empty specimen tube, m_1	g
Mass of specimen tube and product, m_2	g
Mass of product, $m = (m_2 - m_1)$	g
% yield	

(Specimen results on page 187.)

Questions

Answers on page 187

1. Why is it important to use dry chlorine in this experiment?
2. What impurity would be present in the product if damp chlorine were used? Write an equation for the reaction giving this impurity.
3. Calculate and comment on the percentage yield of your product.
4. Why is your product stored in a desiccator?

The next exercise is about modifications to the method you have just used.

EXERCISE 97

Answers on page 188

a Figures 36 and 37 below show two assemblies for preparing the chlorides of the elements in Period 3.

Which apparatus would be more suitable for:

i) $SiCl_4$, ii) PCl_3, iii) S_2Cl_2?

In making your choice, you should consider both the state of each chloride at room temperature (20°C) and the melting point of the element.

Figure 36

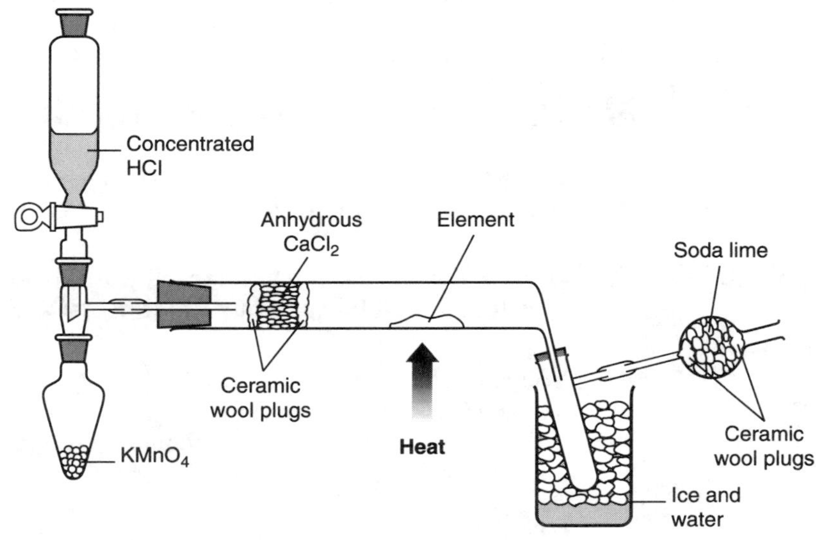

Figure 37

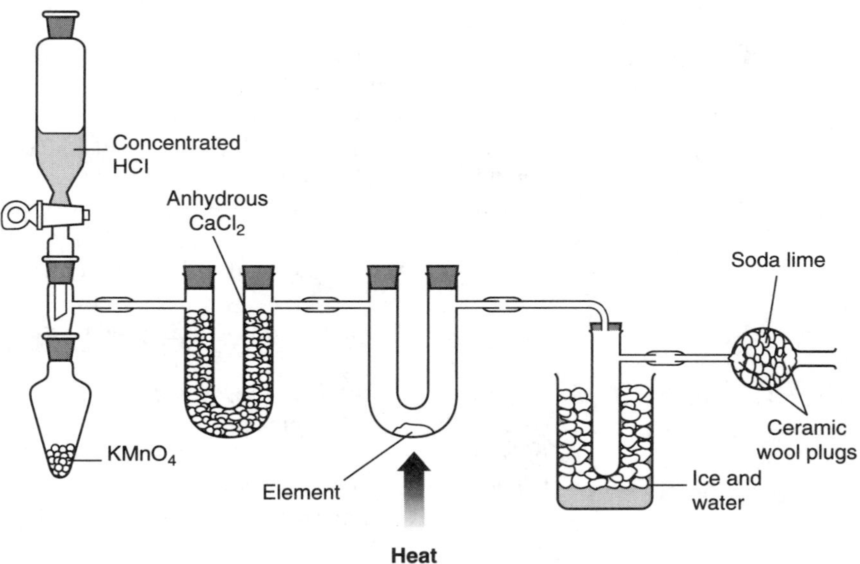

b How would you heat each of the three elements in part **a** in preparing its chloride? We suggest you choose from the following alternatives:
'strongly', 'enough to start the reaction', 'enough to melt the element'.

In making your choice, consider the melting point of each element and its reactivity with chlorine.

c Bearing in mind the melting point and boiling point of sulphur, what would you have to avoid in the preparation of disulphur dichloride?

So far, you have learned about preparing chlorides by direct synthesis. Although ionic chlorides may also be prepared in this way, there is an alternative method, which you should know from your pre-A-level work.

If necessary, consult a textbook on the preparation of ionic salts. Then go on to do the next exercise.

EXERCISE 98
Answers on page 188

a Outline a method, other than direct synthesis, by which you could prepare a sample of lithium chloride or sodium chloride, starting with a sample of the metal.
b Why would this method not be suitable for anhydrous magnesium chloride?

In addition to knowing how to prepare chlorides of various elements you need to be able to determine their composition. We deal with this in the next section.

16.3 Formula determination of chlorides

The most straightforward way to determine the composition of a chloride, given simple laboratory apparatus, is to use a titration method.

OBJECTIVE

When you have finished this section you should be able to:
- **calculate the formula of a chloride** using data from a silver nitrate titration.

You have already performed a silver nitrate titration in The Mole unit of ILPAC Volume 1 in order to determine the number of molecules of water of hydration in hydrated barium chloride. You should therefore be able to calculate an empirical formula using titration data. In The Mole unit you met the calculation in several stages. To give you practice in following it through as a single process, try the exercises which follow. The first one is broken down into separate steps as a guide.

EXERCISE 99
Answers on page 188

0.767 g of a chloride of phosphorus was dissolved in water and made up to 250 cm^3 of solution. After neutralisation, 25.0 cm^3 of this solution required 18.4 cm^3 of 0.100 M $AgNO_3$ for complete precipitation of the chloride.
a Calculate the amount of chloride ion in 25.0 cm^3 of solution.
b Calculate the amount and hence the mass of chloride ion in the whole sample.
c Calculate the mass and hence the amount of phosphorus in the whole sample.
d Calculate the amount of chlorine combined with one mole of phosphorus.
e Hence state the simplest formula of the chloride.

Now try a similar calculation by doing the next exercise.

EXERCISE 100
Answers on page 189

1.420 g of a chloride of sulphur was dissolved in water and the solution made up to a volume of 250 cm^3. 25.0 cm^3 of this solution, after neutralisation, needed 21.0 cm^3 of 0.100 M $AgNO_3$ for complete precipitation of the chloride.
a Calculate the number of moles of chlorine combined with one mole of sulphur.
b If the relative molar mass of the chloride is 135.2 what is its molecular formula?

Now that you have finished the work on chlorides you should be able to answer the following Teacher-marked Exercise, which is an A-level essay question. Look through your notes and make a rough plan before you start writing.

EXERCISE
Teacher-marked

Write an essay on the chlorides of the elements sodium, magnesium, aluminium, silicon, phosphorus and sulphur. You may like to consider their composition, preparation, physical nature and their reactions with water. You should also try to relate these considerations to such properties of the atoms as size and electronic structure.

Describe how you would determine the formula of one of these chlorides in the laboratory, if you were given the relative atomic mass of the parent element.

We now move on to consider the oxides of Periods 2 and 3.

CHAPTER 

OXIDES OF THE ELEMENTS IN PERIODS 2 AND 3

You have already studied the oxides of Groups I, II and VII in some detail, in the s-Block Elements and The Halogens units of this volume. In this chapter you extend your knowledge to include the other elements of Periods 2 and 3.

OBJECTIVES

When you have finished this chapter you should be able to:

- state the changes in the **acid–base nature** of the **oxides** of the elements across Periods 2 and 3;
- explain the change in **bonding and structure** in the **oxides** of the elements in Periods 2 and 3;
- identify a **periodic pattern** in the reactions of the **oxides** of the elements in Periods 2 and 3 with **water**.

We start with an exercise similar to the one you did for the chlorides of the elements in Period 3 where you use electronegativity differences to predict the type of bonding found in these compounds.

EXERCISE 101

Answers on page 190

Use the electronegativity values from your data book to identify:

a the type of bonding found in Period 3 oxides,

b the change in bond type that takes place with increasing atomic number across the period.

Now test your predictions by doing Experiment 14, in which you examine the oxides of the elements in Period 3.

You could, as an alternative, watch part 2 of the ILPAC video programme entitled 'Chorides and Oxides' if it is available.

EXPERIMENT 14 Investigating the properties of Period 3 oxides

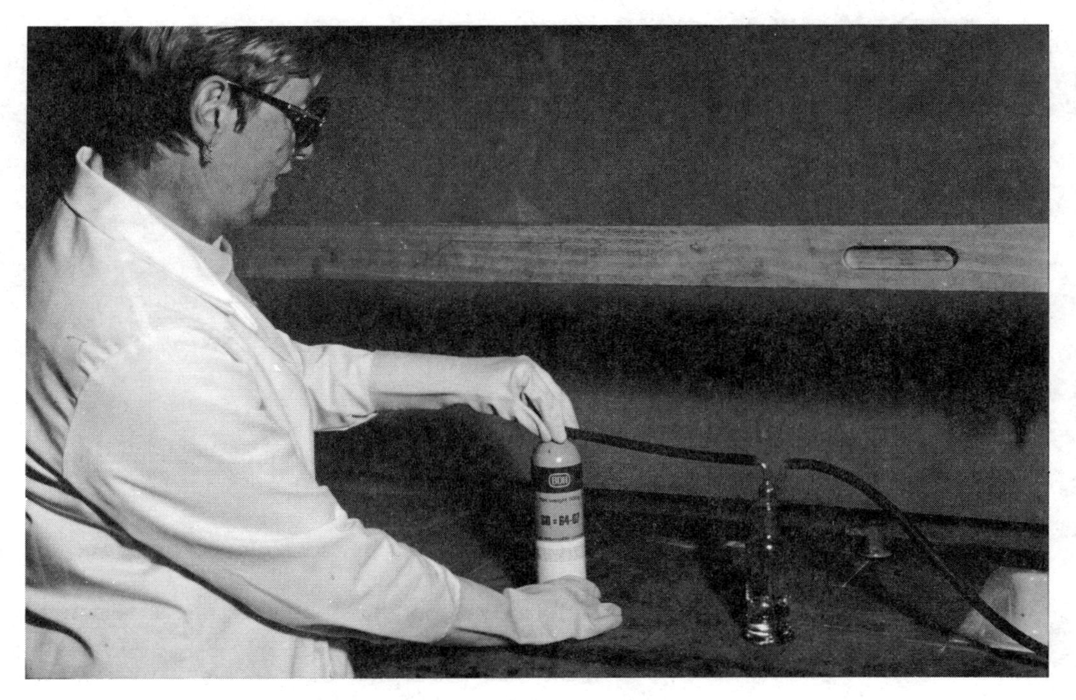

Aim The purpose of this experiment is to examine the oxides of Period 3 elements and describe their bonding and structure.

Introduction

You carry out an investigation along similar lines to the work you did on the chlorides of the elements in Period 3. However, you will not be asked to test the oxides with hexane because unlike the covalent chlorides, most of the oxides are not composed of discrete molecules. Therefore they are unlikely to dissolve in hexane and simple experiments cannot distinguish between insolubility and slight solubility.

Requirements

- safety spectacles
- access to a fume cupboard
- 6 test-tubes
- test-tube rack
- 1 measuring cylinder, 10 cm^3
- 1 measuring cylinder, 100 cm^3
- distilled water
- thermometer, 0–100°C
- 1 spatula
- universal indicator solution and colour chart
- teat-pipette
- pH paper
- splints
- sodium peroxide, Na_2O_2
- magnesium oxide, MgO
- aluminium oxide, Al_2O_3
- phosphorus(V) oxide, P_4O_{10}
- silicon(IV) oxide, SiO_2
- access to sulphur dioxide cylinder or generator, SO_2
- Drechsel bottle
- glass tubing with right-angled bend
- rubber tubing for connections.

HAZARD WARNING

Phosphorus(V) oxide is corrosive and irritates eyes, skin and lungs. Sodium peroxide is also corrosive and a powerful oxidant. Sulphur dioxide is a toxic gas with a choking smell. Therefore you must:

- **do the experiment at the fume cupboard;**
- **wear safety spectacles;**
- **avoid contact with skin.**

Procedure

A. **Appearance**

Examine your oxide samples, and in a larger copy of Results Table 18 note for each:

a whether it is solid, liquid or gaseous,

b its colour (if any).

B. **On mixing with water**

1. Set up six test-tubes, side by side.
2. Into each tube pour about 5 cm^3 of distilled water.
3. In the first test-tube place a thermometer.

   a Note the temperature.

   b Add half a spatula-tip of sodium peroxide and stir carefully with the thermometer.

   c Note, after about one minute, i) the temperature, ii) whether the solid has dissolved and iii) anything else you see. For example, is gas evolved at any time? If so, is the gas acidic? Can you identify it using a simple test?

   d Add 2–4 drops of universal indicator solution, compare the colour with the chart provided, and note the pH indicated, or use a piece of pH paper.

4. Repeat the above steps 3**a**–**d** using, in turn, magnesium oxide, aluminium oxide, silicon(IV) oxide and phosphorus(V) oxide.

5. Measure the pH of the water in the sixth test-tube by adding 2–4 drops of universal indicator solution for comparison with the above.

6. Bubble sulphur dioxide slowly through the water in the sixth test-tube until there is no further change in the colour of the indicator. Note the final pH of the solution. (You will probably be given sulphur dioxide in liquid form in a cylinder. To obtain the gas you carefully open the valve and the sudden decrease in pressure inside the cylinder causes the surface liquid to vaporise. Make sure there is a Drechsel bottle between the cylinder and the water in case of suck-back. Alternatively, your teacher may suggest other ways of generating the gas.)
7. To test the solubility of sulphur dioxide lower the delivery tube from your generator to the bottom of the 100 cm^3 measuring cylinder filled with water. Pass a slow steady stream of gas through the water and when the air has been expelled from your apparatus look for a change in the size of the sulphur dioxide gas bubbles as they rise up through the water.

Results Table 18

	Na_2O_2	MgO	Al_2O_3	SiO_2	P_4O_{10}	SO_2
Appearance						
On mixing with water						
Initial temperature						
Final temperature						
Does it dissolve?						
pH of solution						
Other observation(s) (if any)						

(Specimen results on page 190.)

Questions

Answers on page 191

1. Use your experimental results, your data book and your textbook(s) if necessary to complete a larger copy of Table 30.

Table 30

Formula of oxide	Na_2O_2*	MgO	Al_2O_3	SiO_2	P_4O_{10}*	SO_2*	Cl_2O*
Melting point/°C							
Boiling point/°C							
State at s.t.p.							
Action of water							
pH of aq. solution							
Acid–base nature							
Conductivity of liquid							
Solubility in hexane							
Structure							
Bonding							

*These substances represent the most familiar or readily available oxides of that element. In general the other oxides of that element have similar properties.

2. Write equations for any reactions which took place when you added the oxides to water.
3. Comment on the change in structure and bonding in the oxides between sodium and chlorine.
4. How does the acid–base nature of the oxides of the elements in Period 3 change with increasing atomic number?
5. Can you relate this change to the change in structure and bonding that takes place along the period?
6. Do your conclusions about the bonding of the oxides of the elements in Period 3 confirm your predictions in Exercise 101?

You are now in a position to predict the structure and bonding of Period 2 oxides and relate these to their acid–base nature. You do this in the next exercise.

EXERCISE 102

Answers on page 192

Complete a large copy of Table 31. Remember that Li_2O, BeO and B_2O_3 are likely to have much in common with those diagonally below them in Period 3.

Table 31

Formula of oxide	Li_2O	BeO	B_2O_3	CO_2*	N_2O_4*	O_2	F_2O*
State at s.t.p.							
Conductivity of liquid		Fairly poor	Very poor				
Acid–base nature							
Structure							
Bonding							

*These substances represent the most familiar or readily available oxides of that element.

You should now be able to answer the next exercise.

EXERCISE 103

Answers on page 192

a State the name and formula of the main product formed when each of the following elements reacts with an excess of dry oxygen in the absence of a catalyst.
i) Na
ii) Al
iii) S

b Briefly state the bonding in, and the structure of, the three compounds formed in **a**.

c Which one of these oxides has the lowest melting point?

d Which one of these oxides dissolves in water to form an alkaline solution?

e Write an equation for the reaction in **d**.

To help you consolidate your knowledge of the oxides of Periods 2 and 3 you should now answer the following Teacher-marked Exercise, which is an A-level essay question. Look through your notes and make a rough plan before you start writing.

EXERCISE

Teacher-marked

Write an account of the more important oxides of the elements from sodium (Na; $Z = 11$) to chlorine (Cl; $Z = 17$), remembering that some of the elements have more than one well-characterised oxide. You may like to consider their composition, structure, thermal stability, and behaviour with water and/or acids and alkalis, but your account need not be concerned with all these points nor confined to them.

HYDRIDES OF THE ELEMENTS IN PERIODS 2 AND 3

In the s-Block Elements and The Halogens units of this volume you studied the hydrides of Groups I, II and VII. You learned that most of the s-block hydrides are ionic whereas the halogen hydrides (halogen halides) are covalent. In this chapter we consider the hydrides of all the elements in Periods 2 and 3.

OBJECTIVES

When you have finished this chapter you should be able to:

- state which **hydrides of Periods 2 and 3** react with **water** and write the appropriate equations;
- describe the **trend in acid–base nature** of the **hydrides across Periods 2 and 3;**
- **classify** the **hydrides** of the elements in Periods 2 and 3 as **ionic, covalent** or **intermediate.**

Start by reading about the hydrides of Periods 2 and 3. In particular look for the reaction of each one with water. Find a textbook with a section on hydrides if possible, otherwise you will have to look up each compound according to its group in the Periodic Table. Then do the next exercise.

EXERCISE 104

Answers on page 192

Table 32

Empirical formula of hydride	**LiH**	**BeH_2**	**BH_3***	**CH_4†**	**NH_3**	**OH_2**	**FH**
State at r.t.p.		Solid	Gas (B_2H_6)				
Behaviour with water		Reacts H_2 evolved	Reacts H_2 evolved				
Acid–base nature		Basic	Neutral				
Empirical formula of hydride	**NaH**	**MgH_2**	**AlH_3**	**SiH_4‡**	**PH_3**	**SH_2**	**ClH**
State at r.t.p.		Solid	Solid				
Behaviour with water		Reacts H_2 evolved	Reacts H_2 evolved	Virtually insoluble, no reaction			
Acid–base nature		Basic	Basic§	Essentially neutral			

*A series of boron hydrides is formed, the simplest being B_2H_6 (diborane).
†A series of hydrocarbons is formed (see ILPAC Volume 5, Hydrocarbons).
‡A series of silicon hydrides is formed (silanes).
§Could be interpreted as amphoteric.

N.B. Both boron and aluminium form complex ionic hydrides containing BH_4^- and AlH_4^- ions. Sodium tetrahydridoborate(III), $NaBH_4$ (often called sodium borohydride), and lithium tetrahydridoaluminate(III), $LiAlH_4$ (often called lithium aluminium hydride), are widely used as powerful reducing agents in organic chemistry. You will learn more about this in the units on organic chemistry.

a In a larger copy of Table 32 (which you will find on the previous page):
   i) give the physical states of the missing hydrides at room temperature and pressure with the aid of your data book;
   ii) say whether the missing hydrides react with water and, if so, whether hydrogen is given off in the reaction;
   iii) classify the missing hydrides as acidic, basic or neutral depending on whether they are a source of H^+ or OH^- ions in water.

b Write an equation for the reactions with water of:
   i) NaH,
   ii) MgH_2,
   iii) AlH_3.

c Describe the trend in acid–base nature across each period.

The hydrides of Periods 2 and 3 can be classified in relation to their bond-type and structure, and to the electronegativity of the element concerned. The change in acid–base character of the hydrides can also help us in this classification just as the change in the acid–base nature of the oxides correlated with the change in bond-type. As with the oxides, borderline cases exist between the extremes of the periods.

EXERCISE 105
Answers on page 193

a In a copy of Table 33, which you will find on the next page, fill in the electronegativity difference between each element in Periods 2 and 3 and hydrogen. The electronegativity values are in your data book.

b With the aid of the rest of the table classify the hydrides of Periods 2 and 3 as ionic, covalent or borderline and enter your decisions in the appropriate spaces. Don't rely entirely on electronegativity.

c State the ions present in each of the hydrides which you have classified as ionic. Give reasons for your answer.

d You may be surprised by the small electronegativity differences for LiH and NaH which have NaCl type lattices. What do these values suggest about the bonding in LiH and NaH? Explain your answer by considering the size of the H^- ion shown in Fig. 38 below.

Figure 38
Relative sizes of the halide and hydride ions/nm.

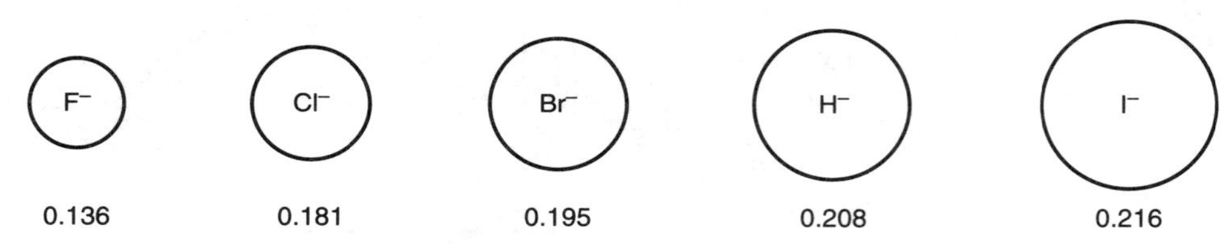

You have now completed your main work on hydrides. We suggest you revise this topic and answer the following Teacher-marked Exercise.

EXERCISE
Teacher-marked

Compare and contrast the physical and chemical properties of the simple hydrides of each of the following elements:

sodium, calcium, carbon, nitrogen, oxygen, fluorine.

In your answer, attempt to relate these properties to the type of bonding encountered in these hydrides. To end this section, we give an exercise to summarise the evidence from the hydrides for diagonal relationships in the Periodic Table.

EXERCISE 106
Answers on page 194

In what ways do the hydrides of Li and Mg, Be and Al, and B and Si illustrate the diagonal relationships between these elements?

Table 33

Empirical formula of hydride	**LiH**	**BeH_2**	**BH_3**	**CH_4**	**NH_3**	**OH_2**	**FH**
Electronegativity difference							
Acid–base nature	Basic	Basic	Neutral	Neutral	Basic	Neutral	Acidic
Structure	Giant ionic	Polymeric	Simple molecular	Simple molecular	Simple molecular	Simple molecular	Simple molecular
Bonding	Appreciably ionic	Mainly covalent	Covalent	Covalent	Covalent	Covalent	Covalent
Classification							
Empirical formula of hydride	**NaH**	**MgH_2**	**AlH_3**	**SiH_4**	**PH_3**	**SH_2**	**ClH**
Electronegativity difference							
Acid–base nature	Basic	Basic	Normally basic	Essentially neutral	Very slightly basic	Weakly acidic	Strongly acidic
Structure	Giant ionic	Giant lattice	Giant lattice	Simple molecular	Simple molecular	Simple molecular	Simple molecular
Bonding	Appreciably ionic	Mainly covalent	Mainly covalent	Covalent	Covalent	Covalent	Covalent
Classification							

End-of-unit test

To find out how well you have learned the material in this unit, try the test which follows. Read the notes below before starting.
1. You should spend about 90 minutes on this test.
2. Hand your answers to your teacher for marking.

Questions 1–5 concern the properties of a number of chlorides as shown in the table below.

Table 34

	State at room temperature	Effect of gentle heat	Action of water
A	Solid	Stable	Dissolves, no hydrolysis
B	Solid	Stable	Partially hydrolysed
C	Liquid	Stable	Not soluble, no hydrolysis
D	Liquid	Stable	Completely hydrolysed
E	Liquid	Decomposes	Completely hydrolysed

Select, from A to E, the set of properties which best fits each of the following.
1. Phosphorus trichloride. (1)
2. Tetrachloromethane. (1)
3. Barium chloride. (1)
4. Silicon tetrachloride. (1)
5. Aluminium chloride. (1)

Questions 6–10 concern the bonding and acid–base nature of the oxides, chlorides and hydrides of the elements lithium to argon in the Periodic Table.

	Bonding	Acid–base nature
A	Giant covalent	Weakly acidic
B	Covalent molecular	Acidic
C	Covalent molecular	Neutral
D	Ionic	Basic
E	Ionic	Neutral

Select, from A to E, the most appropriate classification for each of the substances described below.
6. A hydride that dissolves in water to produce a solution with a low pH value. (1)
7. A chloride that is a liquid at 298 K (25°C) and is resistant to hydrolysis. (1)
8. A compound formed between a Group I and a Group VII element. (1)
9. An oxide with a high melting point that is a poor conductor of electricity in the liquid state. (1)
10. The main constituent of natural gas. (1)

In Questions 11–15 each of the questions or incomplete statements is followed by five suggested answers. Suggest the best answer in each case.

11. Which one of the following hydrides has the highest melting point?
A HCl,
B H_2S,
C NaH,
D PH_3,
E SiH_4, (1)

12. Which of the following oxides is best classified as a basic oxide?
A aluminium oxide (Al_2O_3),
B beryllium oxide (BeO),
C sulphur trioxide (SO_3),
D carbon dioxide (CO_2),
E magnesium oxide (MgO). (1)

13. Which of the following trends is **not** observed across the period from sodium to chlorine?
A The elements become less metallic.
B The elements form anions more readily.
C The hydrides become more acidic.
D The oxides become more basic.
E The chlorides become more covalent. (1)

14.

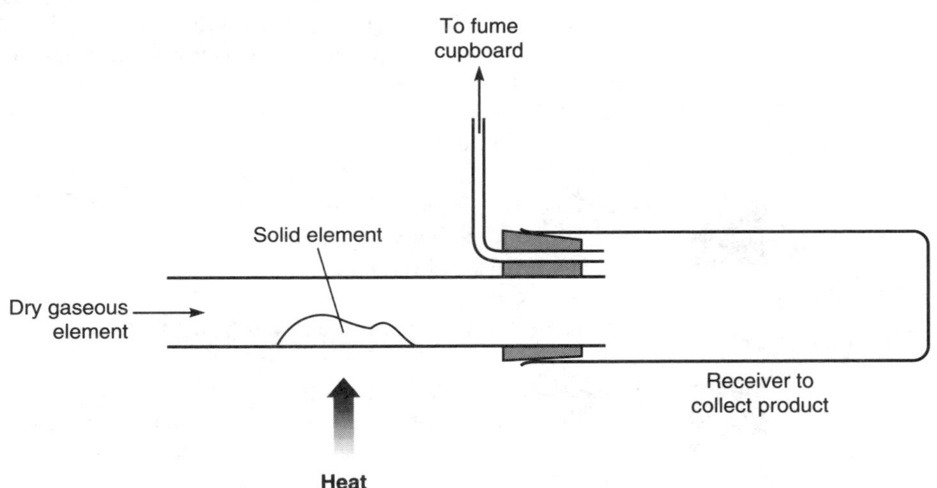

The above diagram shows the apparatus that a student proposed as being suitable for combining various solid elements with various gaseous elements and collecting the products.

Which of the following pairs of elements would be the **most** suitable for use in this apparatus?
A potassium and oxygen,
B sulphur and oxygen,
C silicon and chlorine,
D magnesium and chlorine,
E aluminium and chlorine. (1)

15. The chloride of an element X is a fuming liquid of boiling point 76°C at atmospheric pressure. Exactly 0.01 mol of this chloride was mixed with water and the resulting solution required 100 cm^3 of 0.3 M aqueous silver nitrate for complete precipitation of the chloride. To which group of the Periodic Table does the element X belong?
A Group IV,
B Group V,
C Group VI,
D Group VII,
E Group VIII. (1)

16. **a** Consider the following oxides:
Al_2O_3, CaO, CO, MgO, Na_2O, P_4O_{10}, SO_2, SiO_2.
State which of these oxides are:
i) **basic** and give **two** further examples,
ii) **acidic** and give **two** further examples,
iii) **neutral** and give **one** further example,
iv) **amphoteric** and give **one** further example. (7)
b Describe tests which you would carry out to show how amphoteric character is exhibited chemically, **stating clearly the experimental observations expected.** Write equations for the reactions which occur. (5)
c Consider the following chlorides:
CCl_4, HCl, $MgCl_2$, $NaCl$, PCl_5, $PbCl_2$, $PbCl_4$, $SiCl_4$.
i) State, with **brief** explanation, which of the above chlorides contain dominantly **a** ionic bonding, and **b** covalent bonding. For compounds which you describe as ionic, state whether this is for the anhydrous compound or for aqueous solution or both.
ii) Explain why you may be unable to assign clearly certain of these chlorides to either category. (6)

17. **a** Give the name and formula of
i) an ionic hydride,
ii) a covalent hydride,
iii) a complex hydride.
b How can your example in **a** part iii) be used in preparative organic chemistry? (4)

18. The second short period contains the elements Na, Mg, Al, Si, P, S, Cl, Ar.
a Which element most readily forms a peroxide? Give the formula of the peroxide. (1)
b Which element has an amphoteric hydroxide? Give two equations to illustrate your answer. (3)
c i) Which element forms the most stable hydride containing the hydride ion?
ii) Give the reason for your answer in **c** part i).
iii) Give the reaction of the hydride with water. (4)
d Which element forms a weakly acidic hydride, and two oxides giving acids with water? (1)
e i) Which element has a slightly basic hydride and two acidic oxides?
ii) Give the formula of the hydride.
iii) Is the hydride more, or less, basic than ammonia? (2)
f i) Which element has the largest atomic radius?
ii) Which element has the smallest ionic radius? (2)

(Total: 50 marks)

ANSWERS

Answers for unit – s-Block Elements

(Answers to questions from examination papers are provided by ILPAC and not by the examination boards.)

EXERCISE 1

a Li $1s^22s^1$ Be $1s^22s^2$
Na $1s^22s^22p^63s^1$ Mg $1s^22s^22p^63s^2$
K $1s^22s^22p^63s^23p^64s^1$ Ca $1s^22s^22p^63s^23p^64s^2$
Rb $1s^22s^22p^63s^23p^63d^{10}4s^24p^65s^1$ Sr $1s^22s^22p^63s^23p^63d^{10}4s^24p^65s^2$

b They have one and two electrons respectively in their outer shells.

c In each case, the penultimate shell (the shell next to the outer shell) contains two electrons. There are eight electrons in the penultimate shells of the other elements.

d i) 1^+. A Group I element tends to lose its single outer electron in reactions as it is well shielded from the nucleus by the inner electrons.
ii) 2^+. A Group II element tends to lose its two outer electrons in reactions.

EXERCISE 2

a i) As each group is descended, the next atom in each group has another shell of electrons around the nucleus.
ii) Each Group II atom has one more electron in the outer shell and one more proton in the nucleus than has the Group I atom in the same period. Since the screening of the outer s-electrons from the nucleus is the same for both atoms, the nucleus of the Group II atom exerts a stronger pull on the outer electrons because it has one more proton. This greater 'effective nuclear pull' of Group II atoms reduces their atomic radii.
A similar argument applies to the smaller ionic radii of Group II ions compared to Group I ions.

b Mg

c Mg^{2+}

EXERCISE 3

Table 1

Element	Ionisation energy/kJ mol^{-1} First	Second	Third
Li	520	7300	11800
Na	500	4600	6900
K	420	3100	4400
Rb	400	2700	3800
Cs	380	2400	3300
Be	900	1800	14800
Mg	740	1500	7700
Ca	590	1100	4900
Sr	550	1100	4200
Ba	500	1000	3390

You may find that your data book gives slightly different values but the same general patterns should be apparent.

a The outer s-electron is relatively easy to remove because it is well shielded from the nucleus by the inner electrons. Removal of a second electron involves the removal of an electron from an inner shell, which is closer and not so well shielded; it is therefore more strongly held by the nucleus.

b The two outer s-electrons are relatively easy to remove because they are well shielded from the nucleus by the inner electrons. Removal of a third electron is relatively difficult because the inner electrons are not so well shielded from the nucleus.

c Ionisation energy decreases as each group is descended. This is because the outer electrons are further out and progressively better shielded from the nucleus as each group is descended.
d Reactivity increases down each group because the outer electrons are less strongly held.
e Reactivity decreases because one electron is more easily lost than two.

EXERCISE 4

a As the outer-shell electrons become less strongly held as each group is descended, so also there is less attraction for additional bonding electrons.
b The electronegativity increases because the outer-shell electrons are more strongly held. They are only partially shielded from the extra nuclear charge.
c Cs (lowest electronegativity).
d Be (highest electronegativity, lowest difference).

EXERCISE 5

a i) Be $1s^2 2s^2$
ii) Ba $1s^2 2s^2 2p^6 3s^2 3p^6 3d^{10} 4s^2 4p^6 4d^{10} 5s^2 5p^6 6s^2$
b i) +II
ii) For both of these atoms, there is a big jump between the 2nd and 3rd ionisation energies. Therefore, an oxidation state higher than +II is very unlikely, i.e. it is relatively easy to lose the first two electrons but very difficult to lose a third, for both elements.
iii) Group II (alkaline-earth elements).
c i) Be. The outer electrons in Ba are very well shielded from the nucleus by the inner electrons. Be has far fewer inner electrons; therefore the shielding is not so good.
ii) Smaller. The formation of an ion involves the loss of the complete outer electron shell.

EXERCISE 6

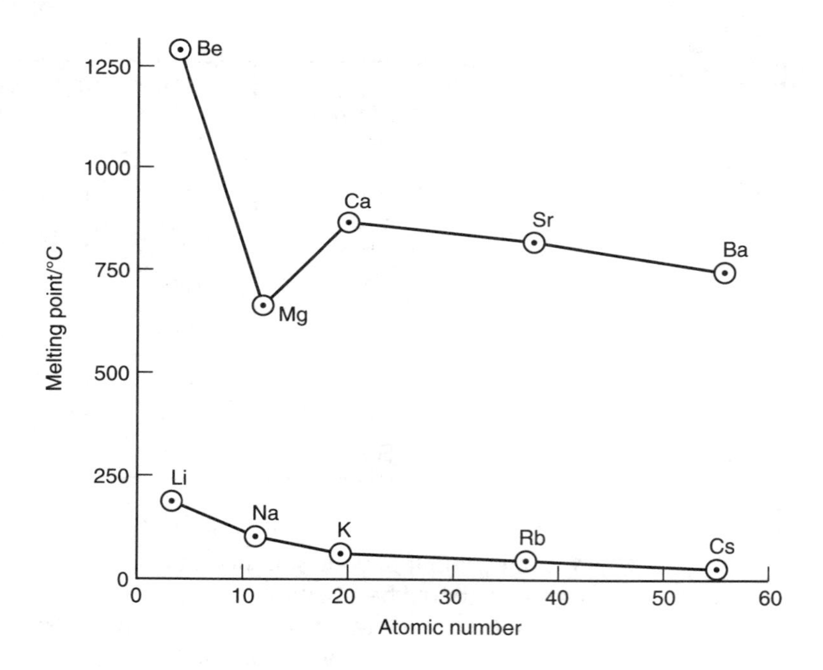

a Melting points generally decrease down each group.
b A metal is regarded as a fairly closely-packed assembly of positive ions 'cemented' together by a mobile electron 'cloud'. As each group is descended, the number of electrons in the cloud remains the same but the ionic size increases. Therefore, the electron cloud becomes more diffuse (or spread out) resulting in weaker attractive forces between the cloud and the ions.

c The melting points in Group II are higher than for the corresponding Group I elements because the ions of Group II are doubly charged and smaller than their Group I neighbours. Thus, the alkaline-earth elements contribute two electrons per atom to the mobile electron 'cloud' whereas the alkali metals only contribute one electron per atom. The greater number of electrons and the smaller ionic size of the Group II elements help to increase the density of the electron cloud and thus increase the attractive forces between the cloud and the ions.

d It has a fairly low melting point for a metal and is a liquid over a range of about 800°C. Water is usually a liquid between 0 and 100°C. In comparison to sodium, this is a much narrower range so that the boiling point is too low to be useful for nuclear reactors. Furthermore, sodium is a far better conductor of heat than water, and despite its lower heat capacity, a flow of sodium can remove heat from a reactor more efficiently. (A surprising additional advantage is that liquid sodium presents fewer corrosion problems!)

EXERCISE 7

Element	Structure	Element	Structure
Li	BCC	Be	HCP
Na	BCC	Mg	HCP
K	BCC	Ca	FCC
Rb	BCC	Sr	FCC
Cs	BCC	Ba	BCC

Key
BCC = body-centred cubic
FCC = face-centred cubic
HCP = hexagonal close-packed

In Group I all the metals have the same crystal structure whereas those of Group II are of more than one type. Since crystal structure affects physical properties, the irregularities in melting point and boiling point of the Group II elements are not altogether surprising.

EXERCISE 8

a The metallic bonds are stronger for Group II elements.

b Metallic bonding becomes weaker as each group is descended.

EXERCISE 9

a $2M (s) + 2H_2O (l) \rightarrow 2MOH (aq) + H_2 (g)$

b Sufficient heat is generated in the reaction between potassium and water to ignite the hydrogen. The sodium–water reaction is not sufficiently exothermic to cause the hydrogen to ignite.

EXERCISE 10

a Calcium reacts vigorously with cold water, producing hydrogen and a whitish suspension of calcium hydroxide, some of which dissolves. Unlike the alkali metals, calcium neither floats nor melts during the reaction.

$$Ca (s) + 2H_2O (l) \rightarrow Ca(OH)_2 (aq) + H_2 (g)$$

b i) Magnesium reacts very slowly with cold water.

ii) Hydrogen is produced. It is tested by removing the tube from the water when one-third to one-half full and holding it, mouth downwards, to a flame. Air enters the tube and the air/hydrogen mixture explodes with a characteristic 'shriek'. (This explosion is harmless on a test-tube scale but **very dangerous on a larger scale**.)

c If the group trend follows the usual pattern, beryllium would be expected to react very weakly with water, if at all, and barium would react very vigorously to produce hydrogen and barium hydroxide.

EXERCISE 11

a v).
b It is important to get the magnesium hot before passing steam over it, and to keep it hot while the steam is being generated.
c $Mg (s) + H_2O (g) \rightarrow MgO (s) + H_2 (g)$.

EXERCISE 12

a Very slowly if at all. (In fact, there is no reaction at room temperature.)
b 0.1 M hydrochloric acid would react more rapidly because it contains a greater concentration of hydrogen ions.
c Since they react rapidly with water, they are likely to react even more rapidly with dilute acids, and explosions are possible.

EXERCISE 13

a i) $Na_2O (s) + \frac{1}{2}O_2 (g) \rightarrow Na_2O_2 (s)$
ii) Sodium monoxide can be made by heating sodium in a limited supply of oxygen or air.
b i) There are no Group II superoxides. (The cations have too great polarising power.)
ii) Beryllium oxide, BeO; magnesium oxide, MgO; calcium oxide, CaO; strontium oxide, SrO; barium oxide, BaO; strontium peroxide, SrO_2 (very low yield); and barium peroxide, BaO_2.
iii) $2BaO_2 (s) \rightarrow 2BaO (s) + O_2 (g)$. Most other peroxides are also decomposed to oxygen and a lower oxide by heat.

EXERCISE 14

a Beryllium oxide, BeO.
b i) $BeO (s) + 2NaOH (aq) + H_2O (l) \rightarrow Na_2Be(OH)_4 (aq)$
Note that sodium beryllate, $Na_2Be(OH)_4$, contains the beryllate ion $[Be(OH)_4]^{2-}$, so that the equation may be written in ionic form:

$$BeO (s) + 2OH^- (aq) + H_2O (l) \rightarrow Be(OH)_4^{2-} (aq)$$

You may also find the formula written as Na_2BeO_2, which is an anhydrous form, and the equation could then be:

$$BeO (s) + 2NaOH (aq) \rightarrow Na_2BeO_2 (aq) + H_2O (l)$$

or $BeO (s) + 2OH^- (aq) \rightarrow BeO_2^{2-} (aq) + H_2O (l)$

ii) $BeO (s) + 2HNO_3 (aq) \rightarrow Be(NO_3)_2 (aq) + H_2O (l)$

EXPERIMENT 1

Specimen results

Results Table 1

Experiment	Observation	Conclusion
Sodium peroxide added to water plus universal indicator	Colour of gas: None Effect on glowing splint: Relights. pH of water: 12 or higher	The gas is oxygen
Sodium peroxide plus water, added to acidified dichromate solution plus 2-methylbutan-1-ol	Colour of organic (top) layer is: Blue Colour of aqueous (bottom) layer is: Very pale green	The colour of the organic layer shows that a peroxide has been formed

Questions

1. **a** $Na_2O_2 (s) + 2H_2O (l) \rightarrow 2NaOH (aq) + H_2O_2 (aq)$
b $2H_2O_2 (aq) \rightarrow 2H_2O (l) + O_2 (g)$
c $2Na_2O_2 (s) + 2H_2O (l) \rightarrow 4NaOH (aq) + O_2 (g)$

2. **a** BaO_2 (s) + $2H_2O$ (l) → $Ba(OH)_2$ (aq) + H_2O_2 (aq)
   b i) BaO_2 (s) + H_2SO_4 (aq) → $BaSO_4$ (s) + H_2O_2 (l)
   ii) It produces barium sulphate, which is insoluble and can be separated easily from the hydrogen peroxide by filtration.
3. **a** Na_2O (s) + CO_2 (g) → Na_2CO_3 (s)
   b $2Na_2O_2$ (s) + $2CO_2$ (g) → $2Na_2CO_3$ (s) + O_2 (g)
   c $4KO_2$ (s) + $2CO_2$ (g) → $2K_2CO_3$ (s) + $3O_2$ (g)

EXERCISE 15

a Li_3N, (Be_3N_2), Mg_3N_2, Ca_3N_2, Sr_3N_2, Ba_3N_2.
Be_3N_2 is formed only with difficulty at temperatures above 500°C.
b i) $6Li$ (s) + N_2 (g) → $2Li_3N$ (s)
ii) $3Mg$ (s) + N_2 (g) → Mg_3N_2 (s)
c No. Li is the only member of Group I which will form the nitride directly. In Group II, all the elements except Be form nitrides readily.
d Li is more like Mg than the other elements in Group I as far as nitride formation is concerned, i.e. both elements form the nitride directly, whereas the other members of Group I do not.

EXERCISE 16

Reducing power increases since it becomes easier to lose the outer electrons as the group is descended. (Reducing agents donate electrons.)

EXERCISE 17

a Metallic character increases down each group.
b i) Cs, ii) Be.
c BeO is amphoteric, i.e. it has some acid character, like non-metal oxides, whereas all the other s-block oxides are basic.

EXERCISE 18

a All the s-block elements except beryllium react directly with hydrogen. (Magnesium reacts under high pressure only.)
b i) $2Na$ (s) + H_2 (g) → $2NaH$ (s)
ii) Ca (s) + H_2 (g) → CaH_2 (s)
c i) All the s-block hydrides except BeH_2 and MgH_2 are ionic.
ii) BeH_2 and MgH_2 are covalent.
d Electrolyse molten lithium hydride (or solutions of other hydrides in molten alkali halides). Hydride ions are converted to hydrogen gas at the **anode**.

$$2H^- \rightarrow H_2 + 2e^-$$

EXPERIMENT 2

Specimen results

Results Table 2
Effect of heat on the s-block carbonates

Carbonate	Time to detect CO_2	Observations
Li_2CO_3	35 s	Lime-water very cloudy
Na_2CO_3	50 s	Slight cloudiness
K_2CO_3	70 s	Slight cloudiness
Rb_2CO_3	not available	–
Cs_2CO_3	65 s	Slight cloudiness
$MgCO_3$	20 s	Lime-water very cloudy
$CaCO_3$	40 s	Lime-water very cloudy
$SrCO_3$	not available	–
$BaCO_3$	no CO_2 detected	No change observed

Results Table 3
Effect of heat on the s-block nitrates

Nitrate	Time to detect O_2 or NO_2	Observations	Effect of adding dilute HCl to cold residue
$LiNO_3$	NO_2 – 35 s	Liquid formed immediately – steamy gas evolved – resolidified after 20 s	No reaction
$NaNO_3$	O_2 – 40 s	Liquid formed after 20 s – no steamy gas – bubbles formed in liquid	Brown fumes evolved
KNO_3	O_2 – 50 s	As for $NaNO_3$	Brown fumes evolved
$RbNO_3$	not available	–	
$CsNO_3$	O_2 – 60 s	As for $NaNO_3$	Brown fumes evolved
$Mg(NO_3)_2$	NO_2 – 25 s	Liquid formed immediately – steamy gas evolved – resolidified after about 20 s	No reaction
$Ca(NO_3)_2$	NO_2 – 30 s	As for Mg	No reaction
$Sr(NO_3)_2$	NO_2 – 32 s	White powder crackled – no melting	No reaction
$Ba(NO_3)_2$	NO_2 – 42 s	White powder melted after 30 s	No reaction

Questions

1. Some of these nitrates are hydrated and therefore dissolve in their own water of crystallisation. The water eventually boils off leaving a white solid.
2. Lithium nitrate and lithium carbonate.
3. Thermal stability of both the nitrates and carbonates increases as each group is descended.
4. Group I nitrates and carbonates are more stable.
5. **a** $4LiNO_3 (s) \rightarrow 2Li_2O (s) + 4NO_2 (g) + O_2 (g)$
   $Li_2CO_3 (s) \rightarrow Li_2O (s) + CO_2 (g)$
   b $2KNO_3 (s) \rightarrow 2KNO_2 (l) + O_2 (g)$. The liquid product is potassium nit**rite**.
   K_2CO_3 is usually reckoned to be thermally stable at Bunsen burner temperatures, although traces of CO_2 may be detected.
   c $2Mg(NO_3)_2 (s) \rightarrow 2MgO (s) + 4NO_2 (g) + O_2 (s)$
   $MgCO_3 (s) \rightarrow MgO (s) + CO_2 (g)$
6. All Group I nitrates (except $LiNO_3$) decompose to the nitrite, which produces NO_2 (amongst other nitrogen compounds) if warmed with dilute acids. This is a useful test for the presence of nitrite ions.

EXERCISE 19

a As each group is descended, the polarising power of the cation decreases. Thus, cations of the upper elements distort the anion electron clouds far more than do those of the lower elements. Anions with highly distorted electron clouds are more readily decomposed than those with little distortion. Therefore, thermal stability increases as each group is descended.

b Mg^{2+} has a much greater polarising power than Na^+ due to its smaller size and greater charge.

EXERCISE 20

a Be^{2+} is a very small, doubly charged ion and thus has a high polarising power. Therefore, Be^{2+} will considerably distort the CO_3^{2-} ion, causing the compound to decompose with ease.

b The polarising power of the singly-charged Li^+ is less than that of Be^{2+} and, therefore, Li^+ will distort CO_3^{2-} to a smaller extent.

c The Bunsen burner flame is not hot enough to reach the decomposition temperature of $BaCO_3$.

EXERCISE 21

a The Li^+ ion is too highly polarising and too small to allow the existence of a stable crystal lattice in which large HCO_3^- ions pack around the small Li^+ ion.

b $2NaHCO_3\ (s) \rightarrow Na_2CO_3\ (s) + CO_2\ (g) + H_2O\ (g)$

c i) The heat causes the $NaHCO_3$ to decompose and produce CO_2. This CO_2 causes the cakes to rise.

ii) Rainwater contains dissolved CO_2. As the water trickles down the roof of a limestone ($CaCO_3$) cave, a chemical reaction occurs between the $CaCO_3$ and $CO_2\ (aq)$ producing a dilute solution of $Ca(HCO_3)_2$. As drops of the solution hang from the roof of the cave, water evaporates causing the formation of a deposit of $CaCO_3$ on the roof.

$$Ca(HCO_3)_2\ (aq) \rightleftharpoons CO_2\ (g) + H_2O\ (g) + CaCO_3\ (s)$$

As this deposit builds up and grows down from the roof, stalactites are produced. The drops of solution/solid which fall to the bottom cause the upward growth of stalagmites.

d Neither of these substances exist as solids.

e If each solid is heated, only $NaHCO_3$ will produce an appreciable amount of CO_2.

f Thermal stability increases down the group since the polarising power of the cations decreases.

g The cations are too small and highly polarising to allow the existence of a stable crystal lattice.

EXERCISE 22

a $MgSO_4\ (s) \rightarrow MgO\ (s) + SO_3\ (g)$

b Thermal stability should increase since the polarising power of the cations decreases and ionic size increases.

EXERCISE 23

a Group I hydroxides are more thermally stable because the singly-charged cations have less polarising power.

b Thermal stability increases down each group because polarising power decreases with increasing size of the cation.

c Yes. The process

$$M(OH)_2\ (s) \rightarrow MO\ (s) + H_2O\ (g)$$

becomes more and more endothermic as Group II is descended. This suggests that the process becomes less energetically favourable as the group is descended.

d It is the only hydroxide which decomposes at Bunsen burner temperatures because the small Li^+ ion has considerable polarising power.

$$2LiOH\ (s) \rightarrow Li_2O\ (s) + H_2O\ (g)$$

EXPERIMENT 3

Specimen results

Results Table 4

Cation solution	**Number of drops of anion solution added to give a precipitate**			
	OH^-	**SO_4^{2-}**	**SO_3^{2-}**	**CO_3^{2-}**
Mg^{2+}	5	40+	40+	25
Ca^{2+}	20	40+	10	8
Sr^{2+}	30 (slight)	8	2	4
Ba^{2+}	40+	1	1	2

Your results will probably differ from ours in the numbers of drops used, but the trends should be fairly clear.

Questions

a The solubility of the hydroxides increases down Group II.
b The solubility of the sulphates decreases down Group II.
c The solubility of the sulphites decreases down Group II.
d The solubility of the carbonates decreases down Group II.

EXERCISE 24

a The solubility of the hydroxides increases down Group II. For all the other salts listed, the solubility generally decreases down Group II. (The only exception to these simple rules is that calcium nitrate is more soluble than magnesium nitrate.)
b Yes, the trends revealed by the table are the same as those revealed by the experiment.
c Doubly charged anions give compounds which are less soluble than those containing singly charged anions.

EXERCISE 25

a $BaSO_4$ is extremely insoluble and thus only faint traces can be absorbed into the blood system.
b i) A white precipitate will appear. Barium chloride is used because it is fairly soluble in water, but barium sulphate is insoluble. The sulphate is the only common barium compound which will form a white precipitate in acid solution.
ii) Ba^{2+} (aq) + SO_4^{2-} (aq) → $BaSO_4$ (s)
iii) The addition of HCl prevents the precipitation of $BaCO_3$ and $BaSO_3$ which could be mistaken for $BaSO_4$. If any CO_3^{2-} or SO_3^{2-} ions are present, they are removed by reaction with H^+ ions.

$$CO_3^{2-} (aq) + 2H^+ (aq) \rightarrow H_2O (l) + CO_2 (g)$$

$$SO_3^{2-} (aq) + 2H^+ (aq) \rightarrow H_2O (l) + SO_2 (g)$$

c i) The test for CO_2 is more sensitive using $Ba(OH)_2$. A smaller amount of CO_2 produces a precipitate because $BaCO_3$ is less soluble than $CaCO_3$.
Both sodium hydroxide and barium hydroxide solutions absorb CO_2 producing CO_3^{2-} ions. In sodium hydroxide, these remain in solution, but in barium hydroxide a precipitate forms because $BaCO_3$ is insoluble. The precipitate shows that contamination has occurred.
ii) Barium compounds are poisonous, and more expensive.
iii) $Ba(OH)_2$ (aq) + CO_2 (g) → $BaCO_3$ (s) + H_2O (l)

EXERCISE 26

a

Compound	Solubility/mol per 100 g of water (298 K)
LiOH	5.16×10^{-1}
NaOH	1.05
KOH	1.71
RbOH	1.69 (303 K)
Li_2CO_3	1.75×10^{-2}
Na_2CO_3	6.60×10^{-2}
K_2CO_3	8.11×10^{-1}
Rb_2CO_3	1.95

b In both cases, the solubility generally increases down the group.
c The trend for Group I carbonates (increase) is opposite to that for Group II (decrease). The trends are the same for the hydroxides.
d Both the hydroxides and the carbonates of Group I are more soluble than those of Group II.
e Yes, the Group I hydroxides are more soluble than the Group I carbonates.

EXERCISE 27

a

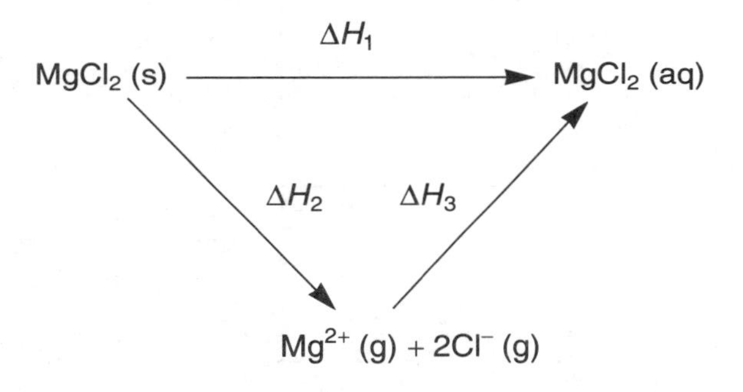

$\Delta H_1 = \Delta H_2 + \Delta H_3$

i.e. $\Delta H_{sol} = -\Delta H_{lat} + \Delta H_{hyd}$

$= +2526 \text{ kJ mol}^{-1} + -1920 \text{ kJ mol}^{-1} + -2(364) \text{ kJ mol}^{-1}$

$= \mathbf{-122 \text{ kJ mol}^{-1}}$

b

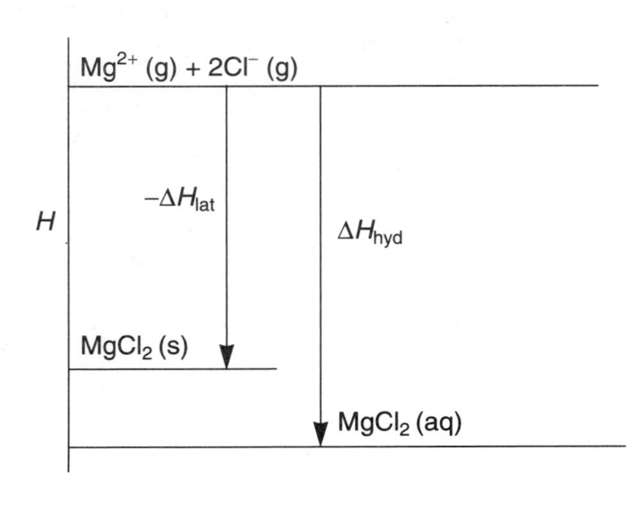

c Since ΔH_{sol} is negative and fairly large, anhydrous magnesium chloride would be expected to be soluble in water.

EXERCISE 28

a The larger the ion, the weaker the electric field around it (you could say that the charge is spread out over a much larger surface area) and water molecules are attracted less strongly. This means that fewer water molecules are bonded to the ion and the enthalpy of hydration, resulting from this bonding, is smaller.

b The larger the ion, the less close it can approach another ion of opposite charge and the smaller the energy released as it approaches, i.e. the less negative the lattice enthalpy.

c If r_{anion} is small, changing r_{cation} has a proportionally greater effect on $(r_{anion} + r_{cation})^2$ than if r_{anion} is large. For instance, suppose $r_{anion} = 6$ units and r_{cation} changes from 3 units to 4 units. Then the expression $1/(r_{anion} + r_{cation})^2$ changes from 1/81 to 1/100, i.e. by 19%. However, if $r_{anion} = 2$ units, the same change in r_{cation} changes the expression from 1/25 to 1/36, i.e. by 31%.

EXERCISE 29

a i) $$M^{2+}(g) + A^{2-}(g) \rightarrow M^{2+}A^{2-}(s)$$

ii) $$M^{2+}(g) + A^{2-}(g) + aq \rightarrow M^{2+}(aq) + A^{2-}(aq)$$

b

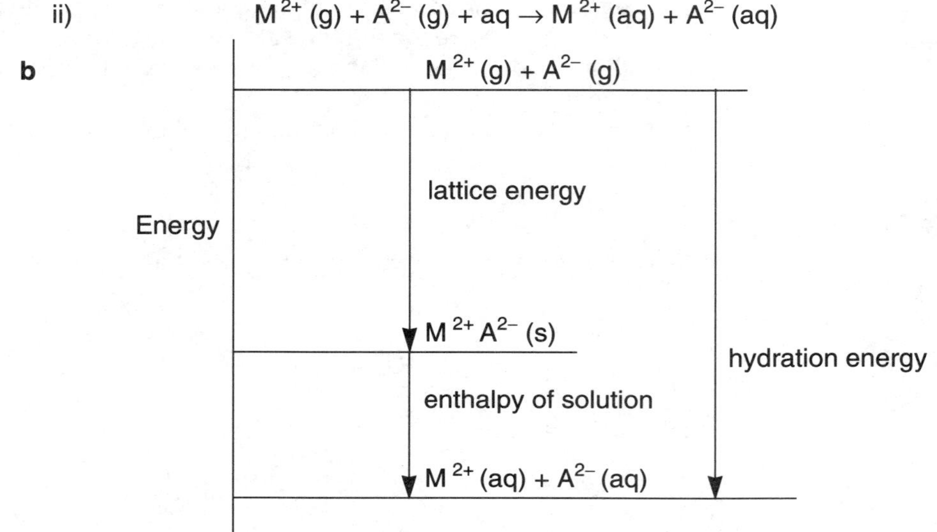

c The magnesium ion, Mg^{2+}, is very much smaller than the barium ion, Ba^{2+}. Consequently, it has a stronger electric field around it and more water molecules are attracted strongly enough to remain bound, in layers, around it. This process of solvation releases sufficient energy to break up the crystal lattice. For Ba^{2+}, the hydration energy is insufficient to break up the crystal lattice and so the salt remains undissolved.

EXERCISE 30

Table 5

Property	Li	Rest of Group I	Mg
Oxide formation	Li_2O (monoxide) formed by direct combination	Peroxides and superoxides formed	MgO (monoxide) formed by direct combination
Nitride formation	Li_3N formed by direct combination	No direct combination	Mg_3N_2 formed by direct combination
Effect of heat on nitrates	Li_2O formed with NO_2 (brown fumes) and O_2	Stable nitrites (NO_2^-) and oxygen produced	MgO formed with NO_2 (brown fumes) and O_2
Effect of heat on carbonates	Li_2O formed with CO_2	Hardly any decomposition at Bunsen temperatures	MgO formed with CO_2
Effect of heat on hydroxides	Li_2O formed with H_2O	Thermally stable	MgO formed with H_2O
Physical state of hydrogen-carbonates	$LiHCO_3$ does not exist as a solid	Stable white solids	$Mg(HCO_3)_2$ does not exist as a solid
Solubility of carbonates	Sparingly soluble	Fairly soluble	Sparingly soluble
Solubility of hydroxides	Fairly soluble	Soluble	Sparingly soluble

EXERCISE 31

a The polarising power of Li^+ is less than that of Be^{2+}, because it has a smaller charge. (Li^+ and Be^{2+} are almost the same size.)

b The polarising power of Mg^{2+} is less than that of Be^{2+}, because it is larger. (Mg^{2+} and Be^{2+} have the same charge.)

c The answers to **a** and **b** suggest that Li^+ and Mg^{2+} might have roughly equal polarising powers.

d Each cation distorts a particular anion to approximately the same extent. Therefore, the anions decompose in a similar way when heated.

EXERCISE 32

a The decomposition of sodium chloride into its elements will require a considerable input of energy.

b In the electrolysis of aqueous sodium hydroxide, hydrogen ions, H^+, are released at the cathode in preference to sodium ions, Na^+, despite the very small concentration of H^+.

c Sodium chloride is obtained from underground deposits formed when prehistoric seas dried up.

EXERCISE 33

a A molten mixture of sodium chloride and calcium chloride.

b The addition of calcium chloride lowers the melting point so that electrolysis can proceed at a lower temperature. This saves energy and reduces vaporisation of sodium.

c Calcium is not discharged to any appreciable extent because, under the conditions of the cell, sodium ions accept electrons more readily than calcium. (Calcium comes above sodium in the electrochemical series.)
d B is the anode (graphite) and C the cathode (steel).
e Chlorine is produced at the anode, and emerges at D.

$$2Cl^- \rightarrow Cl_2 + 2e^-$$

Sodium is produced at the cathode and, because of its low density, it rises into a circular trap to emerge at F.

$$Na^+ + e^- \rightarrow Na$$

f Most metals react readily with chlorine. The net reaction at a metal anode is usually the dissolution of the anode rather than the discharge of an anion.
g G is a steel mesh which ensures that molten sodium and chlorine do not come into contact.
h The refractory (heat-resistant) lining, H, protects the steel cell wall and reduces heat losses.

EXERCISE 34

a $MgCO_3 \cdot CaCO_3$ (s) $\rightarrow$ CaO (s) + MgO (s) + $2CO_2$ (g)
b CaO is first converted to the hydroxide on contact with sea-water.

$$CaO\ (s) + H_2O\ (l) \rightarrow Ca(OH)_2\ (s)$$

$Ca(OH)_2$ is more soluble than $Mg(OH)_2$ (see page 29). Therefore, when some $Ca(OH)_2$ dissolves, sufficient hydroxide ions are produced to cause the precipitation of $Mg(OH)_2$.

$$Mg^{2+}\ (aq) + 2OH^-\ (aq) \rightarrow Mg(OH)_2\ (s)$$

c The crystals are heated in a stream of hydrogen chloride gas which carries away the water without allowing hydrolysis to occur. If the crystals are heated alone, partial hydrolysis produces some oxide.

$$MgCl_2 \cdot 6H_2O\ (s) \rightarrow MgO\ (s) + 2HCl\ (g) + 5H_2O\ (g)$$

Some texts give:

$$MgCl_2 \cdot 6H_2O\ (s) \rightarrow Mg(OH)Cl + HCl\ (g) + 5H_2O\ (g)$$

EXERCISE 35

a The addition of sodium chloride lowers the melting point of the electrolyte. This saves energy and reduces the vaporisation of magnesium. However, only a small amount can be added, otherwise sodium would be discharged rather than magnesium.
b The anode is the central graphite rod, B. The iron tank acts as the cathode, C.
c Graphite does not react with chlorine as most metals do. Graphite cannot dissolve to produce cations and electrons, as most metal anodes do. So the discharge of anions (Cl^-) is the only possible anode reaction.
d D is a porous tube which prevents chlorine from coming into contact with molten magnesium.
e Domestic gas (methane) is passed through the cell from E to F in order to keep out oxygen and nitrogen, both of which would react with the magnesium as it floats to the top of the melt.
f Sodium chloride is readily available as a raw material, whereas magnesium chloride is not. The production of magnesium chloride requires a considerable input of energy and also uses other manufactured chemicals. The cost of electrolysis is greater because the discharge of magnesium requires two electrons per atom. (In practice, magnesium is cheaper because it is produced on a much larger scale.)

g Both workers and local residents must be protected from the possible leakage of toxic chlorine gas by good design and regular monitoring of all vessels and pipework in contact with chlorine, which is, of course, highly corrosive as well as toxic. Alarm systems must be installed to give warnings of escaping chlorine. In addition, workers must be protected from heat and from possible failure of electrical insulation.

h The ideal site would be close to sources of dolomite and sea-water in order to decrease the costs of transporting raw materials. It would also be close to the users of the finished products, or at least to a good transport system, but the transport of raw materials is more costly because of their vastly greater bulk. The availability of cheap electrical power (e.g. from a local hydroelectric source) would also be important. To minimise the risk to local residents the plant should be as far away as possible from centres of population, consistent with reasonable access to a labour force, and in the direction of the prevailing wind so that any leakage of chlorine is dispersed before it does too much harm.

EXERCISE 36

a The electrolyte is concentrated brine obtained from underground rock salt deposits.

b The electrolyte flows continuously through the cell from B to C to replenish Na^+ and Cl^- ions as they are discharged. The concentration of Cl^- ions must be kept high in order to prevent the discharge of OH^- ions releasing oxygen instead of chlorine.

c The use of a mercury cathode, D, suppresses the discharge of H^+ ions, the process which would occur at cathodes made of most other materials. The discharge of H^+ ions in the upper cell is not desirable because it would make the solution alkaline, and chlorine reacts with alkalis. The mercury is recirculated by a pump, E.

d Titanium must be resistant to attack by chlorine and must not lose electrons too readily, to ensure that chlorine gas is discharged.

e Upper compartment: $2Cl^- \rightarrow Cl_2\ (g) + 2e^-$

$Na^+ + e^- \rightarrow Na\ (l)$ (dissolves in mercury)

Lower compartment: $2Na/Hg\ (l) + 2H_2O\ (l) \rightarrow 2NaOH\ (aq) + H_2\ (g) + 2Hg\ (l)$

f The interconversion of sodium metal and aqueous sodium ions is represented by the equation

$$Na^+\ (aq) + e^- \rightleftharpoons Na\ (s)$$

In the upper compartment, the flowing mercury is the cathode: its negative charge attracts sodium ions and shifts the equilibrium to the right. In the lower compartment, graphite cathodes float above the mercury amalgam, making the latter the anode and shifting the equilibrium to the left.

EXERCISE 37

a Potassium nitrate, KNO_3 (saltpetre).

b Sodium carbonate, Na_2CO_3.

c Magnesium sulphate, $MgSO_4{\cdot}7H_2O$.

d Sodium hydrogencarbonate, $NaHCO_3$ ('bicarb'); magnesium hydroxide, $Mg(OH)_2$ ('magnesia').

e Sodium hydroxide, NaOH.

f Sodium chloride, NaCl ('rock salt').

g Liquid sodium.

h Sodium hydrogencarbonate, $NaHCO_3$.

i Potassium ('potash') is one of the three major plant nutrients (with nitrogen and phosphorus). Potassium is usually added to fertilisers in the form of potassium chloride. Magnesium and calcium may also be classed as major plant nutrients although the amounts required are less and it is therefore less often necessary to add them to fertilisers.

j Calcium carbonate, $CaCO_3$ (limestone); calcium hydroxide, $Ca(OH)_2$ (lime).

k Calcium oxide, CaO (lime or quick-lime).

l Magnesium is a component of magnalium (an alloy with aluminium).

Answers for unit – The Halogens

EXERCISE 38

a F: $1s^22s^22p^5$
Cl: $1s^22s^22p^63s^23p^5$
Br: $1s^22s^22p^63s^23p^63d^{10}4s^24p^5$
I: $1s^22s^22p^63s^23p^63d^{10}4s^24p^64d^{10}5s^25p^5$

b The penultimate shell of F contains only two electrons; the other penultimate shells contain 8 or 18 electrons.

c F^-: $1s^22s^22p^6$ oxidation state –I
Cl^-: $1s^22s^22p^63s^23p^6$ oxidation state –I

EXERCISE 39

a As the group is descended, an extra shell of electrons is added to the atom of each successive element.

b In the formation of a covalent bond, there is an overlap of atomic orbitals which draws the nuclei closer together. Furthermore, the ion has an extra electron which is repelled by the other electrons and there is no compensatory extra charge on the nucleus.

EXERCISE 40

a F^-: 0.133 nm, Na^+: 0.102 nm, Mg^{2+}: 0.072 nm.

b Ionic radius decreases with increasing atomic number because the effective nuclear charge increases. This pulls the electrons closer to the nucleus.

EXERCISE 41

a $Cl(g) + e^- \rightarrow Cl^-(g)$; $\Delta H^\ominus = -349\ kJ\ mol^{-1}$
$Br(g) + e^- \rightarrow Br^-(g)$; $\Delta H^\ominus = -325\ kJ\ mol^{-1}$
$I(g) + e^- \rightarrow I^-(g)$; $\Delta H^\ominus = -295\ kJ\ mol^{-1}$

b Electron affinity becomes less negative (i.e. there is less affinity for electrons) with increasing atomic number. (Note that as we are dealing with negative values, electron affinity actually **increases** – this is why it is better to say 'becomes less negative'.) This is because the outer electrons become more shielded from the nucleus as the atomic size increases, so the tendency to attract another electron decreases as the group is descended.

c Electron affinity of F = $-350\ kJ\ mol^{-1}$. Ionisation by electron loss is the opposite process to electron gain, so the corresponding energy change is reversed in sign.

d The low value for F is probably due to the repulsion between the incoming electron and the electrons in the outer shell. This incoming electron must get closer to the outer-shell electrons in the case of F because of its very small size, compared to the other halogens.

EXERCISE 42

a F: 4.0, Cl: 3.0, Br: 2.8, I: 2.5.

b Electronegativity decreases as the group is descended. This is because the outer electrons become progressively better shielded from the nucleus as the atomic size increases. Thus, electrons in a covalent bond are attracted less and less to the halogen as its atomic number increases.

EXERCISE 43

a There is a decrease in bond dissociation energy except between F_2 and Cl_2.

b I_2 dissociates most readily and Cl_2 least readily.

c Bond energy decreases in the order Cl_2, Br_2, I_2, owing to the increasing length of the halogen–halogen bond. The increasing bond length is due to the increasing atomic size of the halogen with increasing atomic number.

d This is probably due to the repulsion of non-bonding pairs of electrons on each fluorine atom at each end of the F—F bond. The fluorine atoms are so small that the repulsions between these non-bonding electrons are much greater than in the case of Cl_2, because of their closer proximity. (See the diagram on the top of the next page.)

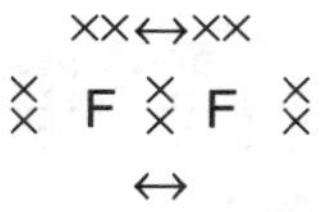

xx↔xx
x F x F x
↔
greater repulsion

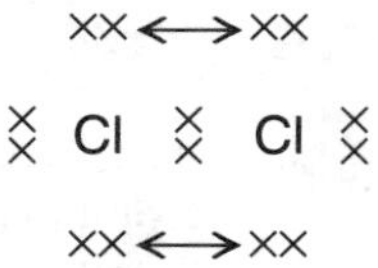

xx⟷xx
x Cl x Cl x
xx⟷xx
weaker repulsion

EXERCISE 44

a

	Melting point/K	Boiling point/K
F_2	53	85
Cl_2	172	238
Br_2	266	332
I_2	387	457

b Melting points and boiling points increase down the group.
c F_2: gas, Cl_2: gas, Br_2: liquid, I_2: solid.

EXERCISE 45

a Van der Waals forces increase as the number of electrons increases. The greater the number of electrons, the greater the possibility that temporary dipoles will be large, and therefore the stronger the attractive forces.
b Van der Waals forces increase as the group is descended.
c Van der Waals forces are much greater in I_2 than in Cl_2.

EXERCISE 46

Table 7

Name of element	Formula	Colour and physical state at room temperature and pressure
Fluorine	F_2	yellow gas
Chlorine	Cl_2	light green gas
Bromine	Br_2	dark orange liquid
Iodine	I_2	black solid

EXERCISE 47

No value is assigned for fluorine because it reacts violently with water.

EXERCISE 48

Iodine solution is made by dissolving iodine in a dilute solution of potassium (or sodium) iodide. It dissolves because of the formation of the triiodide ion, I_3^-, which is soluble.

$$I_2\,(aq) + I^-\,(aq) \rightleftharpoons I_3^-\,(aq)$$

Because this reaction is readily reversible, the solution is usually regarded as iodine solution and is simply written as I_2 (aq) in equations.

EXPERIMENT 4

Specimen results

Results Table 5

	Nature of each layer	Chlorine water	Bromine water	Iodine solution
Colour of aqueous solution		faint green	orange-brown	reddish brown
Colour of each layer after shaking with Volasil 244	Upper layer aqueous	no colour	red-brown	violet
	Lower layer organic	no colour	yellow	light brown
Colour of each layer after shaking with ethoxyethane	Upper layer organic	no colour	orange-brown	light brown
	Lower layer aqueous	no colour	yellow	yellow
Colour of each layer after shaking with cyclohexane	Upper layer organic	no colour	orange-brown	violet
	Lower layer aqueous	no colour	yellow	light brown

Questions

1. The halogens are more soluble in organic solvents than in water because if dilute aqueous solutions of the coloured halogens are mixed with organic solvents, most of the colour is transferred to the organic solvent.
2. Iodine has a significantly different colour in the organic layer than in the aqueous layer. Iodine in hexane is purple (or violet). Iodine in dichloromethane is also purple when dilute, but red when more concentrated.
3. To distinguish between a dilute solution of iodine and a more concentrated solution of bromine, add a few cm^3 of hexane to each solution and shake. The iodine appears purple in hexane while the bromine appears brown.

EXERCISE 49

a $H_2 + X_2 \rightarrow 2HX$

b Reactivity with hydrogen decreases as the group is descended.

c The energy of the light source splits the chlorine molecules into highly reactive chlorine atoms which then react with hydrogen molecules in a rapid chain reaction.

d i) H_2 and F_2 react spontaneously at room temperature. (Even in the dark at –200°C.)
ii) $H_2 + Br_2$ react only on heating and in the presence of a platinum catalyst.
iii) $H_2 + I_2$ combine only partially and slowly, even on heating.

EXERCISE 50

a i)

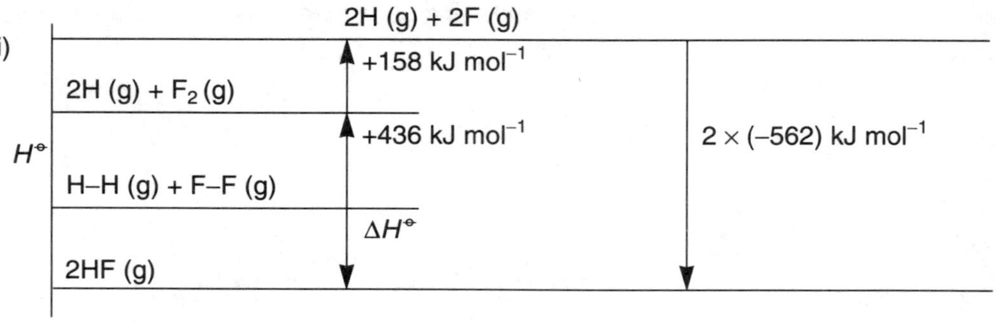

2H (g) + 2F (g)

+158 kJ mol^{-1}

2H (g) + F_2 (g)

+436 kJ mol^{-1}

$2 \times (-562)$ kJ mol^{-1}

$H^{\ominus}$

H–H (g) + F–F (g)

$\Delta H^{\ominus}$

2HF (g)

$\Delta H^{\ominus} = 2(-562) + 158 + 436 = $ **-530 kJ mol^{-1}**

ii)

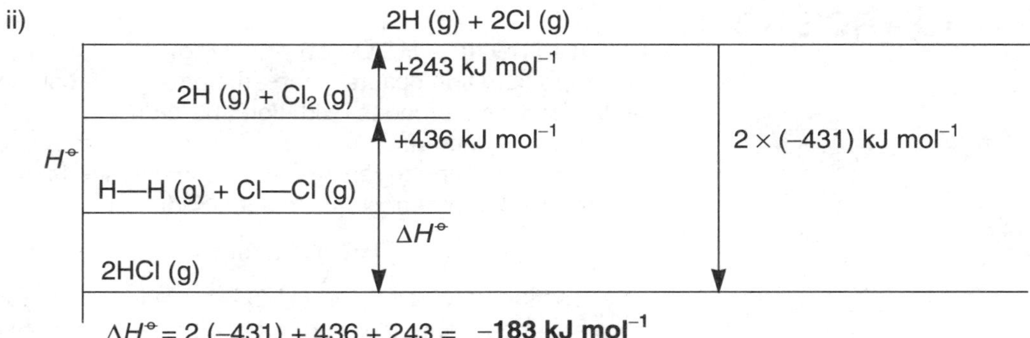

$\Delta H^\ominus = 2\,(-431) + 436 + 243 =$ **-183 kJ mol^{-1}**

b The H_2/F_2 reaction is more feasible.

c The small bond energy of F—F and the large bond energy of H—F.

EXERCISE 51

a i) $Xe\ (g) + 2F_2\ (g) \rightarrow XeF_4\ (s)$ ii) +IV.

b i) +II, ii) +VI,
iii) +II, iv) +IV.

c Some of the noble gases are not inert; they form compounds with some elements such as fluorine and oxygen.

EXERCISE 52

a

Table 9

Reactant	Fluorine	Chlorine	Bromine	Iodine
Sulphur powder	Ignites spontaneously to form SF_6	Reacts if heated to form S_2Cl_2	Reacts if heated to form S_2Br_2	No reaction
Red phosphorus	Ignites spontaneously to form PF_5	On heating forms PCl_3 and PCl_5	Reacts spontaneously to form PBr_3	Solid spontaneously forms PI_3
Iron filings	Ignites if warmed to form FeF_3	Reacts on heating to form $FeCl_3$	Reacts if heated to form $FeBr_3$	Reacts if heated to form FeI_2
Sodium	Reacts explosively to form NaF	Continues to burn in chlorine to form NaCl	Continues to burn in vapour to form NaBr	Continues to burn in vapour to form NaI

b The solids melt on gentle heating. The rate of reaction is much greater because liquid iodine is far more concentrated than the vapour.

c F_2 brings out the highest oxidation states of the elements and I_2 brings out a lower oxidation state.

EXERCISE 53

a Chlorine reacts with the water in the litmus paper to form hydrochloric acid and chloric(I) acid.

$$Cl_2\ (g) + H_2O\ (l) \rightarrow HCl\ (aq) + HClO\ (aq)$$

The formation of the two acids turns the litmus paper red and the chloric(I) acid then bleaches it.

b $2F_2\ (g) + 2H_2O\ (l) \rightarrow 4HF\ (aq) + O_2\ (g)$
(Traces of H_2O_2 and ozone, O_3, are also formed.)

c $2HClO\ (aq) \rightarrow 2HCl\ (aq) + O_2\ (g)$

d Bromine reacts with water, though less readily than chlorine.
$Br_2\ (l) + H_2O\ (l) \rightleftharpoons HBrO\ (aq) + HBr\ (aq)$
Iodine does not react with water to any appreciable extent.

EXERCISE 54

a $\overset{0}{Cl_2}$ (g) + H_2O (l) → $H\overset{+1}{Cl}O$ (aq) + $H\overset{-1}{Cl}$ (aq)

b Disproportionation occurs when an element in a compound or in a free state undergoes simultaneous oxidation and reduction, i.e. the element appears in two products with increased and decreased oxidation numbers.

For example, in the reaction in part **a**, chlorine is both oxidised to chloric(I) acid and reduced to hydrochloric acid (chloride ion).

Ox(Cl) changes from 0 to +1 and to −1

c The reaction between F_2 and H_2O is not a disproportionation reaction because F appears in only one of the products. The reaction between Br_2 and H_2O is a disproportionation reaction since Br is simultaneously oxidised and reduced to HBrO and HBr.

EXPERIMENT 5

Specimen results

Results Table 6

Aqueous halogen	Original colour	Colour after adding NaOH (aq)	Colour after adding H_2SO_4 (aq)
Bromine water	orange-brown	very pale yellow	orange-brown
Iodine solution	reddish-brown	very pale yellow	reddish-brown

Questions

1. $3Br_2$ (aq) + $6OH^-$ (aq) → $5Br^-$ (aq) + BrO_3^- (aq) + $3H_2O$ (l)

   $3I_2$ (s) + $6OH^-$ (aq) → $5I^-$ (aq) + IO_3^- (aq) + $3H_2O$ (l)
2. Both of the above reactions are disproportionation reactions.
3. Both reactions are reversible because the halogen colour returns in both cases when the colourless halogen–alkali mixtures are acidified.
4. Chlorine reacts with cold alkali to form chlorate(I) ion, ClO^-.

   Cl_2 (aq) + $2OH^-$ (aq) → Cl^- (aq) + ClO^- (aq) + H_2O (l)

   ClO^- (aq) is stable at room temperature whereas BrO^- and IO^- are not.

EXERCISE 55

a $3ClO^-$ (aq) → $2Cl^-$ (aq) + ClO_3^- (aq)
chlorate(I) chlorate(V)

b $3Cl_2$ (g) + $6OH^-$ (aq) → $5Cl^-$ (aq) + ClO_3^- (aq) + $3H_2O$ (l)

c IO^-, BrO^-, ClO^- (IO^- disproportionates most readily, ClO^- least readily.)
IO^- is not formed when I_2 reacts with sodium hydroxide even at 0°C. This suggests that IO^- is very unstable and immediately disproportionates to I^- and IO_3^-. BrO^- disproportionates at 20°C whereas ClO^- is stable at 20°C.

d

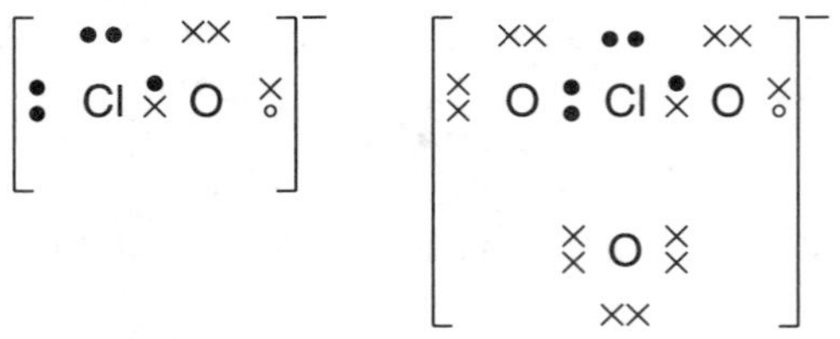

```
 [   ••   ××  ]−        [ ××   ••   ××  ]−
 [ : Cl ⁘ O ×° ]        [ ×× O : Cl ⁘ O ×° ]
 [            ]        [                ]
                        [      ×× O ××   ]
                        [        ××      ]
```

EXERCISE 56

a i) $\overset{+1}{H_2}\overset{-2}{S}$ (aq) + $\overset{0}{Br_2}$ (aq) → $2\overset{+1}{H}\overset{-1}{Br}$ (aq) + $\overset{0}{S}$ (s)

ii) $\overset{0}{Al}$ (s) + $1^1/_2\overset{0}{I_2}$ (s) → $\overset{+3}{Al}\overset{-1}{I_3}$ (s)

iii) $\overset{0}{Cl_2}$ (g) + $\overset{+1}{H_2}\overset{-2}{O}$ (l) → $\overset{+1}{H}\overset{+1}{Cl}\overset{-2}{O}$ (aq) + $\overset{+1}{H}\overset{-1}{Cl}$ (aq)

iv) $2\overset{+1}{Na_2}\overset{+2}{S_2}\overset{-2}{O_3}$ (aq) + $\overset{0}{I_2}$ (aq) → $\overset{+1}{Na_2}\overset{+2.5}{S_4}\overset{-2}{O_6}$ (aq) + $2\overset{+1}{Na}\overset{-1}{I}$ (aq)

b i) S^{2-} is oxidised to S; Br_2 is reduced to Br^-.
ii) Al is oxidised to Al^{3+}; I_2 is reduced to I^-.
iii) Cl_2 is simultaneously oxidised to ClO^- and reduced to Cl^-.
iv) $S_2O_3^{2-}$ is oxidised to $S_4O_6^{2-}$; I_2 is reduced to I^-.

EXERCISE 57

a Yes **b** No **c** Yes **d** Yes **e** No

EXPERIMENT 6

Specimen results

Results Table 7

			Chlorine water	**Bromine water**	**Iodine solution**
1.	Initial colour		almost none	orange	brown
2.	Colour after shaking with KI		brown	brown	
	Colour of each layer after shaking with Volasil 244	Upper	violet	violet	
		Lower	yellow	yellow	
	Conclusion		I^- oxidised	I^- oxidised	
3.	Colour after shaking with KBr		orange		unchanged
	Colour of each layer after shaking with Volasil 244	Upper	red		violet
		Lower	almost none		yellow
	Conclusion		Br^- oxidised		no reaction
4.	Colour after shaking with KCl			same	same
	Colour of each layer after shaking with Volasil 244	Upper		red	violet
		Lower		almost none	yellow
	Conclusion			no reaction	no reaction

Questions

1. **a** I_2 (aq) does not oxidise Cl^- (aq) or Br^- (aq).
   b Br_2 (aq) oxidises I^- (aq) but not Cl^- (aq).
   c Cl_2 (aq) oxidises both Br^- (aq) and I^- (aq).
   d The experiment should confirm your predictions.
2. $Cl_2 \text{ (aq)} + 2Br^- \text{ (aq)} \rightarrow 2Cl^- \text{ (aq)} + Br_2 \text{ (aq)}$
   $Cl_2 \text{ (aq)} + 2I^- \text{ (aq)} \rightarrow 2Cl^- \text{ (aq)} + I_2 \text{ (aq)}$
   $Br_2 \text{ (aq)} + 2I^- \text{ (aq)} \rightarrow 2Br^- \text{ (aq)} + I_2 \text{ (aq)}$

EXERCISE 58

Table 11

a

	F	Cl	Br	I
$\Delta H^\ominus_{at}$/kJ mol^{-1}	+79	+122	+112	+107
$\Delta H^\ominus_{e}$/kJ mol^{-1}	–328	–350	–325	–295
$\Delta H^\ominus_{hyd}$/kJ mol^{-1}	–506	–364	–335	–293
$\Delta H^\ominus_{r}$/kJ mol^{-1}	–755	–592	–548	–481

b For the reaction $\frac{1}{2}X_2 \text{ (standard state)} \rightarrow X^- \text{ (aq)}$
$\Delta H^\ominus_r$ is numerically greatest for F_2, decreasing to the smallest value for I_2. This suggests that the order of oxidising power (tendency to accept electrons) is $F_2 > Cl_2 > Br_2 > I_2$.

c Hydration energy shows the most pronounced trend and this is sufficient to mask the irregularities in the other energy factors.

EXERCISE 59

a A hint of metallic character might appear as the group is descended since electronegativity decreases with increasing atomic number.

b I_2 appears to have a metallic lustre, supporting the idea that it possesses a hint of metallic character.

EXERCISE 60

a

Table 12

	Formula	Molar mass /g mol^{-1}	Melting point/K	Boiling point/K	Physical state at s.t.p.
Hydrogen fluoride	HF	20.0	190	293	liquid
Hydrogen chloride	HCl	36.4	159	188	gas
Hydrogen bromide	HBr	80.9	186	206	gas
Hydrogen iodide	HI	127.9	222	238	gas

b With the exception of HF (which has the highest boiling point), the boiling points of the hydrogen halides increase with molar mass.

c The melting points follow a similar trend to boiling points.

d The van der Waals forces between the hydrogen halide molecules increase with molar mass. Thus, more energy is required to separate the molecules.

EXERCISE 61

Measurements of molar mass show that HF is associated in the liquid state, i.e. it exists as $(HF)_n$, where n is at least 2. This association is due to the presence of hydrogen bonds which operate between the HF molecules.

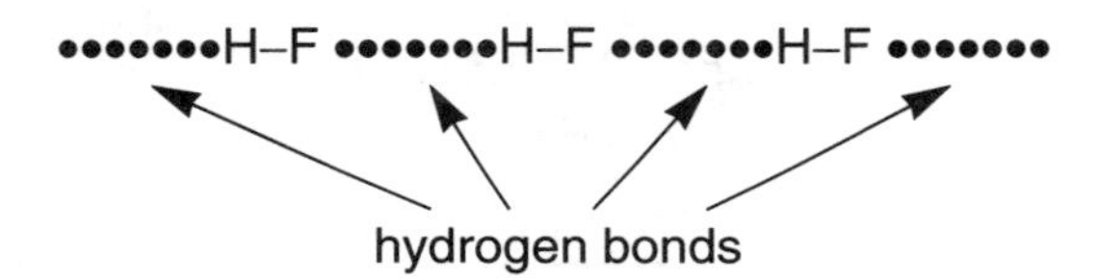

Hydrogen bonding only occurs in compounds with N—H, O—H or F—H bonds (with the exception of a few special cases such as $CHCl_3$ and HCN) because the atoms covalently bonded to the hydrogen are highly electronegative and small in size. Thus, HCl molecules are not hydrogen bonded because although Cl is very electronegative, it is much larger than N, O or F. Therefore, more energy is required to separate individual HF molecules than HCl molecules, and hence the boiling point of HF is greater than that of HCl.

EXERCISE 62

a Bond dissociation energy decreases with increasing molar mass. As the atomic radii of the halogens increase so do the hydrogen–halogen bond lengths. The longer the bond, the easier it is to break.

b i) $2HI\ (g) \rightarrow H_2\ (g) + I_2\ (g)$

ii) HI has the weakest bond and is therefore the most easily decomposed, even by a hot wire. HCl (g) and HBr (g) are not decomposed at the temperature of the hot wire.

It is also clear from ΔH_f° values that HI is the most unstable hydrogen halide with respect to decomposition to its elements.

EXERCISE 63

a Hydrofluoric acid, HF (aq); hydrochloric acid, HCl (aq); hydrobromic acid, HBr (aq); hydriodic acid, HI (aq).

b Hydrofluoric acid is a weak acid (only about 10% of the HF molecules ionise in 0.1 M solution) for the following reasons:

i) The H—F bond is very strong.
ii) Hydrogen bonds between HF molecules make ionisation more difficult.
The other hydrogen halides have weaker hydrogen–halide bonds and do not form hydrogen bonds.

c Acid strength decreases slightly in the order HI > HBr > HCl. This is mainly due to the increase in bond energy in passing from HI to HCl.

EXERCISE 64

HF is a weak acid, i.e. it is only partially ionised into H_3O^+ and F^-. This is partly due to the very strong H—F bond and partly due to hydrogen bonding between adjacent molecules.

Some of the F^- ions react with HF molecules to form HF_2^- ions:

$$F^- (aq) + HF (aq) \rightarrow HF_2^- (aq)$$

The HF_2^- ion is hydrogen bonded and stabilised by electron delocalisation:

$$[F\cdots\cdots H—F]^- \leftrightarrow [F—H\cdots\cdots F]^-$$

Thus, hydrofluoric acid contains two anions, F^- and HF_2^-, and when it reacts with an alkali, two salts are formed, e.g. KF and KHF_2.

There is no hydrogen bonding in the other hydrohalic acids; they each contain only one type of ion and form only one salt when reacting with an alkali. They are completely ionised in dilute aqueous solution.

HCl (aq), HBr (aq) and HI (aq) are all strong acids, i.e. they are almost completely dissociated into H^+ (aq) (or H_3O^+ (aq)) and X^- (aq). No HX_2^- ions exist with these acids so only one series of salts can be formed.

EXPERIMENT 7

Specimen results

Results Table 8

Test	Chloride	Bromide	Iodide
Action of MnO_2 and conc. H_2SO_4	Steamy fumes in cold. Pale green gas on warming Choking smell	Steamy brown fumes in cold. More on warming. Choking smell	Steamy violet fumes in cold. More on warming. Bad egg smell
Suspected product	Cl_2(HCl)	Br_2(HBr)	I_2(HI, H_2S)
Confirmatory test	Blue litmus bleached. Starch/ iodide paper blue	Red colour when bubbled into hexane	Violet colour in hexane
Action of conc. H_2SO_4	Steamy fumes in cold. No green gas even on heating	Steamy fumes in cold. Brown gas on warming	Steamy violet fumes in cold. More on warming Bad egg smell
Suspected product	HCl	HBr(Br_2)	I_2(HI, H_2S)
Confirmatory test	White smoke with ammonia. Blue litmus turns red but not bleached	White smoke with ammonia. Red colour in hexane	Violet colour in hexane
Action of conc. H_3PO_4	Steamy fumes on warming	Steamy fumes on warming	Steamy fumes on warming
Suspected product	HCl	HBr	HI
Confirmatory test	White smoke with ammonia	White smoke with ammonia	White smoke with ammonia

Questions

1. **a** KCl (s) + H_2SO_4 (l) → $KHSO_4$ (s) + HCl (g) (K_2SO_4 at high temperature only)

   b $2KCl$ (s) + H_3PO_4 (l) → K_2HPO_4 (s) + $2HCl$ (g)

   c KBr (s) + H_2SO_4 (l) → HBr (g) + $KHSO_4$ (s)

   $2HBr$ (g) + H_2SO_4 (l) → SO_2 (g) + $2H_2O$ (l) + Br_2 (l)

   d $2KBr$ (s) + H_3PO_4 (l) → K_2HPO_4 (s) + $2HBr$ (g)

   e KI (s) + H_2SO_4 (l) → $KHSO_4$ (s) + HI (g)

   $2HI$ (g) + H_2SO_4 (l) → SO_2 (g) + $2H_2O$ (l) + I_2 (s) or

   $8HI$ (g) + H_2SO_4 (l) → H_2S (g) + $4I_2$ (s) + $4H_2O$ (l)

   f $2KI$ (s) + H_3PO_4 (l) → K_2HPO_4 (s) + $2HI$ (g)

2. Concentrated H_2SO_4 alone is not a sufficiently strong oxidising agent to oxidise HCl (g) to Cl_2 (g). This is due to the strong H—Cl bond. The combination of concentrated H_2SO_4 and MnO_2 can oxidise HCl (g) to Cl_2 (g).
3. Concentrated H_2SO_4 alone is a sufficiently strong oxidising agent to oxidise HI to I_2. This is due to the weakness of the H—I bond. A more powerful oxidising agent such as concentrated H_2SO_4 and MnO_2 will merely produce similar results.

EXERCISE 65

HI, HBr, HCl, HF (HI most readily oxidised).

The oxidation of a hydrogen halide by sulphuric acid can be represented by the equation:

$$2H{-}X + H_2SO_4 \rightarrow X{-}X + 2H_2O + SO_2$$

In energy terms, the difference between one halide and another lies in the differences in E(H—X) and E(X—X). Since two H—X bonds have to be broken for each X—X bond formed, differences in E(H—X) are more important. The group trend in E(H—X) is very pronounced; the H—I bond is the weakest and HI is therefore most readily oxidised.

EXERCISE 66

i) The salt contains the bromide ion.
ii) $NaBr$ (s) + H_2SO_4 (l) → HBr (g) + $NaHSO_4$ (s)
iii) $2HBr$ (g) + H_2SO_4 (l) → SO_2 (g) + $2H_2O$ (l) + Br_2 (g)
The brown fumes are formed because the concentrated sulphuric acid oxidises HBr to Br_2.

EXERCISE 67

Preparation of HF and HCl. Both of these gases may be prepared by heating a halide salt with concentrated sulphuric acid.

$$CaF_2\ (s) + H_2SO_4\ (l) \rightarrow CaSO_4\ (s) + 2HF\ (g)$$

$$NaCl\ (s) + H_2SO_4\ (l) \rightarrow NaHSO_4\ (s) + HCl\ (g)$$

HCl may be collected by downward delivery. HF is usually made in small quantities only and not collected since it attacks glassware.

Preparation of HBr and HI. Both of these gases are prepared by heating the appropriate halide salt with a non-oxidising, non-volatile acid such as orthophosphoric acid, H_3PO_4.

$$2NaBr\ (s) + H_3PO_4\ (l) \rightarrow Na_2HPO_4\ (s) + 2HBr\ (g)$$
$$2NaI\ (s) + H_3PO_4\ (l) \rightarrow Na_2HPO_4\ (s) + 2HI\ (g)$$

Both gases may be collected by downward delivery.

EXPERIMENT 8

Specimen results

Results Table 9

Test	Chloride	Bromide	Iodide
Action of $AgNO_3$ (aq)	White ppt	Pale yellow ppt	Yellow ppt
Effect of standing in **a** dark **b** light	 No change Darkens rapidly	 No change Darkens slightly	 No change No change
Action of $AgNO_3$ (aq) followed by dilute HNO_3 (aq)	White ppt insoluble in HNO_3 (aq)	Pale yellow ppt. insoluble in HNO_3 (aq)	Yellow ppt insoluble in HNO_3 (aq)
Action of $AgNO_3$ (aq) followed by NH_3 (aq)	White ppt soluble in NH_3 (aq)	Pale yellow ppt. slightly soluble in NH_3 (aq)	Yellow ppt. insoluble in NH_3 (aq)
Action of $Pb(NO_3)_2$(aq)	White ppt	White ppt	Yellow ppt
Action of H_2O_2 (aq) and dilute H_2SO_4 (aq)	No change	No change	Brown colour Violet in hexane

Questions

1. **a** $Ag^+ (aq) + Cl^- (aq) \rightarrow AgCl (s)$

   $Ag^+ (aq) + Br^- (aq) \rightarrow AgBr (s)$

   $Ag^+ (aq) + I^- (aq) \rightarrow AgI (s)$

   b $Pb^{2+} (aq) + 2Cl^- (aq) \rightarrow PbCl_2 (s)$

   $Pb^{2+} (aq) + 2Br^- (aq) \rightarrow PbBr_2 (s)$

   $Pb^{2+} (aq) + 2I^- (aq) \rightarrow PbI_2 (s)$

2. **a** Add silver nitrate solution to each solution in turn, followed by dilute or concentrated ammonia solution. A white precipitate is obtained with the chloride ion, which is soluble in dilute ammonia solution. A pale yellow precipitate is obtained with the bromide ion, which is slightly soluble in dilute ammonia solution and soluble in concentrated ammonia solution.

   b Add lead ions to bromide and iodide solutions separately. A white precipitate is obtained with the Br^- ions and a yellow precipitate with the I^- ions.

3. **a** $2I^- (aq) + H_2O_2 (aq) + 2H^+ (aq) \rightarrow I_2 (aq) + 2H_2O (l)$

   b H_2O_2 is not a sufficiently strong oxidising agent to oxidise Cl^- (aq) and Br^- (aq) ions.

4. The light converts some of the silver halide to small particles of metallic silver, which darkens the precipitates.

EXERCISE 68

a When potassium manganate(VII) crystals are mixed with concentrated hydrochloric acid, an immediate reaction occurs at room temperature, giving a light green gas.

$$2KMnO_4 (s) + 16HCl (aq) \rightarrow 2KCl (aq) + 2MnCl_2 (aq) + 8H_2O (l) + 5Cl_2 (g)$$

b When KCl (aq) is mixed with $AgNO_3$ (aq) a white precipitate appears which dissolves on addition of concentrated aqueous ammonia.

$$Cl^- (aq) + Ag^+ (aq) \rightarrow AgCl (s)$$

$$AgCl (s) + 2NH_3 (aq) \rightarrow (Ag(NH_3)_2)^+ (aq) + Cl^- (aq)$$

c When Br_2 (aq) is added to KI (aq), the resulting solution is a deep orange-brown colour (much deeper than the original bromine water colour). This is due to the liberation of iodine.

$$Br_2\,(aq) + 2KI\,(aq) \rightarrow I_2\,(aq) + 2KBr\,(aq)$$

On addition of sodium thiosulphate, the solution becomes colourless.

$$I_2\,(aq) + 2S_2O_3^{2-}\,(aq) \rightarrow 2I^-\,(aq) + \underset{\text{tetrathionate ion}}{S_4O_6^{2-}}\,(aq)$$

EXERCISE 69

a Transfer 25.0 cm^3 aliquots of hydrogen peroxide solution by pipette into each of three clean conical flasks. Add a few cm^3 of dilute sulphuric acid to each flask followed by about 10 cm^3 of potassium iodide solution. Titrate each solution with 0.10 M sodium thiosulphate solution run in from a burette. When the iodine colour has faded to pale yellow, add approximately 2 cm^3 of fresh starch solution. This gives a deep blue colour. Continue titrating until the solution just turns colourless and record the volume of sodium thiosulphate added from the burette. Use the average of the three titres (which should agree to within 0.1 cm^3) in the calculation.

Since the concentrations of the acid and the potassium iodide solutions are not given, it would be wise to add a little more of each to see that no more iodine is produced (i.e. to check that an excess of each had, in fact, been added).

b Suppose that a 25.0 cm^3 aliquot needed 24.0 cm^3 of 0.10 M sodium thiosulphate solution. From the equations given,
1 mol of H_2O_2 gives 1 mol of I_2 which reacts with 2 mol of $S_2O_3^{2-}$ $\therefore$ 1 mol of H_2O_2 is equivalent to 2 mol of sodium thiosulphate ion.
Let A refer to H_2O_2 and B refer to $S_2O_3^{2-}$. Substituting into the expression

$$\frac{c_A V_A}{c_B V_B} = \frac{a}{b}$$

where $c_A = ?$ $\quad c_B = 0.10\ \text{mol dm}^{-3}$
$V_A = 25.0\ \text{cm}^3$ $\quad V_B = 24.0\ \text{cm}^3$
$a = 1$ $\quad b = 2$

$$\frac{c_A \times 25.0\ \text{cm}^3}{0.10\ \text{mol dm}^{-3} \times 24.0\ \text{cm}^3} = \frac{1}{2}$$

gives

$$\therefore c_A = \frac{0.10\ \text{mol dm}^{-3} \times 24.0\ \text{cm}^3}{2 \times 25.0\ \text{cm}^3} = \mathbf{0.048\ mol\ dm^{-3}}$$

EXERCISE 70

a

Table 13

	F	Cl	Br	I
+VII		Cl_2O_7		I_2O_7
+VI		Cl_2O_6	BrO_3	
+V				I_2O_5
+IV		ClO_2	BrO_2	I_2O_4
+III				
+II				
+I		Cl_2O	Br_2O	
0				
–I	OF_2,O_2F_2			

b Electronegativities (Pauling) are: O(3.5), F(4.0), Cl(3.0), Br(2.8), I(2.5). Thus the electronegativity differences between oxygen and the halogens are small, the maximum being 1.0 between oxygen and iodine. Therefore the bonds in the oxides are predominantly covalent.

c Cl, Br and I can all increase their oxidation state from –I to +VII. This is achieved by promotion of electrons into the vacant outer-shell d-orbitals (which are close in energy to the s- and p-orbitals in the same shell) during bonding.

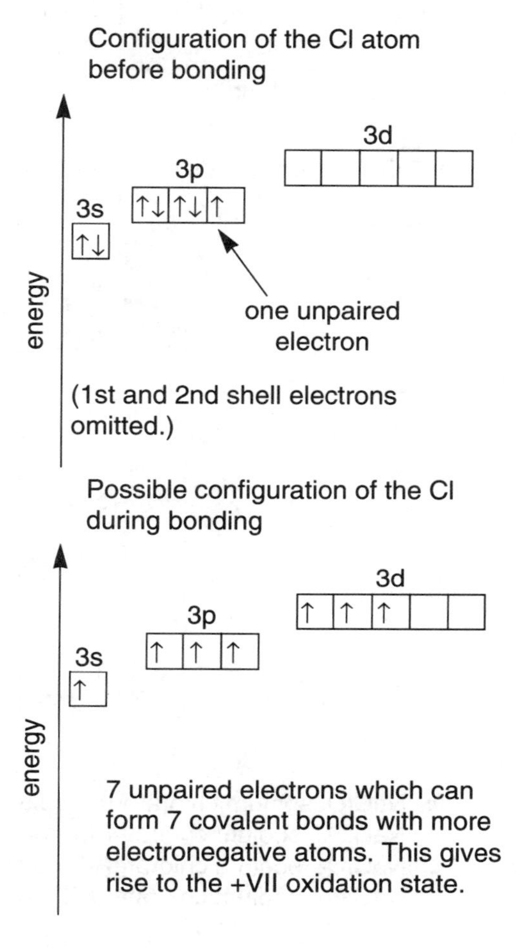

d Oxygen has an oxidation state of +I in O_2F_2, and +II in OF_2.

e The first-named element in a binary compound is usually the more electropositive. Compare, for instance, the names sodium oxide and oxygen fluoride.

f Acidic (like SO_2, SO_3, CO_2, etc.).

$$Cl_2O_7\text{ (l)} + H_2O\text{ (l)} \rightarrow 2HClO_4\text{ (aq)} \qquad \text{(chloric(VII) acid)}$$

EXERCISE 71

F_2O consists of angular molecules similar to those of H_2O. The bond angle is less than the tetrahedral angle (109.5°) because the lone pairs on the oxygen atom repel each other more strongly than the bonding pairs.

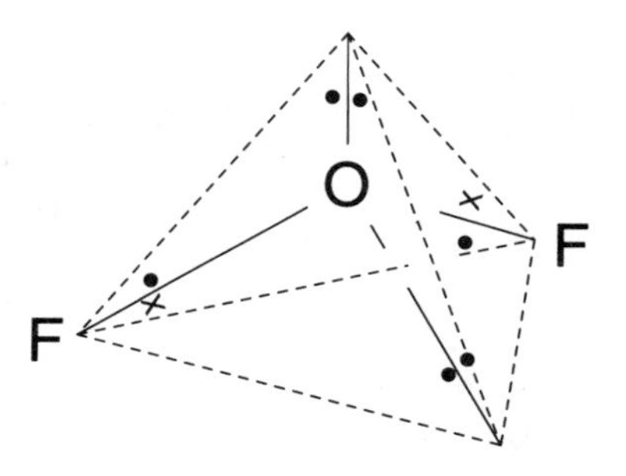

EXERCISE 72

a

Table 14
Oxoacids of chlorine

Formula	IUPAC name	Old name	Acid strength	Oxidation state of halogen	Name and formula of anion
HClO	chloric(I) acid	hypochlorous acid	very weak	+I	ClO^- chlorate(I)
$HClO_2$	chloric(III) acid	chlorous acid	weak	+III	ClO_2^- chlorate(III)
$HClO_3$	chloric(V) acid	chloric acid	strong	+V	ClO_3^- chlorate(V)
$HClO_4$	chloric(VII) acid	perchloric acid	very stong	+VII	ClO_4^- chlorate(VII)

b

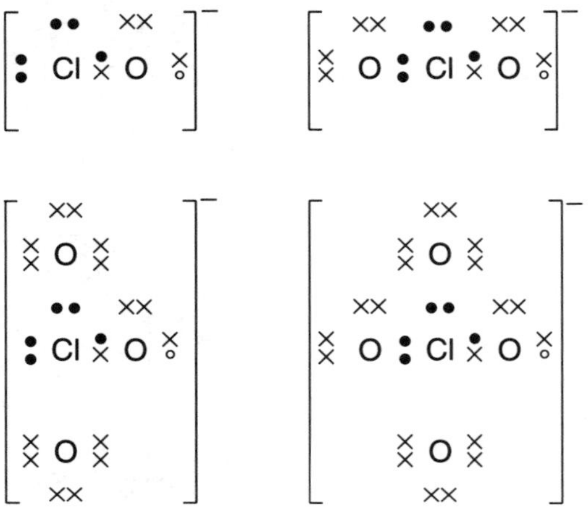

```
 ⎡   ••   ××   ⎤−        ⎡    ××   ••   ××   ⎤−
 ⎢ : Cl ×• O ×∘ ⎥        ⎢ ×× O : Cl ×• O ×∘ ⎥
 ⎣              ⎦        ⎣                    ⎦

 ⎡   ××           ⎤−     ⎡        ××            ⎤−
 ⎢ ×× O ××        ⎥      ⎢      ×× O ××         ⎥
 ⎢   ••   ××      ⎥      ⎢   ××   ••   ××       ⎥
 ⎢ : Cl ×• O ×∘   ⎥      ⎢ ×× O : Cl ×• O ×∘    ⎥
 ⎢ ×× O ××        ⎥      ⎢      ×× O ××         ⎥
 ⎣   ××           ⎦      ⎣        ××            ⎦
```

c NaClO, sodium chlorate(I) (sodium hypochlorite).
$NaClO_2$, sodium chlorate(III) (sodium chlorite).
$NaClO_3$, sodium chlorate(V) (sodium chlorate).
$NaClO_4$, sodium chlorate(VII) (sodium perchlorate).

d Chloric(VII) acid, $HClO_4$.

EXERCISE 73

a HIO, HBrO, HClO (→ increasing acid strength).
Acid strength increases with increasing electronegativity of the halogen X.

H—O—X

As the electronegativity of X increases, the electrons in the O—X bond are drawn nearer to X, leaving a slightly positive charge on the O. This draws the electrons in the H—O bond nearer to the O for the more electronegative halogen, enabling the H—O bond to break much more easily. Thus, more H^+ ions are produced for HClO than HBrO and HIO.

b HIO weaker than HIO_3.
The greater number of O atoms in HIO_3 produces a larger positive charge on I compared to HIO. The electrons in the H—I bond for HIO_3 are therefore drawn closer to the I, causing the bond to break with relative ease. Thus, more H^+ ions are formed in a given amount of HIO_3 compared to HIO.

EXERCISE 74

a $HIO\ (aq) \rightarrow H^+\ (aq) + IO^-\ (aq)$
$HIO\ (aq) \rightarrow I^+\ (aq) + OH^-\ (aq)$

b Metals tend to form cations in their reactions and since iodine can form I^+ ions, it must possess slight metallic character.

EXERCISE 75

a $\overset{+5}{IO_3^-}\ (aq) + \overset{-1}{I^-}\ (aq) + H^+\ (aq) \rightarrow \overset{0}{I_2}\ (aq) + H_2O\ (l)$
∴ oxidised species is I^- and reduced species is IO_3^-.
The balanced half-equations are

$2IO_3^-\ (aq) + 12H^+\ (aq) + 10e^- \rightarrow I_2\ (aq) + 6H_2O\ (l)$

$2I^-\ (aq) \rightarrow I_2 + 2e^-$ (Multiply this equation by 5.)

Combining the two half-equations we get

$2IO_3^-\ (aq) + 12H^+\ (aq) + 10I^-\ (aq) \rightarrow 5I_2\ (aq) + I_2\ (aq) + 6H_2O\ (l)$

or $IO_3^-\ (aq) + 6H^+\ (aq) + 5I^-\ (aq) \rightarrow 3I_2\ (aq) + 3H_2O\ (l)$

b $\overset{+2}{S_2O_3^{2-}}\ (aq) + \overset{0}{I_2}\ (aq) \rightarrow \overset{-1}{I^-}\ (aq) + \overset{+2.5}{S_4O_6^{2-}}\ (aq)$
∴ oxidised species is $S_2O_3^{2-}$ and reduced species is I_2.
The balanced half-equations are:

$2S_2O_3^{2-}\ (aq) \rightarrow S_4O_6^{2-}\ (aq) + 2e^-$

$I_2\ (aq) + 2e^- \rightarrow 2I^-\ (aq)$

Combining the two half-equations we get

$2S_2O_3^{2-}\ (aq) + I_2\ (aq) \rightarrow S_4O_6^{2-}\ (aq) + 2I^-\ (aq)$

EXPERIMENT 9

Specimen results

Results Table 10

Solution in flask	iodide/iodate/acid mixture					25.0 cm^3
Solution in burette	sodium thiosulphate			0.10 mol dm^{-3}		
Indicator	starch					
		Trial	1	2	3	4
Burette readings	Final	30.4	30.30	30.20	30.40	–
	Initial	0.0	0.00	0.00	0.20	–
Volume used/cm^3		30.4	30.30	30.20	30.20	–
Mean titre/cm^3	30.20					

Calculations

1. $n = cV = 0.10\ mol\ dm^{-3} \times (30.2/1000)\ dm^3 = 30.2 \times 10^{-4}$ mol
2. Amount of iodine atoms = amount of thiosulphate = 30.2×10^{-4} mol
3. $n = cV = 0.10\ mol\ dm^{-3} \times (5.0/1000)\ dm^3 = 5.0 \times 10^{-4}$ mol
4. Amount of I from KI = total amount – amount from KIO_3
   $= (30.2 - 5.0) \times 10^{-4}$ mol
   $= 25.2 \times 10^{-4}$ mol
5. 5.0×10^{-4} mol of KIO_3 reacts with 25.2×10^{-4} mol of KI
   ∴ 1 mol of KIO_3 reacts with (25.2/5.0) mol of KI = 5 mol
   This is in agreement with the equation
   $IO_3^-\ (aq) + 6H^+\ (aq) + 5I^-\ (aq) \rightarrow 3I_2\ (aq) + 3H_2O\ (l)$

EXERCISE 76

a Relative molecular mass of KIO_3 = 39 + 127 + 48 = 214
i.e. 1 dm^3 of (*M*/60) KIO_3 contains (214/60) g = 3.57 g
∴ 250 cm^3 requires (3.57/4) = **0.89 g**

b From the equations given,
1 mol of IO_3^- produces 3 mol of I_2 which react with 6 mol of $S_2O_3^{2-}$.
$\therefore$ 1 mol of IO_3^- is equivalent to 6 mol of $S_2O_3^{2-}$
Let A refer to IO_3^- and B refer to $S_2O_3^{2-}$
Substituting into the expression,

$$\frac{c_A V_A}{c_B V_B} = \frac{a}{b}$$

where $c_A = 1/60\ \text{mol dm}^{-3}$ $\quad c_B = ?$ $\quad a = 1$
$V_A = 25.0\ \text{cm}^3$ $\quad V_B = 20.0\ \text{cm}^3$ $\quad b = 6$

gives $$\frac{\frac{1}{60}\ \text{mol dm}^{-3} \times 25.0\ \text{cm}^3}{c_B \times 20.0\ \text{cm}^3} = \frac{1}{6}$$

$$\therefore\ c_B = \frac{\frac{1}{60}\ \text{mol dm}^{-3} \times 25.0\ \text{cm}^3 \times 6}{20.0\ \text{cm}^3} = \frac{2.5\ \text{mol dm}^{-3}}{20} = \mathbf{0.125\ mol\ dm^{-3}}$$

c To a 25 cm^3 aliquot of HCl (aq) add excess KI (aq) and KIO_3 (aq). Titrate the liberated I_2 with sodium thiosulphate solution of known concentration to the usual 'decolorisation of starch indicator' end point.
From the chemical equations, 1 mol of H^+ is equivalent to 1 mol of $S_2O_3^{2-}$. The concentration of H^+ can be calculated by substituting in the equation

$$\frac{c_A V_A}{c_B V_B} = \frac{1}{1}$$ where A refers to H^+ and B refers to $S_2O_3^{2-}$

d i) $S_2O_3^{2-}$: *Ox*(S) = +2
ii) From the equations for the reactions,
2 mol of $S_2O_3^{2-}$ reacts with 1 mol of I_2 released by 1 mol of Br_2
$\therefore$ 20 cm^3 of 0.1 M $Na_2S_2O_3$ reacts with 10 cm^3 of 0.1 M I_2
released by 10 cm^3 of 0.1 M Br_2
If only 10 cm^3 of 0.1 M Br_2 remains, then 50 – 10 = 40 cm^3 must have reacted, i.e. 40 cm^3 of 0.1 M Br_2 reacts with 10 cm^3 of 0.1 M $S_2O_3^{2-}$
$\therefore$ **4** mol of Br_2 reacts with 1 mol of $S_2O_3^{2-}$
iii) In reactants, *Ox*(Br) = 0 and *Ox*(S) = +2
In products, *Ox*(Br) = –1 (assumed to be Br^-)
8 Br atoms change oxidation number by –1 each. Total change = –8
$\therefore$ total change for S atoms must be +8, i.e. +4 each for 2 atoms
$\therefore$ *Ox*(S) in products = +2 + (+4) = **+6**
iv) The most likely product with *Ox*(S) = 6 is SO_4^{2-}
$\therefore$ half-equations can be written:

$$4Br_2\ (aq) + 8e^- \rightarrow 8Br^-\ (aq)$$
$$S_2O_3^{2-}\ (aq) + 5H_2O\ (l) \rightarrow 2SO_4^{2-}\ (aq) + 10H^+\ (aq) + 8e^-$$

Combining these half-equations gives:

$$S_2O_3^{2-}\ (aq) + 4Br_2\ (aq) + 5H_2O\ (l) \rightarrow 2SO_4^{2-}\ (aq) + 10H^+\ (aq) + 8Br^-\ (aq)$$

EXERCISE 77

a i) Sodium chlorate(I) (sodium hypochlorite).
ii) Sodium chlorate(V) (sodium chlorate).
iii) Sodium chlorate(I) (sodium hypochlorite).
iv) Potassium iodate(V).
v) Sodium chlorate(V).
vi) Potassium iodate(V).

b Chlorine gas is liberated when sodium chlorate(I) comes into contact with an acid.

EXPERIMENT 11

Specimen results

Results Table 13
Tests on unknown substance D

Method	Observations	Inferences
a A few crystals of D were heated in an ignition tube, gently at first and then more strongly	Some decrepitation at first. Solid eventually melted to a clear liquid which turned brown, then red, on further heating and gave off a little purple vapour. Cooled to a colourless solid	Purple vapour must be iodine, probably from thermal decomposition of potassium iodide
b The residue from **a** was cooled and one drop of concentrated H_2SO_4 was added. Then a few more drops were added	The mixture immediately darkened (almost black) and steamy fumes with a choking and 'bad egg' smell were released. A brownish liquid condensed on the tube just above the mixture	HI produced (displaced from iodide by non-volatile H_2SO_4). Some oxidation of HI to iodine by concentrated H_2SO_4, which was reduced to H_2S
c 10 drops of dilute H_2SO_4 were added to 5 drops of $KMnO_4$ solution followed by a few crystals of D. The mixture was then warmed	The solution immediately changed from purple to dark brown. No further change on warming	I^- oxidised to I_2 (brown in solution as I_3^-)

Results Table 14 Tests on unknown substance E

	Method	Observations	Inferences
a	A few crystals of E were heated in an ignition tube, gently at first and then more strongly	No change at first, but solid soon melted to colourless liquid and effervesced. Gas was colourless at first, then tinged with purple. Red liquid eventually formed on strong heating which cooled to a colourless solid	Purple vapour must be iodine but E is not the same as D. Perhaps D is produced from E by decomposition
	Gas was tested with damp litmus papers, blue and red	No colour change	Neutral gas (or CO_2) produced
	Gas was drawn into teat pipette and bubbled through a little lime-water	No change	No CO_2 produced
	A glowing splint was lowered into the tube	The splint relit	O_2 produced, probably by decomposition of potassium iodate(V)
b	The residue from **a** was cooled and one drop of conc. H_2SO_4 was added. Then a few more drops were added	The mixture immediately turned almost black and colourless fumes with a choking 'bad egg' smell were released. A brownish liquid condensed on the tube above the mixture	HI produced (displaced from iodide by non-volatile H_2SO_4). Some oxidation of HI to iodine by concentrated H_2SO_4, which was reduced to H_2S. This suggests that the residue contains I^-, thus E is very likely to be KIO_3
c	10 drops of dilute H_2SO_4 were added to 5 drops of $KMnO_4$ solution followed by a few crystals of E. The mixture was then warmed	No change observed apart from dissolving of crystals	No redox reaction occurs. This is consistent with the identity suggested for E, i.e. KIO_3
d	A few crystals of D and E were dissolved separately in about 2 cm^3 of distilled water in each of two tubes. The solutions were then mixed	D dissolved very easily, E less easily. Both solutions were colourless and remained so on mixing (perhaps a slight yellow colouration)	No apparent reaction. This again is consistent with KI (aq) and KIO_3 (aq) in neutral solution
e	Dilute H_2SO_4 was added dropwise to the mixed solutions from **d**	Solution turned dark brown with some blackish precipitate	I_2 formed by redox reaction between I^- and IO_3^- in presence of H^+

Results Table 15 Experiments to test inferences

Inference tested	**Test and observations**	**Conclusion**
Iodine produced by reaction of D and E in acid solution	About 1 cm^3 of Volasil 244 was added to mixture of D, E and acid (**e** above). The tube was shaken gently The upper layer of Volasil 244 turned purple	Iodine confirmed
D is potassium iodide	A few crystals of D were dissolved in distilled water and a few drops of dilute HNO_3 were added followed by $AgNO_3$ solution Yellow precipitate formed	Yellow precipitate of AgI confirms that D is potassium iodide

Final conclusion. D is potassium iodide, KI, and E is potassium iodate(V), KIO_3.

EXERCISE 78

a Dried-up prehistoric seas, now underground due to movement of the earth's crust.

b $Mg^{2+}(aq) + 2OH^-(aq) \rightarrow Mg(OH)_2(s)$ and $Ba^{2+}(aq) + SO_4^{2-}(aq) \rightarrow BaSO_4(s)$

c Evaporate the brine to give solid sodium chloride. Mix this with a powerful oxidising agent, such as manganese(IV) oxide, and react with concentrated sulphuric acid. This method would be unsatisfactory because of a high energy requirement for evaporation and high cost of reagents. (This is based on chemistry in this unit but alternatives might be accepted.)

d

$$H^+(aq) + e^- \rightarrow H \qquad H + H \rightarrow H_2(g)$$

As H^+ is discharged, more water dissociates, building up the concentration of $OH^-(aq)$.

$$H_2O(l) \rightarrow H^+(aq) + OH^-(aq)$$

e i) Hydrogen and chlorine could react, possibly explosively, to form hydrogen chloride.

$$H_2(g) + Cl_2(g) \rightarrow 2HCl(g)$$

ii) Chlorine would react with hydroxide ions to form chlorate(I) ions and perhaps chlorate(V) ions.

$$Cl_2(aq) + OH^- \rightarrow Cl^-(aq) + ClO^-(aq)$$

$$3ClO^-(aq) \rightarrow 2Cl^-(aq) + ClO_3^-(aq)$$

f Chloroethene (also known as vinyl chloride) is polymerised to form poly(chloroethene), generally known as PVC (polyvinyl chloride).

g Hydrogen and chlorine can be combined together safely using a suitable catalyst in the absence of light to make hydrogen chloride. Chlorine is bubbled into cold sodium hydroxide solution (not too concentrated) to form a solution of sodium(I) chlorate, sold as commercial bleach. Equations above in answer **e**.

h The fact that sodium reacts with water to form hydrogen and sodium ions suggests that sodium produces ions by losing electrons more readily than hydrogen does and, conversely, that hydrogen ions add electrons more readily than sodium ions.

$$2H^+(aq) + 2e^- \rightarrow H_2(g) \qquad Na^+(aq) + e^- \rightarrow Na(s)$$

i The diaphragm allows passage of **all** components of the electrolyte, whereas the membrane allows **only** hydrated sodium ions.
j The brine needs to be of higher purity in the membrane cell.
k The mercury cell gives sodium hydroxide of higher concentration (50%) than the diaphragm cell (10%): the membrane cell is nearly as good (up to 40%). The mercury cell produces much purer sodium hydroxide than the diaphragm cell: the membrane cell is even better.
l i) Mercury cells are very expensive to build. Diaphragm cells are cheaper initially but the diaphragms need frequent replacement. Energy costs for these two cells are similar but the membrane cell is cheaper to run.
ii) Large-scale use of mercury can give rise to highly toxic effluent if not very carefully controlled. In the diaphragm process, very careful control is necessary to prevent the possibility of hydrogen and chlorine coming together to form a very explosive mixture.
iii) There is much capital 'tied up' in existing plant – this has to be recovered from profits before the capital cost of a new plant can be considered.
m The plant should be near salt deposits and have good transport facilities by road, rail and sea for distribution of the products. It should have access to cheap electrical power, perhaps hydroelectricity. In order to meet environmental standards, it should be not too close to (and preferably downwind of) centres of population (consistent with the needs of a labour force).

Answers for unit – The Periodic Table

EXERCISE 79

a Atomic radius decreases across both Periods 2 and 3.
b In moving across each of these periods from left to right, each successive element gains an additional proton in its nucleus and an additional electron in its outermost shell. The electrons added to the outer shell shield one another only weakly from the extra positive charge on the nucleus, so the atomic radius decreases sharply.
c In Groups I, II and VII there is a marked increase in atomic radius between the first and the last elements, but the greater part of this increase occurs between the first and third elements of the group. The trend is similar for Groups III to VI, but the most marked increase is that between the first and the second elements.
d There is not much decrease in radius with increasing atomic number in either transition series, and there is an actual increase towards their ends. Electrons are being added to an inner d-subshell, and they shield the outer-shell electrons from the nucleus rather more effectively than new outer-shell electrons would. The increasing positive charge of the nucleus is therefore compensated, and the decrease in atomic radius is lessened and then averted.
e Gallium might be expected to have a greater atomic radius than aluminium because its outer electrons are in a higher energy shell. Two opposing factors influence the trend in atomic radius down any group; firstly, the occupation of additional electron shells, which tends to increase the radius and, secondly, the increased nuclear charge, which tends to draw the shells closer to the nucleus. The effect of the nuclear charge is, of course, reduced by shielding and the extent of this reduction depends on the nature and number of the inner electrons. In this case, there are 18 extra electrons, as opposed to 10 between boron and aluminium, and 10 of these are in the 3d-subshell. They only partially shield the 4p-electrons from the greatly increased nuclear charge so that the outer shell is closer to the nucleus than might be expected.
f i) Each noble gas would be expected to have the smallest covalent radius in its period. (Some evidence is seen by considering the compound XeF_2, in which the Xe—F bond length is reported to be 0.200 nm. Subtracting the average covalent radius for F, 0.071 nm, gives 0.129 nm for Xe, smaller than I at 0.133 nm.)

ii) Group O would be expected to show a similar trend in radii to elements in other groups – the radii would increase with increasing atomic number. Evidence for this comes from the van der Waals radii of the noble gases, which would be proportional to their covalent radii. These are:

Noble gas	Van der Waals radius/nm
Ne	0.160
Ar	0.192
Kr	0.197
Xe	0.217
Rn	–

EXERCISE 80

a In each period there is a decrease in ionic radius for the first three elements, followed by a sharp rise with the fourth element. There is then a steady decrease to the Group VII element.

b While there is a single trend in atomic radius (decrease across each period) there are two separate trends in ionic radius. The change from one trend to another occurs at the point where the elements change from being typical metals, losing electrons to form positive ions, to being typical non-metals, gaining electrons to form negative ions.

c The four ions which are purely hypothetical are C^{4+}, C^{4-}, Si^{4+} and Si^{4-}.

d Yes – Groups III, V and VI do show a similar trend – ionic radii increase down each group with increasing atomic number.

e Period 2 cations are isoelectronic with He but the anions are isoelectronic with Ne. Period 3 cations are isoelectronic with Ne but the anions are isoelectronic with Ar.

EXERCISE 81

a The halogens are found at the peaks of the ionisation energy graph (excluding the noble gases).

b The halogens are found at the troughs of the atomic radius graph. Each halogen has the smallest atoms of the elements in its period (excluding the noble gases).

c This suggests an inverse relationship between atomic radius and ionisation energy. For example, in the halogens, the small radius indicates that the outer electrons are strongly attracted by the nucleus. More energy is therefore needed to remove an electron, which explains why each halogen has the highest first ionisation energy in its period, apart from the noble gases.

EXERCISE 82

a

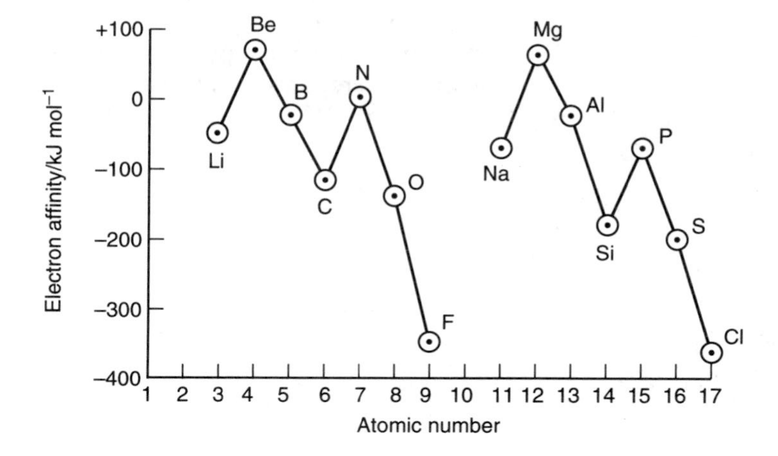

b Yes, the pattern shown in Period 3 is similar to the pattern shown in Period 2, although the maximum reached with nitrogen in Period 2 is higher than the maximum with phosphorus in Period 3.

c Beryllium and nitrogen show positive and small negative electron affinity values respectively indicating that these elements have little tendency to accept electrons. In Be the 2s subshell is full and more energy is needed to add a third electron to the 2p subshell, while in N, the added electron has to overcome the repulsive force of electrons already present in each singly occupied 2p orbital.

EXERCISE 83

a Between boron and fluorine and between aluminium and chlorine the atomic radius decreases while the atomic volume increases overall.

b The fact that atoms are getting smaller while taking up more space suggests that there is a change in the type of structure adopted by these elements.

EXERCISE 84

a and **b**

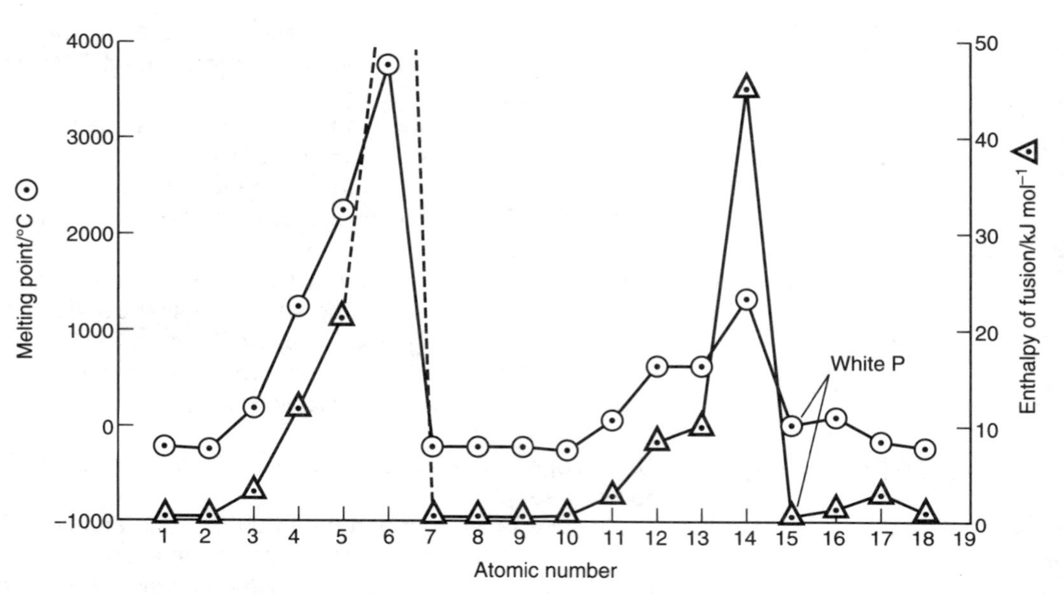

c The temperature at which a substance melts is obviously related to the amount of heat needed to melt it. This explains why the graph of enthalpy of fusion parallels the melting point graph.

d The elements at the peaks of each graph are in Group IV.

e Elements with the highest melting points and enthalpies of fusion have structures with strong bonds between their atoms. This suggests giant covalent structures for Group IV elements.

f Melting point and enthalpy of fusion are periodic since the pattern shown by Period 2 elements is repeated fairly closely in Period 3.

EXERCISE 85

Table 21

a

Element	**Lithium**	**Beryllium**	**Boron**	**Carbon (graphite)**	**Nitrogen**	**Oxygen**	**Fluorine**	**Neon**
Bonding	Metallic	Metallic	Covalent	Covalent	Covalent	Covalent	Covalent	—
Structure	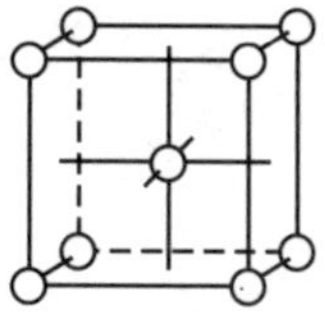	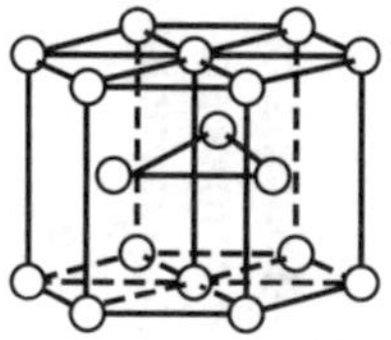	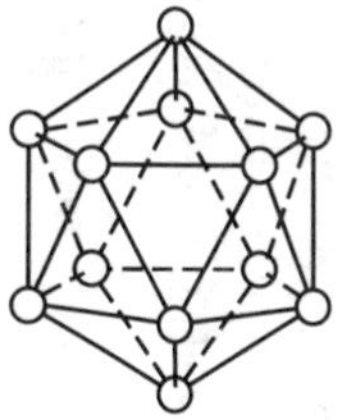	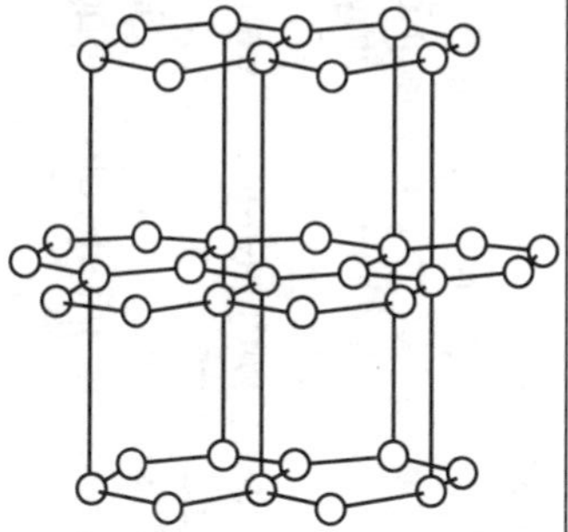				
Type	BCC	HCP	Giant molecular	Giant molecular	Simple molecular	Simple molecular	Simple molecular	Atomic
Element	**Sodium**	**Magnesium**	**Aluminium**	**Silicon**	**Phosphorus (white)**	**Sulphur**	**Chlorine**	**Argon**
Bonding	Metallic	Metallic	Metallic	Covalent	Covalent	Covalent	Covalent	—
Structure	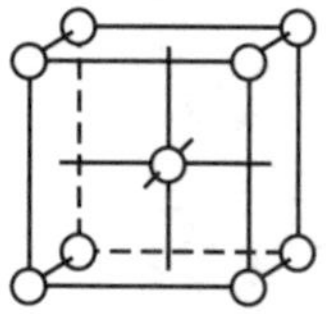	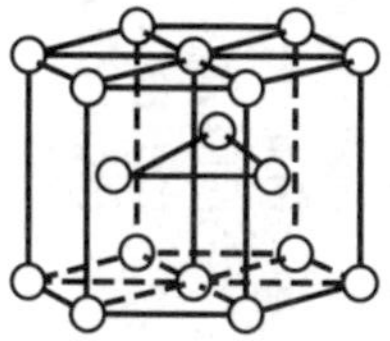	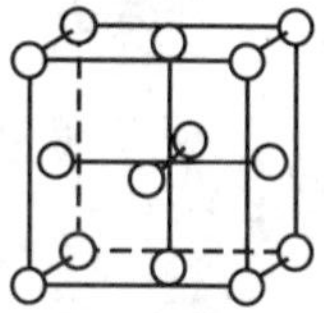	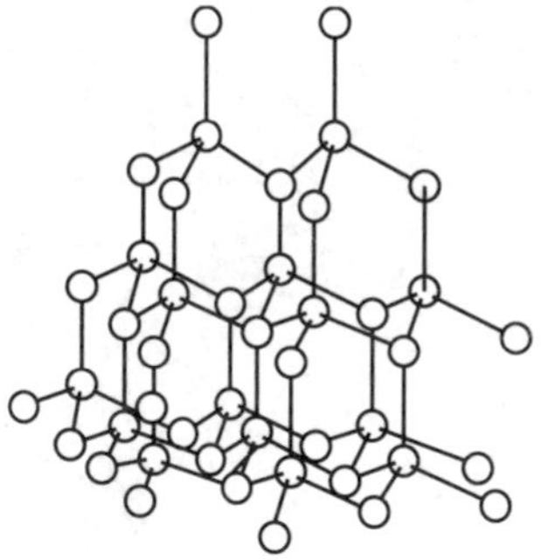	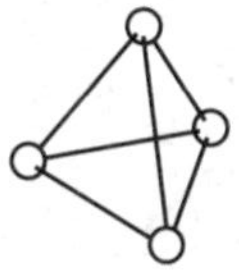	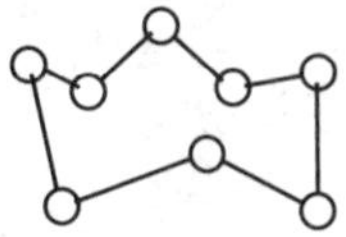		
Type	BCC	HCP	FCC (CCP)	Giant molecular	Simple molecular	Simple molecular	Simple molecular	Atomic

b i) The strength of the bonding between atoms increases steadily from lithium to boron. Lithium and beryllium both have giant metallic structures but in beryllium the bonds are stronger since there are two bonding electrons per atom instead of one. Boron has a giant molecular structure with the strongest bonds of the three.

Between sodium and aluminium the bonds between atoms also increase steadily in strength. The structures are all metallic, but the number of electrons available for bonding increases from one to three per atom.

ii) There is nothing in the structural arrangements shown in Table 21 to suggest that graphite should have a higher melting point than boron. However, each carbon atom has four outer electrons available for bonding while each boron atom has three, and C—C bonds are stronger than B—B bonds.

Similar arguments apply to aluminium and silicon. (Beware of stating that covalent bonding is necessarily stronger than metallic bonding – see the Bonding and Structure unit of ILPAC Volume 3.)

iii) Between carbon and nitrogen and again between silicon and phosphorus there is a dramatic change in structure from giant molecular, with covalent bonds between atoms, to simple molecular with only van der Waals forces between the molecules. This explains the sharp decreases in both melting point and enthalpy of fusion.

c In these groups the small molecules of the elements, or single atoms for Group O, are held together by weak van der Waals forces. The energy needed to break these down is far less than the energy needed to break four covalent bonds per atom in the carbon structure. This explains the large enthalpy of fusion of carbon compared with elements in the following groups.

d The table does show a repeating pattern, with metallic structures followed by giant covalent, followed by simple molecular, moving from left to right. Boron resembles silicon, rather than aluminium in its own group, in having a giant molecular structure. Apart from this diagonal relationship, structure is periodic.

EXERCISE 86

a Metallic bonding persists in the liquid state and has to be overcome for a metal to vaporise. However, most non-metals melt to give relatively free atoms or molecules which need little further energy to vaporise them.

b The sharpest changes in melting point and boiling point take place between C and N and between Si and P.

c These changes correspond to changes from giant molecular to simple molecular structures in each case.

d A plot of enthalpy of vaporisation would have the same general shape as the boiling point plot.

e In fusion (melting), the solid structure is disrupted but the atoms or molecules remain close together in the liquid, and attractive forces are much stronger than in the gaseous state. In vaporisation, the particles are completely separated and this requires more energy than fusion.

EXERCISE 87 a and b

Table 22

		Na	Mg	Al	Si	P (white)	S	Cl	Ar
Dry O_2 and heat	A	Very vigorous	Very vigorous	Vigorous at first	Slow	Vigorous	Slow	No reaction	No reaction
	B	Na_2O_2	MgO	Al_2O_3 on surface	SiO_2	P_4O_6 and P_4O_{10}	SO_2	——	——
Dry Cl_2 and heat	A	Very vigorous	Vigorous	Vigorous	Slow	Slow	Slow		No reaction
	B	NaCl	$MgCl_2$	$AlCl_3$	$SiCl_4$	PCl_3 and PCl_5	SCl_2 and S_2Cl_2		——
Dry H_2 and heat	A	Very vigorous	Vigorous	No reaction	No reaction	No reaction	Very slow	Vigorous in sunlight	No reaction
	B	NaH	MgH_2	——	——	——	H_2S	HCl	——
Cold H_2O	A	Very vigorous	Slow	No reaction	No reaction	No reaction	No reaction	Slow	No reaction
	B	NaOH	Mg $(OH)_2$ on surface	——	——	——	——	HClO (aq)	——
Cold dilute HCl	A	Violent	Very vigorous	Vigorous if oxide layer removed	No reaction	No reaction	No reaction	No reaction	No reaction
	B	NaCl	$MgCl_2$	$AlCl_3$	——	——	——	——	——
Mg and heat	A	No reaction		No reaction	Slow	Vigorous	Vigorous	Vigorous	No reaction
	B	——		——	Mg_2Si	Mg_3P_2	MgS	$MgCl_2$	——

A = Ease of reaction: violent, very vigorous, vigorous, slow, very slow, no reaction.
B = Main product (compound of given element).

EXERCISE 88

a The s-block elements react vigorously when heated with oxygen, chlorine or hydrogen to form ionic solids. The other elements are less reactive. Thus, aluminium reacts with chlorine and also with oxygen (until surface oxidation to Al_2O_3 prevents further reaction), but not with hydrogen. From silicon onwards reactions with oxygen, chlorine and hydrogen are slow or non-existent, apart from the reactions of phosphorus with oxygen, phosphorus with chlorine and chlorine with hydrogen. The latter reaction occurs in sunlight and proceeds by a free radical mechanism. (For more details of this type of reaction, see ILPAC Volume 5, Hydrocarbons.)

b Oxygen, chlorine and hydrogen all react most vigorously with strongly reducing elements which tend to give up electrons and allow the formation of O^{2-}, Cl^- and H^- ions. As elements' reducing power decreases with increasing atomic number so does their reactivity with oxygen, chlorine and hydrogen.

c The elements' reactivity with magnesium increases across the period. There is no reaction with any of the metals, a slow reaction with silicon, and a vigorous reaction when heated with phosphorus, or sulphur or chlorine. This is the opposite of the trend found with the non-metals oxygen, chlorine and hydrogen.

d Magnesium reacts most effectively with elements which have oxidising properties and which tend to accept electrons. Such elements are found from Group IV onwards, i.e. towards the right-hand side of the Periodic Table.

e Many metals react with dilute acid to form a salt and water. Sodium, magnesium and aluminium (provided its oxide layer has been removed) all show this reaction, while silicon and the remaining elements in the period do not. A non-metal would be expected to form a compound with a reactive metal like magnesium. This reaction occurs with silicon and the elements beyond it. From these two pieces of evidence, then, the change occurs on passing from the Group III metal aluminium to the Group IV non-metal silicon.

f Similar reactions usually occur in Period 2, although differences emerge because of the atypical behaviour of the top element in each group. Be tends to resemble Al in, for example, not reacting directly with hydrogen. Thus the point of change from metal to non-metal occurs further to the left in Period 2.

EXERCISE 89

a

Table 24

General formula and ratio O/X		Formulae of oxides in Groups of Period 2							Formulae of oxides in Groups of Period 3						
		1	2	3	4	5	6	7	1	2	3	4	5	6	7
X_2O_7	3.5*														Cl_2O_7
XO_3	3.0													SO_3	Cl_2O_6
X_2O_5	2.5					N_2O_5							P_4O_{10}		
XO_2	2.0				CO_2	NO_2†				MgO_2		SiO_2		SO_2	ClO_2
X_2O_3	1.5			B_2O_3		N_2O_3					Al_2O_3		P_4O_6		
XO	1.0		BeO		CO	NO	O_2	F_2O_2	Na_2O_2	MgO					
X_2O	0.5	Li_2O				N_2O		F_2O	Na_2O						Cl_2O

Table 25

General formula and ratio Cl/X		Formulae of chlorides in Groups of Period 2							Formulae of chlorides in Groups of Period 3						
		1	2	3	4	5	6	7	1	2	3	4	5	6	7
XCl_5	5												PCl_5		
XCl_4	4				CCl_4							$SiCl_4$		SCl_4	
XCl_3	3			BCl_3		NCl_3					$AlCl_3$†		PCl_3		
XCl_2	2		$BeCl_2$				OCl_2			$MgCl_2$				SCl_2	
XCl	1	$LiCl$						FCl	$NaCl$					S_2Cl_2	Cl_2

*This column shows the number of atom of O per atom of X.

†In some contexts the dimeric formulae are more appropriate.

Table 26

General formula and ratio H/X		Formulae of hydrides in Groups of Period 2							Formulae of hydrides in Groups of Period 3						
		1	2	3	4	5	6	7	1	2	3	4	5	6	7
XH_4	4				CH_4							SiH_4			
XH_3	3			BH_3	C_2H_6	NH_3					AlH_3	Si_2H_6	PH_3		
XH_2	2		BeH_2		C_2H_4		OH_2			MgH_2				SH_2	
XH	1	LiH			C_2H_2		O_2H_2	FH	NaH						ClH

b The basic pattern shown more or less by each group of compounds is a regular increase in the number of atoms of oxygen, chlorine or hydrogen that combines with one atom of the element, reaching a maximum in Group IV. It then decreases to reach a minimum in Group VII. The pattern is complicated in Period 2 by the prolific compound formation of carbon, nitrogen and oxygen and in Period 3 by phosphorus, sulphur and chlorine which show additional higher oxidation states in oxides and halides.

c Phosphorus, sulphur and chlorine show a wide range of oxidation states because they are able to expand their octets by utilising the unused d-orbitals in the third shell which are available for bonding in certain circumstances. Consider, for example, phosphorus. One of the electrons in the 3s orbital can be excited into one of the vacant 3d orbitals leaving five unpaired electrons which can form five covalent bonds with combining elements. For further details, see ILPAC Volume 12, The p-Block Elements.

EXERCISE 90

a

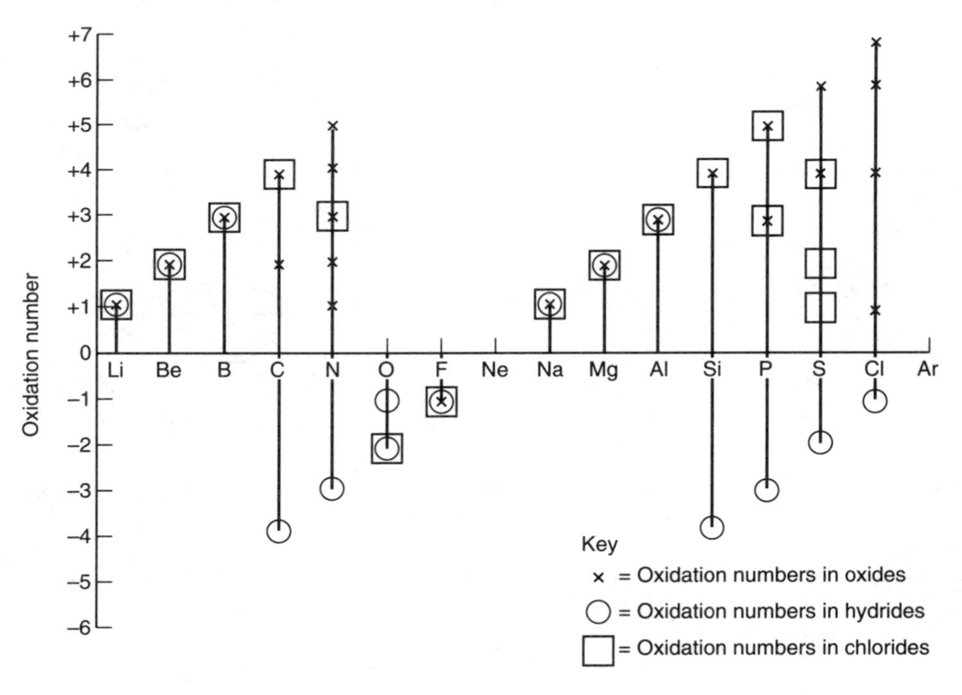

b Phosphorus, sulphur and chlorine can all expand their octets and form compounds with oxidation states higher than those expected for their groups by excitation of the outer electrons into the vacant 3d orbitals. The excitation is helped by the approach of a highly electronegative combining atom. Oxygen and chlorine are much more electronegative than hydrogen so they can effect the excitation whereas hydrogen cannot.

EXERCISE 91

Electronegativity differences (on the Pauling scale) are as follows:

NaCl	(3.0 – 0.9) = 2.1	
$MgCl_2$	(3.0 – 1.2) = 1.8	Increasing covalent character
$AlCl_3$	(3.0 – 1.5) = 1.5	
$SiCl_4$	(3.0 – 1.8) = 1.2	Decreasing ionic character
PCl_3	(3.0 – 2.1) = 0.9	
S_2Cl_2	(3.0 – 2.5) = 0.5	↓

EXPERIMENT 12

Specimen results

Results Table 16

	NaCl	$MgCl_2$	$AlCl_3$	$SiCl_4$	PCl_3	S_2Cl_2
Appearance	Colourless solid	Colourless solid	Colourless solid	Colourless liquid	Colourless liquid	Yellow liquid
On mixing with water		(Hydrated)	(Anhydrous)			
Initial temp.	17°C	17°C	17°C	17°C	17°C	17°C
Final temp.	17°C	19°C	49°C	19°C	27°C	20°C
Does it dissolve?	Yes	Yes	Yes	Yes	Yes (eventually)	Yes
pH of solution	7	6	4 or less	Below 4	Below 4	Below 4
Other observations (if any)	None	None	Vigorous reaction. Acid gas – white fumes with NH_3	Acid gas – white fumes with NH_3. White particles in liquid	Acid gas – white fumes with NH_3	Cloudy solution formed
On mixing with cyclohexane						
Initial temp.	16°C	16°C	16°C	16°C	17°C	17°C
Final temp.	16°C	16°C	16°C	16°C	17°C	17°C
Does it dissolve?	No	No	Very slightly	Slightly soluble if at all	Yes	Yes
Other observations (if any)	None	None	None	Two layers	None	None

Questions

Table 27 Properties of chlorides of Period 3

1.

Formula of chloride	**NaCl**	**$MgCl_2$**	**$AlCl_3$**	**$SiCl_4$**	**PCl_3**	**S_2Cl_2**	**Cl_2**
Melting point/°C	80	714	190	–70	–112	–80	–101
Boiling point/°C	1467	1412	183	58	76	136	–34.6
Physical state at r.t.p.*	Solid	Solid	Solid	Liquid	Liquid	Liquid	Gas
$\Delta H_f^{\ominus}$/kJ mol^{-1}	–411	–642	–695	–640	–339	–60.2	0
$\Delta H_f^{\ominus}$ per mole of Cl/kJ mol^{-1}	–411	–321	–232	–160	–113	–30.1	0
Conductivity of liquid	Good	Good	Poor	Very poor	Very poor	Very poor	Very poor
Action of water	Dissolves	Dissolves	Reacts	Reacts	Reacts	Reacts	Reacts
pH of aqueous solution	7	6.5	3	2	2	2	2
Solubility in hexane	Insoluble	Insoluble	Insoluble	Dissolves	Dissolves	Dissolves	Dissolves
Structure	Giant	Giant	Simple molecular†	Simple molecular	Simple molecular	Simple molecular	Simple molecular
Bonding	Ionic	Ionic	Covalent	Covalent	Covalent	Covalent	Covalent

*r.t.p. = room temperature and pressure (i.e. 25°C and 1 atm).
†The solid has a layer structure. The vapour contains Al_2Cl_6 molecules.

2. **a** $AlCl_3$ (s) + $6H_2O$ (l) → $[Al(H_2O)_6]^{3+}$ (aq) + $3Cl^-$ (aq)
hexaaquaaluminium(III) ion
The $[Al(H_2O)_6]^{3+}$ ions dissociate to form H_3O^+ ions giving rise to an acidic solution. There is also some HCl gas produced. See the p-Block Elements unit of ILPAC Volume 12 for further details.
b $SiCl_4$ (l) + $(x + 2)H_2O$ (l) → $SiO_2{\cdot}xH_2O$ (aq) + 4HCl (g)
hydrated silicon(IV) oxide
(Some books refer to hydrated silicon(IV) oxide as silicic acid and give it the formula H_2SiO_3 or $Si(OH)_4$. These species may exist in solution but it seems likely that a range of hydrates such as $SiO_2{\cdot}2H_2O$ and $SiO_2{\cdot}H_2O$ exist which we represent as $SiO_2{\cdot}x\,H_2O$. The hydrated oxide appears as a colloidal solution or a gel.)
c PCl_3 (l) + $3H_2O$ (l) → H_2PHO_3 (aq) + 3HCl (aq)
phosphonic acid
Phosphonic acid H_2PHO_3 is sometimes called phosphorous acid and given the formula H_3PO_3.
3. Yes, the experimental results do confirm predictions made from electronegativity values. Aluminium, silicon, phosphorus and sulphur all show hydrolytic reactions typical of covalent chlorides while sodium chloride behaves like a typical ionic chloride. You probably used hydrated magnesium chloride for your test, in which case it would simply have dissolved. With anhydrous $MgCl_2$ a vigorous reaction occurs with a trace of hydrogen chloride indicating a degree of covalent character.

EXERCISE 92

Table 28 a

Formula of chloride	LiCl	$BeCl_2$	BCl_3	CCl_4	NCl_3	OCl_2	FCl
State at r.t.p.	Solid	Solid	Liquid	Liquid	Liquid	Gas	Gas
Conductivity of liquid	Good	Very poor	Very poor	Very poor	Very poor	Very poor	Very poor
Action of water	Dissolves	Reacts	Reacts	Immiscible	Reacts	Reacts	Reacts
Structure	Giant	Chain polymer	Simple molecular	Simple molecular	Simple molecular	Simple molecular	Simple molecular
Bonding	Ionic	Covalent	Covalent	Covalent	Covalent	Covalent	Covalent

b $BeCl_2 (s) + H_2O (l) \rightarrow BeO (s) + 2HCl (g)$

$BCl_3 (l) + 3H_2O (l) \rightarrow H_3BO_3 (aq) + 3HCl (g)$

$NCl_3 (l) + 3H_2O (l) \rightarrow 3HClO (aq) + NH_3 (g)$

$Cl_2O (g) + H_2O (l) \rightarrow 2HClO (aq)$

$ClF (g) + H_2O (l) \rightarrow HOF (aq) + HCl (aq)$

EXERCISE 93

One factor which affects the degree of ionic character in a compound is the extent of polarisation of the anion by the cation. The smaller and more highly charged the cation, the more likely it is to polarise the anion. In $CaCl_2$, the calcium ion is capable of polarising the chloride ion to some extent. This decreases the degree of ionic character and makes the compound susceptible to hydrolysis.

EXERCISE 94

When $MgCl_2 \cdot 6H_2O$ is heated alone the following reaction occurs to form a basic chloride.

$$MgCl_2 \cdot 6H_2O (s) \rightleftharpoons Mg(OH)Cl^* (s) + HCl (g) + 5H_2O (l)$$

On stronger heating, magnesium oxide is formed

$$Mg(OH)Cl (s) \rightleftharpoons MgO (s) + HCl (g)$$

However, heating in a stream of hydrogen chloride will produce anhydrous $MgCl_2$, because the continual presence of this gas inhibits hydrolysis by reversing the above reactions.

EXERCISE 95

The small and highly charged beryllium cation has a strong polarising effect on the chloride ions resulting in a high degree of covalent character. This makes the compound very susceptible to hydrolysis.

$$BeCl_2 (s) + H_2O (l) \rightleftharpoons BeO (s) + 2HCl (g)$$

The larger magnesium cation is less polarising than the beryllium cation and therefore $MgCl_2$ is only partially hydrolysed to form Mg(OH)Cl.

*Various formulae have been assigned to this basic chloride including $MgO \cdot MgCl_2$ and $Mg(OH)_2 \cdot MgCl_2$ as well as the one we have used.

EXERCISE 96

a

Table 29

Element	Formula of chloride	Physical state of chloride at s.t.p.	Type of bonding found in chloride
Hydrogen	HCl	Gas	Covalent
Barium	$BaCl_2$	Solid	Ionic
Nitrogen	NCl_3	Liquid	Covalent
Silicon	$SiCl_4$	Liquid	Covalent

b i) $HCl\ (g) + H_2O\ (l) \rightarrow H_3O^+\ (aq) + Cl^-\ (aq)$

ii) $SiCl_4\ (l) + 4H_2O\ (l) \rightarrow SiO_2{\cdot}2H_2O\ (aq) + 4HCl\ (g)$

(A range of hydrates are formed for hydrated silicon(IV) oxide. See the answer to question 2, Experiment 12.)

EXPERIMENT 13

Specimen results

Results Table 16

Mass of aluminium	0.25 g
Mass of empty specimen tube, m_1	10.20 g
Mass of specimen tube and product, m_2	10.60 g
Mass of product, $m = (m_2 - m_1)$	0.40 g
% yield	33%

Questions

1. Any moisture present in the apparatus, such as water vapour mixed with the chlorine, would hydrolyse the aluminium chloride as it formed.
2. The product would contain aluminium oxide as an impurity. It would be formed by the reaction

$$2AlCl_3\ (s) + 3H_2O\ (g) \rightarrow Al_2O_3\ (s) + 6HCl\ (g)$$

3. Using the data from the specimen results the calculation is as follows:

$$Al\ (s) + 1\tfrac{1}{2}Cl_2\ (g) \rightarrow AlCl_3\ (s)$$

First, calculate the mass of $AlCl_3$ that would theoretically be formed from 0.25 g of Al

27 g of Al produces 133.5 g of $AlCl_3$

$$1.0 \text{ g of Al produces } \frac{133.5 \text{ g}}{27} \text{ of } AlCl_3$$

$$0.25 \text{ g of Al produces } \frac{133.5 \text{ g}}{27} \times 0.25 = 1.2 \text{ g of } AlCl_3$$

$$\% \text{ yield} = \frac{\text{actual mass of product}}{\text{theoretical mass of product}} \times 100$$

$$\therefore \% \text{ yield} = \frac{0.40 \text{ g}}{1.2 \text{ g}} \times 100 = \mathbf{33\%}$$

This experiment often gives low yields. Likely reasons are:

a Some product remains in the combustion tube and receiver bottle.

b Some product is carried away with excess chlorine.

c Some aluminium reacts with residual air to form oxide which remains in the combustion tube.

d Some product is hydrolysed by residual water vapour.

4. A desiccator is necessary to prevent hydrolysis by moist air.

EXERCISE 97

a i) Figure 36 for $SiCl_4$ (melting point of Si is 1410°C).

ii) Figure 36 for PCl_3 (melting point of red P is 590°C).

iii) Figure 37 for S_2Cl_2 (melting point of rhombic S is 113°C).

b Si should be heated **strongly**, red P should be heated **enough to start the reaction**, and S should be heated **enough to melt the element**.

c Sulphur melts at just over 100°C and boils at 444°C, so that it is important to avoid unchanged sulphur distilling over and getting mixed in with the product.

EXERCISE 98

a If either lithium or sodium is added to water an aqueous solution of the metal hydroxide is obtained. Samples of their chlorides may be prepared by neutralising the hydroxide with hydrochloric acid followed by evaporation to dryness or crystallisation.

In each case take a known volume of alkali solution and titrate it with dilute hydrochloric acid until it reaches pH 7. This can be done either directly, using a pH meter, or indirectly, using an indicator with an end point at around pH 7, such as bromothymol blue. For the indirect method, the neutralisation is then repeated without the indicator, using the volume of acid determined previously.

Finally evaporate off about half the neutralised mixture to remove some of the excess water and leave the concentrated solution to cool and crystallise.

b Using the above neutralisation method it would be possible to prepare hydrated magnesium chloride, $MgCl_2{\cdot}6H_2O$. However, there is no way of preparing anhydrous $MgCl_2$ directly from this, as it is hydrolysed by its own water of crystallisation to form Mg(OH)Cl.

EXERCISE 99

a $Ag^+ (aq) + Cl^- (aq) \rightarrow AgCl (s)$

Amount of Cl^- in 25 cm^3 of solution = amount of Ag^+ used = cV

$$= 0.100 \text{ mol dm}^{-3} \times \frac{18.4}{1000} \text{dm}^3 = \mathbf{1.84 \times 10^{-3} \text{ mol}}$$

b Amount of Cl^- in whole sample $= 1.84 \times 10^{-3} \text{ mol} \times \frac{250 \text{ cm}^3}{25.0 \text{ cm}^3}$

$$= \mathbf{1.84 \times 10^{-2} \text{ mol}}$$

Mass of chloride ion in whole sample $= n \times M$

$\therefore$ mass of Cl^- in whole sample $= 1.84 \times 10^{-2} \text{ mol} \times 35.5 \text{ g mol}^{-1}$

$$= \mathbf{0.653 \text{ g}}$$

c Mass of P in the whole sample = (mass of sample) − (mass of Cl^- in sample)

$$= 0.767\ \text{g} - 0.653\ \text{g}$$

$$= 0.144\ \text{g}$$

$\therefore$ amount of P in the whole sample $= \dfrac{m}{N}$

$$= \frac{0.144\ \text{g}}{31.0\ \text{g mol}^{-1}} = \mathbf{3.68 \times 10^{-3}\ mol}$$

d Amount of chlorine combined with one mole of phosphorus:

3.68×10^{-3} mol of P combines with 1.84×10^{-2} mol of Cl^-

$\therefore$ 1 mol of P combines with $\dfrac{1.84 \times 10^{-2}\ \text{mol}}{3.68 \times 10^{-3}}$

$$= \mathbf{5.00\ mol\ of\ Cl\ atoms}$$

e The simplest formula of the chloride is $\mathbf{PCl_5}$.

EXERCISE 100

a 1. $Ag^+ (aq) + Cl^- (aq) \rightarrow AgCl (s)$
Amount of Cl^- in 25 cm^3 of solution = amount of Ag^+ used = cV

$$= 0.100\ \text{mol dm}^{-3} \times \frac{21.0}{1000}\ \text{dm}^3 = \mathbf{2.10 \times 10^{-3}\ mol}$$

2. Amount of Cl^- in whole sample $= 2.10 \times 10^{-3}\ \text{mol} \times \dfrac{250\ \text{cm}^3}{25.0\ \text{cm}^3}$

$$= 2.10 \times 10^{-2}\ \text{mol}$$

3. Mass of chloride in whole sample = $n \times M$
$= 2.10 \times 10^{-2}\ \text{mol} \times 35.5\ \text{g mol}^{-1}$
$= 0.746$ g

4. Mass of S in the whole sample
= 1.420 g − 0.746 g
= 0.674 g

5. Amount of S in the whole sample $= \dfrac{m}{M}$

$$= \frac{0.674\ \text{g}}{32.1\ \text{g mol}^{-1}}$$

$$= 2.10 \times 10^{-2}\ \text{mol}$$

There are equal amounts of chloride ion and sulphur, therefore one mole of chloride is combined with each mole of sulphur.

b The molar mass of the chloride is 135.2.
Since S and Cl atoms occur in equal numbers the molecular formula is $(SCl)_n$.
For $n = 1$ molar mass = 67.6, for $n = 2$ molar mass = 135.2.
The molecular formula is $\mathbf{S_2Cl_2}$.

EXERCISE 101

a Electronegativity differences (on the Pauling scale) are as follows:

Na_2O_2 (3.5 – 0.9) = 2.6
MgO (3.5 – 1.2) = 2.3
Al_2O_3 (3.5 – 1.5) = 2.0
SiO_2 (3.5 – 1.8) = 1.7
P_2O_3 (3.5 – 2.1) = 1.4
SO_2 (3.5 – 2.5) = 1.0
Cl_2O_7 (3.5 – 3.0) = 0.5

From these electronegativity differences we predict ionic bonding for Na_2O_2, MgO and predominantly ionic bonding for Al_2O_3.

The electronegativity difference for SiO_2 corresponds to just over 50% ionic character, so that we would expect a large degree of covalency. The degree of covalent character increases further after silicon.

b The type of bonding in Period 3 oxides changes from ionic to covalent with increasing atomic number, across the period.

EXPERIMENT 14

Specimen results

Results Table 18

	Na_2O_2	MgO	Al_2O_3	SiO_2	P_4O_{10}	SO_2
Appearance	White or pale yellow solid	White solid	White solid	White solid	White solid	Colourless gas
On mixing with water						
Initial temperature	22°C	22°C	23°C	23°C	22°C	22°C
Final temperature	24°C	23°C	23°C	23°C	25°C	23°C
Does it dissolve?	Yes	Partially	No	No	Yes	Yes
pH of solution	12	9	7	7	below 4	below 4
Other observation(s) (if any)	Vigorous reaction. Colourless gas given off. Relights glowing splint	None	None	None	Vigorous reaction; steamy fumes evolved	

Questions 1.

Table 30

Formula of oxide	Na_2O_2*	**MgO**	Al_2O_3	SiO_2	P_4O_{10}*	SO_2*	Cl_2O*
Melting point/°C	460	2900	2040	1610 (quartz)	580	–75	–20
Boiling point/°C	Decomposes	3600	2980	2230 (quartz)	300	–10	2
State at s.t.p.	Solid	Solid	Solid	Solid	Solid	Gas	Gas
Action of water	Reacts	None apparent	None apparent	Insoluble	Reacts	Reacts	Reacts
pH of aq. solution	11–12	8–9	7–8	6–7	Below 3	3 or less	3 or less
Acid–base nature	Basic	Basic	Amphoteric	Acidic	Acidic	Acidic	Acidic
Conductivity of liquid	Good	Good	Good	Very poor	Very poor	Very poor	Very poor
Solubility in hexane	Insoluble	Insoluble	Insoluble	Insoluble	Slightly soluble	Dissolves	Dissolves
Structure	Giant	Giant	Giant	Giant	Simple molecular	Simple molecular	Simple molecular
Bonding	Ionic	Ionic	Ionic	Covalent	Covalent	Covalent	Covalent

*These substances represent the most familiar or readily available oxides of that element.

2. **a** $Na_2O_2 (s) + 2H_2O (l) \rightarrow 2NaOH (aq) + H_2O_2 (aq)$

$$2H_2O_2 (aq) \rightarrow 2H_2O (l) + O_2 (g)$$

b Magnesium oxide reacts slightly in cold water and moderately in hot to form the hydroxide, which is very slightly soluble.

$$MgO (s) + H_2O (l) \rightarrow Mg(OH)_2 (s)$$

c $P_4O_{10} (s) + 6H_2O (l) \rightarrow 4H_3PO_4 (aq)$

d $SO_2 (g) + H_2O (l) \rightarrow H_2SO_3 (aq)$

e $Cl_2O (g) + H_2O (l) \rightarrow 2HClO (aq)$

3. The oxides change from being giant ionic structures in Groups I, II and III through a giant covalent structure for silicon(IV) oxide, to simple covalent molecular structures for phosphorus, sulphur and chlorine.
4. The acid–base nature changes from basic for the s-block oxides through amphoteric for aluminium oxide to acidic for the oxides of the remaining elements.
5. As the structure and bonding of the oxides change from giant ionic to simple molecular across the period so their acid–base nature changes from basic to acidic.
6. In general, the observed reactions of Period 3 oxides do fit in with the bond type predicted from electronegativity differences. Aluminium oxide, although insoluble in water, reacts with both acids and bases, reflecting its intermediate bond type. Silicon(IV) oxide is also insoluble in water but reacts with alkalis behaving as a typical acidic oxide. The covalent oxides beyond silicon are all acidic, reacting directly with water to give acidic solutions.

EXERCISE 102

Table 31

Formula of oxide	Li_2O	BeO	B_2O_3	CO_2*	N_2O_4*	O_2	F_2O*
State at s.t.p.	Solid	Solid	Solid	Gas	Liquid	Gas	Gas
Conductivity of liquid	Good	Fairly poor	Very poor	Very poor	Very poor	Very poor	Very poor
Acid–base nature	Basic	Amphoteric	Amphoteric	Acidic	Acidic	Acidic	Acidic
Structure	Giant	Giant	Giant	Simple molecular	Simple molecular	Simple molecular	Simple molecular
Bonding	Ionic	Intermediate	Covalent	Covalent	Covalent	Covalent	Covalent

*These substances represent the most familiar or readily available oxides of that element. In general the other oxides of that element have similar properties apart from CO which is neutral.

EXERCISE 103

a i) Na_2O_2 sodium peroxide
ii) Al_2O_3 aluminium oxide
iii) SO_2 sulphur dioxide

b Na_2O_2 and Al_2O_3 are giant ionic structures; SO_2 consists of simple covalent molecules.

c SO_2 has the lowest melting point.

d Na_2O_2 gives an alkaline solution when dissolved in water.

e $Na_2O_2\ (s) + 2H_2O\ (l) \rightarrow 2NaOH\ (aq) + H_2O_2\ (aq)$ (followed by decomposition of H_2O_2)
$2H_2O_2\ (aq) \rightarrow 2H_2O\ (l) + O_2\ (g)$

EXERCISE 104

a

Table 32

Empirical formula of hydride	**LiH**	**BeH_2**	**BH_3***	**CH_4†**	**NH_3**	**OH_2**	**FH**
State at r.t.p.	Solid	Solid	Gas (B_2H_6)	Gas	Gas	Liquid	Gas
Behaviour with water	Reacts H_2 evolved	Reacts H_2 evolved	Reacts H_2 evolved	No reaction	Dissolves and reacts	No reaction	Dissolves and reacts
Acid–base nature	Basic	Basic	Neutral	Neutral	Basic	Neutral	Weakly acidic
Empirical formula of hydride	NaH	MgH_2	AlH_3	SiH_4‡	PH_3	SH_2	ClH
State at r.t.p.	Solid	Solid	Solid	Gas	Gas	Gas	Gas
Behaviour with water	Reacts H_2 evolved	Reacts H_2 evolved	Reacts H_2 evolved	Very slightly soluble. No reaction	Virtually insoluble. No reaction	Dissolves and reacts	Dissolves and reacts
Acid–base nature	Basic	Basic	Basic§	Essentially neutral	Very slightly basic	Neutral	Strongly acidic

*A series of boron hydrides is formed, the simplest being B_2H_6 (diborane).
†A series of hydrocarbons is formed (see ILPAC Volume 5, Hydrocarbons).
‡A series of silicon hydrides is formed (silanes).
§Could be interpreted as amphoteric.

b i) $NaH (s) + H_2O (l) \rightarrow NaOH (aq) + H_2 (g)$
ii) $MgH_2 (s) + 2H_2O (l) \rightarrow Mg(OH)_2 (s) + 2H_2 (g)$
iii) $AlH_3 (s) + 3H_2O (l) \rightarrow Al(OH)_3 (s) + 3H_2 (g)$

c The acid–base nature of the hydrides of the elements in Periods 2 and 3 changes from basic through neutral to acidic from left to right for both periods.

EXERCISE 105

a and **b**

Table 33

Empirical formula of hydride	**LiH**	**BeH_2**	**BH_3**	**CH_4**	**NH_3**	**OH_2**	**FH**
Electronegativity difference	1.1	0.6	0.1	0.4	0.9	1.4	1.9
Acid–base nature	Basic	Basic	Neutral	Neutral	Basic	Neutral	Acidic
Structure	Giant ionic	Polymeric	Simple molecular	Simple molecular	Simple molecular	Simple molecular	Simple molecular
Bonding	Appreciably ionic	Mainly covalent	Covalent	Covalent	Covalent	Covalent	Covalent
Classification	Ionic	Borderline	Covalent	Covalent	Covalent	Covalent	Covalent
Empirical formula of hydride	NaH	MgH_2	AlH_3	SiH_4	PH_3	SH_2	ClH
Electronegativity difference	1.2	0.9	0.6	0.3	0.0	0.4	0.9
Acid–base nature	Basic	Basic	Normally basic	Essentially neutral	Very slightly basic	Weakly acidic	Strongly acidic
Structure	Giant ionic	Giant lattice	Giant lattice	Simple molecular	Simple molecular	Simple molecular	Simple molecular
Bonding	Appreciably ionic	Mainly covalent	Mainly covalent	Covalent	Covalent	Covalent	Covalent
Classification	Ionic	Borderline	Borderline	Covalent	Covalent	Covalent	Covalent

c LiH contains Li^+ and H^- ions. NaH contains Na^+ and H^- ions. Both of these substances produce hydrogen at the anode when electrolysed in the molten state. They are also basic confirming the absence of H^+ ions and the presence of H^- ions, which act as proton acceptors.

$$H^- (aq) + H_2O (l) \rightarrow H_2 (g) + OH^- (aq)$$

d The H^- ion is larger than one might expect. It is therefore polarised by the small Li^+ ion and to a lesser extent by the Na^+ ion. Thus, although these substances have typical ionic properties they also have a high degree of covalent character.

Note that different values of ionic radii are given by different methods of calculation from internuclear distances. Some books list 0.154 nm as the radius of H^-, but our argument still applies.

EXERCISE 106 The hydrides of boron and silicon clearly illustrate the diagonal relationship between the elements. SiH_4 and BH_3 are both neutral, covalent substances with simple molecular structures, whereas AlH_3 does not closely resemble BH_3. Furthermore boron and silicon form a range of other hydrides, most of which are neutral gases with simple covalent molecules.

There are some similarities between BeH_2 and AlH_3 and between LiH and MgH_2, in basic character and bond-type. However, these are not greater than the similarities between hydrides in the same group.